WHAT ARE THEY?

THE HAIRY GIANTS OF VANCOUVER ISLAND . . . THE "MOUTH-MAN" WHO CRAVES ONLY RED MEAT . . . THE THING THAT RIPS TONGUES OUT OF CATTLE . . . THE "WIND MAN" OF RUSSIA . . . THE "STINKERS" OF MALAYA.

These are only a sampling of the published cases of submen, trolls, and what used to be called "Apemen," documented and discussed in this definitive book by an eminent field biologist.

THE ABOMINABLE SNOWMEN (appearing for the first time in an up-to-date and revised edition) is the masterwork on this subject that has challenged the skeptics, and kept thousands of readers utterly spellbound.

ABOMINABLE SNOWMEN

LEGEND COME TO LIFE

An Account of Reports on the
Existence of Ultra-Primitive
Hominids on Five Continents

New Revised Abridgment

IVAN T. SANDERSON
F.L.S., F.R.G.S., F.Z.S.

PYRAMID BOOKS • NEW YORK

DEDICATION

*To Bernard and Monique Heuvelmans
and My own "Alma"*

ABOMINABLE SNOWMEN
Legend Come to Life

A PYRAMID BOOK
Published by arrangement with Chilton Book Company

Chilton Book Company edition published 1961
Pyramid edition published November, 1968

Copyright © 1961, 1968 by Ivan T. Sanderson

PYRAMID BOOKS are published by Pyramid Publications, Inc.,
444 Madison Avenue, New York, New York 10022, U.S.A.

Contents

FOREWORD TO THE REPRINT EDITION

HISTORY is currently taking a most peculiar and remarkable turn. In the dimmest and farthest past, Man presumably knew practically nothing but then throughout thousands of millenia he gradually acquired wisdom and an ever-increasing understanding of his environment. This culminated in the dawn of what we call the scientific age. Then something very curious happened.

On the one hand, our knowledge of the world we live in started to advance with ever-increasing momentum; but, on the other hand, ever more matters that had interested our ancestors were tossed into a sort of intellectual trash can on the grounds that they were preposterous. I am speaking, of course, of what we now call the "Western World." The peoples indigenous to other continents—other than Europe and North America, that is—did not so toss out these things. Now, we of "the West" have reached an impasse.

Starting about 1920, I suspect, there came a great, spontaneous, unheralded, and apparently unprovoked change in public, if not scientific, opinion. People as a whole began to question everything—religion, science, our social organization, and even our history, at least as taught. Things that had been either forgotten or suppressed for over a century if not two suddenly began to crop up all over the place. At first, however, these were mostly of a very factual and pragmatic nature; the revolution in ideas did not come until forty years later—the year in which this book was written.

One of the results of these two changeovers is the "turn" in history which I mentioned at the outset. Year by year, since about A.D. 1920, more and more allegedly new discoveries are being traced ever farther back in historical time. In fact, the history of just about everything has suddenly—speaking historically—started to be pushed ever farther back in time, generally. Take simple items like the first metal working, the first village settlement, the first written records, the first art, the first boats; even the first Man! Forty years ago, anthropologists gave the impression of being convinced that Modern Man first saw the light round about 50,000 years ago. Now, the date (in our years) is heading for the 2-million mark.

By the end of World War I we Westerners seem to have come to the blissful conclusion that, even if we did not have all the details filled in, we knew the overall picture of everything. The Scopes (Monkeyville) Trial was proclaimed a triumph of scientific logic over traditional belief; the Biblical statements on creation were said to be purely allegorical: scientific truth to be proven. Everybody sort of relapsed into a new intellectual utopia. Both religion and science had been challenged but both had proved their points—by sensible compromise, made possible by the equally sensible employment of logic. Both were perfectly correct; it was merely a matter of semantics. It is nowhere stated in the Bible that God created the world precisely on a Friday in the year 4004 B.C. as Bishop Usher has said; science never said that it was created precisely in 4.004-billion B.C. Both were merely figures of speech.

Unfortunately both were figments of the imagination.

Unpleasant things continued to turn up and with increasing regularity and insistence. These were items that did not fit into either the old traditional pattern of Beliefs, or into the new scientific logic. Most of them had been around literally since ever, but they had just died away, increasingly, since the inception and acceptance of scientific methodology. They were dubbed "old wives' tales" and then, despite their persistence among laymen, were progressively denigrated until even the least schooled country bumpkin came to laugh at them. The job was almost completed by 1920. But then something happened.

People started dredging up these old wives' tales and writing about them. They were colorful; they were historic; they were just clean fun. But, as such popular trash began to blossom, people started saying things like: "Hey, That's not so damned stupid as you think. My grandmother . . ." (and so on).

Encouraged by this, more and still more people began so dredging—and in family attics, in historical societies, in old books, and in the classics even unto the Bible. And within a decade, there were those who were showing the audacity to state that some of these things were not *old* wives' tales

8

but factual accounts by their own new wives—"And don't you try to argue with her, bud!"

Thus, certain aspects of history began to reverse themselves; and the classic example is that of which we write, and which we have dubbed ABSMery for short. This began, for the Western world, in 1920-21 with the coining of the catchy monicker "Abominable Snowman." This was greeted with hoots of derision but the utmost glee by the British press.

Nevertheless, it just would not go away, and throughout the twenties and thirties the business built up and up with ever more evidence from (in this case Himalayan) mountaineers, military and other government personnel, and even travelling scientists. Reports kept pouring out of this area, and all to the effect that the initial silly suggestion that there was (is) a creature in central Asia the name of which was (mis) translated as The Abominable Snowman, was actually not silly at all. And so insistent were these reports that the stay-at-home scientists were forced to try to refute the matter.

In this they not only failed miserably, but they opened a new flood gate of derision and speculation among the press and the public because their arguments and their attempted refutations were manifestly so peurile. The net result was a renewed outburst of reports, coming from ever more respected, reliable, and official persons.

This whole business was, up until World War II, an almost exclusively British affair; but immediately thereafter, it became fully international. Swiss, Japanese, Argentinians, Austrians, Russians, Mongolians, Americans, New Zealanders, and even Indians and the local Nepalis and Tibetans got into the act; and still ever more precise and categoric reports that these creatures really exist, and are not just old (Himalayan) wives' tales, resulted. But the stay-at-homes and the other "experts," who had never been within five thousand miles of the Himalayas, continued to rant and to scoff. No such thing *could* be, they stated, because it was *impossible;* however just who said so, they did not offer to state!

Then the whole business broke out like a rash in both North America and Russia.

True scientists began to prick up their ears; proper expeditions were organized; newspapers, and millionaires, and governments poured money into the effort; and truly concrete evidence began to come in. First, it was mere reports: then plaster casts of footprints; then hairs; then piles of excrement; then photographs of "beds"; and finally some still photographs and a film. The embattled experts had now to contend not only with the general public, the travellers, officialdom, the press, and the literate scholars of over half the world, they had also to battle a very firmly entrenched battalion in their own midst. These were an international group of absolutely topnotch scientists, and notably physical anthropologists, holding much higher positions than theirs, and with far greater credits to their titles.

The next, and, as of the time of writing, final stage was then initiated. This was (is) bibliographical and historical research into the matter; and this not only within the limited confines of western literature and record, but worldwide, and with notable emphasis on Asia. Literally within months, the result was a sort of landslide reversal of history. Everywhere one turned, ever more records of these ABSMs cropped up—and everywhere from Indonesia to Sweden, and from China to Ireland. They even turned up all over North, Central, and South America. And as the years have passed, this flood has not only burst the dam but brought to light something else.

This is that the whole business was never an old wives' tale in the first place, but a perfectly straightforward historical record of fact, and of our ancestry and of that of our prehistory, and cultural and political written history. It is only now, after having reached what we thought was the end of a road, that we have really started to uncover just what is what, and what really happened in the past.

This book is an historical record of that history; and a history of this historical reversal.

IVAN T. SANDERSON

Columbia, New Jersey

ABOMINABLE
SNOWMEN

MAP I. DISTRIBUTION OF ABSMS BY CONTINENTS

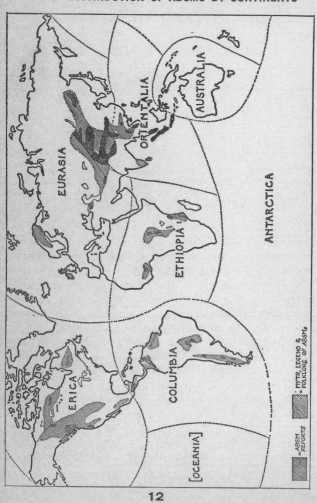

MAP I. DISTRIBUTION OF ABSMS BY CONTINENTS

The surface of the Earth is somewhat clearly divided between areas of two kinds. One, which we call the land but which includes certain peripheral areas at present under shallow seas, forms rafts of certain kinds of rocks of lighter density, some 40 miles thick. The other, which constitutes the ocean floors, is covered by a much thinner layer of these strata. The hydrosphere—or water capsule of our earth—finds its own level due to gravity. As a result, the first areas are subaerial, the latter subaqueous. The former are "landmasses"; the latter "oceans" (with adjacent seas). The first are not, however, the **Continents,** which are specific land areas, with associated promontories and islands, each of which has an unique history, structure, flora, and fauna. These are seven in number, with the islands in the South Pacific forming an additional unit. Current reports of, and myths, legends, and folklore pertaining to, ABSMs are now recorded from five of the Continents.

MAP II. WORLD VEGETATION

MAP II. WORLD VEGETATION

The most important feature of the land-surface of the earth to animals (and thus to men) is the type of vegetation that clothes it. There are seven major types—the equatorial closed-canopy forests; the open orchards and tropical savannahs; the scrublands and hot deserts; the steppes, prairies, and park-lands of the temperate zones; the closed-canopy deciduous and coniferous forests of the higher latitudes; and the tundras and barrenlands of the polar circles. These girdle the earth, in that order, from equator to poles, in successive belts, but all of them waver to north and south and expand or contract, continuously, and in a variety of ways. These variations are due solely to the influence of the major ocean currents. Altitude has no effect on this belting; but on mountains the succession is repeated vertically, irrespective of latitude. ABSMs appear to occur only in mountainous regions and almost exclusively in those which lie in the forest belts. The one exception is eastern Eurasia.

MAP III. HUMAN RACES

16

MAP III. HUMAN RACES

Today, the entire land surface of the earth, apart from Antarctica, the Greenland icecap, and a number of islands, mostly in the polar regions, is officially "inhabited" by Modern Man. Actually, he lives on considerably less than a tenth of the total land surface. Modern Man is divided into two very distinct groups—the Primitives and the Non-Primitives. The former consist of the Australoids of Australia and, in part, Melanesia; the Bushmen of Southwest Africa*; the little Negrillo Pigmies of central Africa*; and the Negrito Pigmies of the Andaman Islands, the Malay Peninsula, and the Philippines.* There are three divisions of the Non-Primitives—the Mongoloid, the Caucasoid, and the Negroid. Of the first, there are five subdivisions; of the second, three; and of the third, two, but with another group—the Hamitic—derived from intermixture with one of the Caucasoid groups. Currently, the West Caucasoids and the Sudanese Negroids have greatly extended their range, notably to the Americas. [* Not on map due to scale.]

17

MAP IV. NORTH AMERICA [VEGETATION]

BOX I = MAP I

‖ = MONTANE BLOCKS

⫽ = LOWLANDS (FOREST, PARK, & PRAIRIE)

≡ = UPLANDS (STEPPES & SCRUBLANDS)

▦ = TROPICAL LOWLAND FORESTS

⋮ = BOTTOMLANDS (TEMPERATE)

▨ = N.W. PACIFIC "RAIN-FOREST"

MAP IV.   NORTH AMERICA [VEGETATION]

This continent should be regarded as reaching from the Arctic Ice Raft to the Isthmus of Tehuantepec. It is divided into three parts: first, into a western and an eastern, by the Great Barrier, the dividing line running roughly down the 110th Meridian. Secondly, the eastern half is sub-divided latitudinally about the 45th parallel; to the north being closed forest and tundra; to the south, open forest (parklands) and prairies. The midwest, southwest, and Mexico are arid and covered with scrub and desert. The rest is mountainous, and forested almost exclusively with conifers. In the Mexican Sierras there are some tropical forests. Along the eastern fringe of the continent lie the Appalachians, and there is another upland area in Labrador. The valley of the Mississippi and its tributaries form extensive, swampy bottomlands.

MAP V. CENTRAL WESTERN NORTH AMERICA

MAP V. CENTRAL WESTERN NORTH AMERICA

This is an arbitrarily chosen area, designed to bring out a number of different physical features. It represents an area of some 1,900,000 square miles, of which some 1,650,000 are land. This is cut diagonally by the Great Barrier—here represented by the Rockies—that extends from the Arctic coast to Vera Cruz on the Gulf coast. To the east of this are lowlands covered, in the north, by the great boreal coniferous forests and, to the south, by the prairies. In the south lies the Great Basin, actually an upland, desert plateau covered with parallel ranges of modest mountains. Between the Sierra Nevada and the Southern Coastal Ranges there is the flat gutter known as the Sacramento Valley. The rest is subdivided into a series of mountain blocks as shown. Each is quite distinct in form, composition, flora, and fauna. It is around the peripheries of these that ABSMs have been reported. The coast, from the Olympics north, is mostly precipitous and without any coastal plain at all.

MAP VI. BRITISH COLUMBIA

PRINCE
RUPERT

SKEENA RIVER

DAWSON
CREEK

PRINCE
GEORGE

TWEEDSMUIR
PARK

TETE JAUNE
CACHE

BELLA
COOLA

BRITISH

COLUMBIA

FRAZIER RIVER

NORTH THOMPSON RIVER

KELSEY
BAY

TOBA
INLET

LYTTON

VANCOUVER ISLAND

HARRISON LAKE

YALE

VANCOUVER

HOPE
RUBY CREEK
FLOOD
AGASSIZ
CHILIWACK

VICTORIA

UNITED STATES

|=ROADS
◉ =TOWNS
⬭ =CITIES

SEATTLE

MAP VI. BRITISH COLUMBIA

This represents an area of some 270,000 square miles. Ninety per cent of this is uninhabited, despite the enormous conglomeration of the City of Vancouver, the old capital of Victoria on Vancouver Island, and the somewhat extensive cultivated areas on that island and about the lower reaches of the Fraser River from Agassiz west. The coastal plains of Puget Sound add only 2 per cent. The whole of it, apart from Vancouver Island, the Fraser delta, and the Puget Sound area, is mightily mountainous and great parts are not truly explored, though there are now excellent large-scale maps resultant from aerial surveys. The Olympic Mountains and the coastal fringe northward around Vancouver Island and north of the lower Fraser River are clothed in an immensely tall, several-layered "Rain Forest" with conifers predominating (the largest trees in the world are found here) and choked with mosses, ferns, and a broadleafed undergrowth. The other areas are heavily forested but for their peaks.

MAP VII. NORTHERN CALIFORNIA

GRANT'S PASS

ROUTE 199

ROUTE 99

SISKIYOU MTS.

CASCADES

ROUTE 96

KLAMATH MTS.

BLUFF CREEK

MT. SHASTA △

HOOPA VALLEY

WILLOW CREEK

EUREKA

ROUTE 299

ROUTE 36

TRINITY MTS.

ROUTE 101

ROUTE 99

ROUTE 20

CLEAR LAKE

= LOWLANDS

MAIN ROADS

SECOND-CLASS ROADS

SAN FRANCISCO

MAP VII. NORTHERN CALIFORNIA

The land area on this map represents approximately 45,000 square miles. All but a small portion at the extreme south around San Francisco, and a sliver of the upper Sacramento Valley, are mountains. These are not excessively high but are very steep and closely packed, with deep narrow gorges between. However, the various blocks contained within this area are not at all homogeneous. The mighty Cascades are volcanic and much larger than the coastal ranges. The Klamaths are the "oldest" from a faunistic point of view; the Trinities are newer and of somewhat different phyto-geographic constitution. Along the coast, from just south of Cape Blanco, but a little way in from that coast, to a little south of San Francisco Bay is the land of the great Redwoods (**Sequoia sempervirens**). The whole mountainous part is clothed in almost unbroken forest, and ABSMs have been reported from Clear Lake in the south to the northern edge of the Siskiyous and beyond to the northeast.

MAP VIII. GUATEMALA

WEST CARIBBEAN

PACIFIC OCEAN

TABASCO

CAMPECHE

THE PETEN

FLORES

BRITISH HONDURAS

CHIAPAS

MAYA MOUNTAINS

LAGUNA DE IZABAL

COBÁN

CUBULCO

MT. SANTA CRUZ QUICHÉ

GUATEMALA CITY

REP. DE HONDURAS

EL SALVADOR

= MONTANE   = LOWLANDS (FORESTED)   = COASTAL SCRUBLANDS   = REPORTED DISTRIBUTION OF AN ABSM

MAP VIII. GUATEMALA

The position of the Republic of Guatemala and the over-all area of this map is shown by the square in the box, which, in turn, encompasses what is popularly called Central America. Guatemala is divided into two very distinct parts—the northern, called the Peten, which is a lowland, heavily forested plateau; and the southern which is mountainous and where there are large numbers of volcanoes, both active and idle. To the west, these mountains are contiguous with the eastern rim of the Chiapas in Mexico. The southern coastal plain is arid. In the northeast corner of the country, which reaches the Bight of Honduras in the Caribbean, there is a limted sealevel triangle containing the so-called "Lake Isabel"—actually the Laguna de Izabal. This is really an arm of the sea and is connected to it by a river-like channel. The area from which ABSMs have been reported centers around the peak named Sanché in the Sierra de Chuacus.

MAP IX. SOUTH AMERICA

MONTANE BLOCKS

UPLANDS (OPEN FORESTS & SAVANNAHS)

LOWLAND FORESTS, WOODLANDS, & PARKS

MAP IX. SOUTH AMERICA

This continent is most notable for its lack of associated islands. It is today composed of three subcontinents joined by extensive lowlands. The former are: first, the Andean chain of mountains and their contained Alto Planos; the ancient Guiana Massif; and, the eastern uplands. The last is divided into two parts—the mountains around the Matto Grosso swamps and the vast arid Caatingas. Between these three major upland blocks there are three enormous drainage basins—those of the Orinoco, Amazon, and La Plata. All these are multiple river systems with innumerable tributaries that meander through extensive forested lowlands. Surrounding the upland massifs and bordering these river basins are intermediate plateaus. These are mostly clothed in savannahs. In the southern tip of the continent, south of the La Plata, these intermediate lowlands are covered with the tall grass Pampas and farther south with scrub. In the extreme northwest there is a block of equatorial forest on the Pacific side of the Andes cut off abruptly to the south by the excessively arid western coastal fringe. ABSMs have been reported from this Colombian area; from the Guiana Massif; from the mountains around the Matto Grosso; and from a few points in the central Andean highlands. "Bigfeet" have long been rumored from the Patagonian region, but the matter is there muddled with the Ground-Sloth business.

MAP X. AFRICA

EURASIA

EL JUF BASIN

AHAGGAR

RUB AL KHALI

GUINEA MASSIF

BODELE BASIN

GORA

DAR FUR

ETHIOPIA

UBANGI-SHARI

BAHR-EL-GHAZAL

GABUN-CAMERUN

CONGO BASIN

TAN-GANYIKA

BENGUELA COLD CURRENT

MOZANBIQUE

KALAHARI

▥ = UPLANDS & MOUNTAINS

▤ = LOWLANDS (SCRUB & DESERT)

▦ = LOWLANDS (EQUATORIAL FOREST)

MAP X. AFRICA

Africa is the second largest and most compact of the continents. Apart from Madagascar, which is hardly a part of it, and Fernando Po in the west, it also is singularly lacking in peripheral islands. Its northern rim is really a part of the continent of Eurasia and, lying as it does today north of the great Sahara Desert, has not only a different climate but, to a large extent, flora and fauna differing from that of the rest of the continent. Africa is divided into three parts—a northern desert belt; a central forested belt; and a southern desert belt. However, further confusion is produced by there being extensive and almost over-all highlands all the way down the eastern half of the continent and other extensive upland blocks in the northern deserts and in the western half of the forested equatorial belt. Africa also has three large basins, but all are inland and without any real outlets. Two—El Juf and the Bodele—now lie in the deserts. The third is that of the Congo, the second biggest riverine system in the world. The tall, closed-canopy, equatorial forests are actually rather limited in extent, and are clearly divided into four parts, in the west and center. The lowland coastal forests of the east are not T-E-F and are more arid. ABSMs are reported from three forest areas, with a rumor from the far southwest.

MAP XI. NORTHERN ORIENTALIA (POLITICAL)

MAP XI. NORTHERN ORIENTALIA (POLITICAL)

Orientalia is today, from a political point of view, an appalling hodge-podge. This continent lies to the south of the southeastern end of Eurasia, all of which is Chinese. (Most countries have for centuries recognized Tibet as being a part of that hegemony.) To the west, it is bordered by Iran and Afghanistan, and a thin eastward extensive of the latter separates it from the U.S.S.R. The greater part of it is covered by India and the two pieces of Pakistan. The eastern half is about equally divided between southern China proper and eight other sovereign states—Burma, Thailand, Laos, Viet Min, Vietnam, Cambodia, Malaya, and Indonesia. In addition, there are sundry territories (such as Sarawak) of other status, and some small colonial possessions. Right in the middle are the independent kindgoms of Nepal, the territory of Sikkim, and the indeterminate Autonomy of Bhutan. The island of Ceylon is an independent country; and there are also sundry tiny enclaves, such as the Portuguese colony of Goa.

MAP XII. ORIENTALIA

MAP XII. ORIENTALIA

Geographically, Tibet is a part of Orientalia but, due to its extreme altitude, it is connected with Eurasia. Orientalia is divided into six parts—India, the Himalayas, Indochina, southern China, Malayo-Indonesia, and the Philippines. (For the last three subdivisions, see Map X.) In this continent we have three major levels—lowlands, mountains, and super-mountains. Most of the first are clothed in equatorial forests but there is a large desert area in western Pakistan, and most of southern China lies in the temperate forest belt and has a distinctly Mediterranean flavor. The mountains fall into seven major and many minor blocks: there are two complexes in India, the Arakan, the Indochinese Massif, the Annams, the southern Chinese Massif, and the Fukien complex. Lesser blocks are on the peninsulas and islands. The Himalayas constitute a special region. The ranges of that name are immensely long but narrow, and are erected upon a huge upland. ⊗ = The Chinese Piedmont.

MAP XIII. EAST AND SOUTH ORIENTALIA

MAP XIII. EAST AND SOUTH ORIENTALIA

The eastern half of Orientalia is also enormously complex from the topographical and phytogeographical points of view. Its central core is the huge Indochinese Peninsula—a vast mass of mountain ranges running from north to south—that lies between the Indian and the Chinese lowlands. This abuts southward onto a vast lowland which constitutes Thailand. From this depends the Malay Peninsula. Around it lie a diadem of islands, starting with the Andamans and Nicobars in the Bay of Bengal on the west; encompassing the greater Indonesian islands of Sumatra, Java, and Borneo on the south; and continuing on via Palawan to the Philippines and Formosa (Taiwan) on the east. Between and among these are literally hundreds of thousands of other smaller islands; plus another string along the coast, terminating in Hainan. The southeastern end of the continent is "Wallace's Line"—running between the Philippines, Borneo, and Java on the one hand, and the Celebes and the Australoid islands on the other.

MAP XIV. MALAYA AND SUMATRA

SIMULUR

NIAS

BATUS

SIBERUT

SIPORA
No. PAGI
So. PAGI

MALAYA

PERAK

SUMATRA

BOEKITS

MENTAWIS

BARISSAN MTS

BANGKA

ENG-GANO

JAVA

= MONTANE
  BLOCKS

= LOWLAND
  FORESTS

Y Y Y Y
Y Y Y Y = LOWLAND
Y Y Y Y   SWAMPS

MAP XIV. MALAYA AND SUMATRA

This small area is one of the most peculiar in the world. In it there are living a large number of animals not found anywhere else, while the only relatives of these are found far away. Most odd, and still least known of all, are the Barissan Mountains of south Sumatra, in and around which ABSMs, particularly in the form of the pigmy **Sedapa,** have been for centuries alleged to exist. These and other unknown primates are reported from the east Sumatran lowland forest and the swamp belt, and from the inner montane block of the Malay Peninsula. The Mentawi Islands have unique apes and monkeys.

MAP XV.   EASTERN EURASIA

MAP XV. EASTERN EURASIA

This most complex geographical setup in the world forms a vast triangle some 3,000 miles along its western face, which is the great barrier abutting onto the Russian steppes; some 2,500 miles along its southern curve, which runs from the Pamirs along the southern rim of the Tibetan Plateau to Sikang; and 3,000 miles from there along its eastern face to meet the Barrier in eastern Siberia. The whole of this is basically a high plateau, the central portion being a hot desert. Upon this, and all around its rim, lie immense mountain ranges. In the south, there is a super-upland, the plateau of Tibet, with even greater ranges upon it. It is an astonishing fact that the greatest of all mountain ranges in the world, that forms the southern rim of the Tibetan Plateau and contains the Everest Block, has no recognized name In English. The Tibetans and the Nepalese know this as the "Mother of All Mountains" or the **Muh-Dzhura rDzhung pBlhüm.** The Karakorams are the western end of this range. ① = The Everest Bloc.

41

1. A Certain Unpleasantness

A BRIEF HISTORY OF ABSMERY

In 1887, a major in the Medical Corps of the British Indian Army, Lawrence Austine Waddell, LL.D., C.B., C.I.E., F.L.S., F.A.I.—i.e Doctor of Laws, Commander of the Bath, Commander of the Indian Empire, Fellow of the Linnean Society, Fellow of the Anthropological Institute—was meandering about in the eastern Himalayas doing what that rather remarkable breed of men were wont to do: that is, a bit of shooting, some subdued exploring, and a certain amount of "politicking." Like many others of his ilk, he wrote a somewhat uninspired and uninspiring book about it, uninspiringly named *Among the Himalayas*. The Major was a normal sort of chappie and a sportsman, but his hunting was not of the feverish ninety-one-gun-in-closet variety of today; quite the contrary, he would take a few birds of types he considered to be legitimate game for his pot or to keep his eye in for grouse-shoots on his next home-leave in Scotland, and he banged away at "tygarr" whenever the local natives could rustle one up. But he was not scrambling about the Himalayas primarily for what we nowadays call "sport." He was just puttering—that lost 19th-century British art—because he had some time off, and official sanction to make use of it as he would.

Despite the limited intelligence attributed to 19th-century British-Indian Army colonels, they were really a most remarkable breed—almost a mutation—for, from some hidden depths of their public-school educations, and the remoter recesses of their ancient family traditions, they dredged up a wealth of wisdom, and they often developed an extraordinarily keen interest in the world about them wherever they happened to land. Most of them were sort of mild philosophers; many turned out to be brilliant linguists and great scholars; and they were often both leaders of men and students of animal life. They have been grossly maligned by almost everybody, laughed at as super-Blimps, and neglected as historians. But if you will just read their maunderings carefully, you will garner therefrom a trove of both literary and factual gems.

Take this Major Waddell, for instance. While pounding over one of the unpleasanter bits of Sikkim, in vile weather, he came upon a set of tracks made by some creature walking on two legs and bare feet that, he says, went on and on, over the freezing snow, not only taking the line of least resistance at every turn but marking out a course in conformity with the easiest gradients that brought whoops of admiration even from the Major's mountain-born porters. He remarks almost casually upon this remarkable achievement and wonders vaguely not what manner of man, but *what sort of creature* could have made them, and why it should have decided to cross this awful pass in the first place. The Major did not realize when he penned this thought just what he was starting; though "starting" is perhaps not the exact word to describe his remarks, for what he recorded was already ancient history when Columbus sailed for the West Indies. It just so happens that, as far as popular recognition is concerned, his was one of the earliest mentions to appear in print in the English language, in what may be called modern times, of what has latterly become known as the "abominable snowman."

At that time nobody in what we now call the Western World paid the slightest attention to this extraordinary report —at least as far as we know. It just went into the record as a statement; for one could hardly, in that day and age, call any pronouncement on the part of anybody with such notable honors a lie, or even a "traveler's tale." It was therefore assumed that some religious chap must have preceded the gallant Major over that particular route and somehow managed not to die of frostbite, sun-blindness, or starvation; and it was remarked that he had done a dashed good job of negotiating the pass. There the matter rested.

Major Waddell's book was one of many written about the end of the last century when the Western World was complacently sure that it knew more or less everything about all countries, with the possible exceptions of Tibet and the holy city of Mecca which, it was then considered, were rather unsporting in that they did not welcome civilized Englishmen. All sorts of sporting gentry went wandering about the fringes of "The Empire" with rod and gun and later wrote about their experiences. Their effusion were read by both the previous and the upcoming genera tions of colonial pioneers, but by few others. What they said was not taken too seriously by the general, nonempire building public. However, many of these gentry also sub mitted official reports on certain less publicized aspects of their activities to their superiors; and these were taken ver seriously.

Unfortunately the great body of such reports are not pub lished and many of them are either lost in some archive or truly lost forever. There are others that are still top-secret and unavailable, so that their very existence is often con jectural. Yet every now and then one stumbles upon such a report that is extremely tantalizing. Tracking down the original is a frightful chore and one of the most time-con suming and frustrating experiences. One is balked at every turn but not, I would stress, by any deliberate or organized defense on the part of authority. Official archives are pre served for the benefit of all and are open to inspection by all, and even the topmost secrets are in time released a mere historical dejecta. The trouble is simply that the origi nal reporters, and more so those reported to, did not lay any store by or place any specific value on esoterica, or anything other than the primary matter at hand, which wa often of a diplomatic or political nature, so that the item that interest us most were never indexed or catalogued You just have to plow through mountains of material quite extraneous to your particular quarry and hope to stumble upon casual asides that are pertinent to it. But one doe occasionally so stumble.

Now I should state, without further ado and quite frankly, that I am prejudiced in favor of official as opposed to any other form of reports and for the following reasons In this country we do not, let's face it, have much respec for the law or its potential until we have recourse to it or it requires our submission. Until we have been on a witnes stand, almost all of us believe that perjury—which is simply a legal term for lying in the law's presence—should be the easiest thing in the world, but even those of us who say that laws are made only to be broken, soon find that it is not. Few think twice about telling a fish story in the corner bar, but there are very few, even congenital idiots, who won't think before telling it in a court of law. When, there fore, somebody voluntarily makes an official statement when there is no profit motive involved, I have always fel it reasonable to assume that it is quite likely true. The British happen to have a particular respect for their law, and British officialdom, despite what has been said about its colonial policies, has always been remarkably altruistic. British consuls and other officials just did not report a lot of rubbish to their service headquarters. Even paper was scarce in minor British outposts and the field officers did not clutter up essential reports with bizarre trivia unless they considered them to be of real import. We approach, therefore, the following official report with a certain quota of awe.

It appears that in 1902 British Indian officialdom was concerned with the stringing of the first telegraph line from Lhasa, the capital of Tibet, to Kalimpong, Darjeeling in Bengal Province of India just south of the Sikkim border (see Map). The job entailed, first, going into Tibet and then stringing the cable out. When the crew reached a pass named Chumbithang near a place called Jelep-La on the Tibet-Sikkim border, an incident occurred that prompted an official report. A dozen workers failed to return to camp one evening and a military posse was sent next day to search for them at the scene of their operations. No trace of the missing men were found, but the soldiers during their wide search for them found a remarkable creature asleep under a rock ledge—or so the report goes. The soldiers were Indians, not Ghurkhas or mountain folk, and this is of significance because had they been they would doubtless have acted differently. The Indians had no qualms about shooting this creature to death immediately. It proved to be human rather than animal in form, though covered with thick hairy fur. Up to this point the report is official. Then it becomes unofficial but for one minor aside to the effect that a full report, together with the beast, was shipped to the senior British political officer then resident in Sikkim, who is correctly named as one Sir Charles Bell.

The unofficial sequence I take from an extraordinary book by John A. Keel entitled *Jadoo*. This is the more startling in that it even mentions an incident apparently lost and certainly forgotten over half a century before, yet states that the information therein given was obtained first-hand. The author states that he met in 1957 in Darjeeling a retired Indian soldier named Bombahadur Chetri, who claimed that he was among the party that killed this creature, and that he personally examined it. He is also alleged to have said that it was about 10 feet tall, covered with hair but for a naked face, and that it had "long yellow fangs." Further, Mr. Keel says that Bombahadur Chetri told him that the carcass had been packed in ice and shipped to this same Sir Charles Bell, but that he did not hear anything further of it. Nor, apparently, did Mr. Keel; and nor have I, though I have spent a lot more time and energy than the item might seem to warrant in a fruitless endeavor to trace further reports, official or otherwise. This is the more aggravating since it is the earliest report that I have found on the actual (or even the alleged) capture of any form of what we shall henceforth be calling an ABSM—i.e. "the abominable snowmen," by what we must, also for lack of any established over-all name, call the "Western World," in the Oriental Region.*

Nevertheless, it is by no means the only such report, nor actually the earliest on record, for as we shall presently see, it was preceded in two if not three other continents by just as definitive statements and in some cases official ones at that.

And this brings up another point that I should endeavor to clear up forthwith.

I would have preferred to start this story where all stories should begin, which is to say at the beginning. However, despite a chronology that I have compiled over the years, such a procedure would be open to at least two serious defects. First, it is almost daily, and now with increasing tempo, being added to almost all along the line, while its origins are regressing ever farther into the recorded past; second, it would be extraordinarily dry and overformal in the eyes of any but extreme specialists. I have felt, therefore, that the history of this whole ABSM business will be much better understood if it is unfolded upon the chronology of *its* discovery and progress; a sort of history of a history. This is, further, herein recorded deliberately from what we called above the "Western" point of view, in that it is a chronological record of how the matter was brought

* The term "ABSM" is coined from the best-known name for one kind of those creatures of which we speak, namely the Abominable Snowman. As is explained later, this term is incorrect, inappropriate, and misleading even in the case in which it was first applied; while it cannot possibly be applied to at least 80 per cent of the apparently most varied and quite different creatures involved, and now reported from five continents. The term "Western World" in this case has a cultural rather than a regional sense; but by the Oriental Region is to be understood a very precise geographical unit.

to the attention of the Western World. In this, it will soon be seen that a greater part of the discoveries made have come to light in reverse. For instance, it has only been within most recent years that the earliest accounts have come to light, and the further research workers probe into the whole matter, the farther back the origins of the whole ABSM affair recede, while the wider does their distribution become both in fact and in report. Thus, in treating of the history of this matter, we must bear in mind that what appear to us to be discoveries are more nearly revelations, because the majority of the world—which is, of course, *non*-Western—has, to some degree or another, known all about the business for centuries, while we have remained completely oblivious of and to it.

For these reasons, I divide our chronology into five stages and call these as follows: (1) the ancient period, prior to the 15th-century expansion of Europe, (2) the dark ages, from 1500 to 1880, (3) that of the Explorers, from about 1880 to 1920, (4) that of the mountaineers, 1920 to 1950 and (5) that of the searchers, from 1950 to 1960. All of this, however, applies primarily and most essentially to the Himalayan area of the Oriental Region wherein this business was primarily unfolded for us. The same periods, of course, exist in time elsewhere, such as North America, but they cannot be founded on the same criteria or named after the same classes of entrepreneurs. Behind this chronology and everywhere lies an immense period of what I call native knowledge. This trails off into the dim mists of the extreme past and into folklore and myth; an area which is only just now being taken into account as serious history rather than mere make-believe. Thus, in other parts of the world our story has often jumped straight out of the "native" period into that of scientific study.

While ABSMs were not only reported but also reported upon, and even officially, in other parts of the world— vide: Canada—long before the travels of Major Waddell, and while specimens (as it now turns out) are alleged to have been captured or killed long before that, we of the West became cognizant of these happenings or alleged happenings only very recently. Also, it now transpires, detailed and more properly critical information on the subject was even being published in eastern Eurasia centuries ago—for instance in Tibet, China, Mongolia, and Manchuria—and some reflections of this had filtered through to Europe as early as Renaissance times, as is exemplified in

48

certain curious statements in the works of Marco Polo. Millions of people were then taking all this as a matter of course but, the whole thing being completely foreign to European conditions or even thought at that time, it made no impression upon what we now call the Western World until our fourth period—namely that of the mountaineers.

Just how foreign it was prior to that period is clearly demonstrated by the reception, or lack of it, given to a report published in a scientific journal (*Proceedings of the Zoological Society of London*) in the year 1915, and the brief comments upon it made at the time. The report was read before the society by a very well-known botanist and scientific explorer named Henry J. Elwes, and consisted of portions of a letter received by that gentleman from a Forestry Officer by the name of J. R. O. Gent who was stationed in Darjeeling. This read as follows:

I have discovered the existence of another animal but cannot make out what it is, a big monkey or ape perhaps—if there were any apes in India. It is a beast of very high elevations and only goes down to Phalut in the cold weather. It is covered with longish hair, face also hairy, the ordinary yellowish-brown colour of the Bengal monkey. Stands about 4 feet high and goes about on the ground chiefly, though I think it can also climb.

The peculiar feature is that its tracks are about 18 inches or 2 feet long and toes point in the opposite direction to that in which the animal is moving. The breadth of the track is about 6 inches. I take it he walks on his knees and shins instead of on the sole of his foot. He is known as the Jungli Admi or Sogpa.[1] One was worrying a lot of coolies working in the forest below Phalut in December; they were very frightened and would not go into work. I set off as soon as I could to try and bag the beast, but before I arrived the Forester had been letting off a gun and frightened it away, so I saw nothing. An old choukidar of Phalut told me he had frequently seen them in the snow there, and confirmed the description of the tracks.

It is a thing that practically no Englishman has ever heard of, but all the natives of the higher villages know about it. All I can say is that it is not the Nepal Langur, but I've impressed upon people up there that I want information the next time one is about.

[1] This is also the name of a known tribal group of people in a remote valley of the Himalayas.

49

This report, which would today probably cause quite a stir in certain circles, though for various and quite opposed reasons, seems hardly even to have been commented upon. It would probably have been dismissed altogether—and, most likely not published in the *Proceedings*—had it not been read by such a person as Elwes. As it was, the general impression left was that perhaps a new species of monkey had been found and some local folklore embellished. But, unexpectedly, Henry Elwes then saw fit to make a statement of his own to the effect that in 1906 he had himself seen the same or a similar creature in another part of the Himalayas. Most aggravatingly, he either did not give further details or they were not recorded at the time, and after he died his notes were lost while no mention of the incident was to be found in any of his published writings. Zoologists were apparently quite impressed at the time because of the standing of Elwes, but the matter never got further than the closed confines of professional zoology.

It was, moreover, not until 1920 that the English-speaking public, outside of the limited audience earlier served by the writings of travelers in the Orient, was in any way made aware of this whole business, and, as is so often the case, it was even then more by accident than by design. This part of our story is most intriguing as well as being a sort of turning point in Western thinking, and not only upon this but upon many other matters. But before telling you the details of this little comedy, I just want to diverge a moment to impress upon you once again the fact that what then took place, while a revelation, was more particularly so to the Anglo-Saxon world. A decade before (1907), a certain then young zoologist named Vladimir A. Khakhlov started an extended survey of similar matters throughout central Eurasia and submitted a long report on it to the Imperial Academy of Sciences in Russia; Netherlands authorities had been pestered with annoying (to officialdom) reports of a like nature emanating from Sumatra; the French had undergone the same in Indo-China; and the Brazilians in their country; while even in British Columbia both the courts and the Crown itself had long been bothered by citizens seeking to make depositions on closely related matters. Thus, in retrospect, the happenings of 1920 lose a great deal of their import if not of their impact.

In that year an incident occurred that was impressive enough but which might have been either wholly or temporarily buried had it not been for a concatenation of almost piffling mistakes. In fact, without these mistakes it is almost certain that the whole matter would have remained in obscurity and might even now be considered in an entirely different light or in the status of such other mysteries as that of "sea-monsters." This was a telegram sent by Lt. Col. (now Sir) C. K. Howard-Bury, who was on a reconnaissance expedition to the Mt. Everest region.

The expedition was approaching the northern face of Everest, that is to say from the Tibetan side, and when at about 17,000 feet up on the Lhapka-La pass saw, and watched through binoculars, a number of dark forms moving about on a snowfield far above. It took them some time and considerable effort to reach the snowfield where these creatures had been but when they did so they found large numbers of huge footprints which Colonel Howard-Bury later stated were about "three times those of normal humans" but which he nonetheless also said he thought had been made by "a very large stray, grey wolf." (the extraordinarily illogical phrasing of this statement will be discussed later on, but it should be noted here that a large party of people had seen several creatures moving about, not just "*a* wolf," and that it is hard to see how the Colonel could determine its color from its tracks. Further, wolves cannot walk on two feet only; and, in any case, there are no wolves there!) However, despite these expressions, the Sherpa porters with the expedition disagreed with them most firmly and stated that the tracks were made by a creature of human form to which they gave the name *Metoh-Kangmi*.

Colonel Howard-Bury appears to have been intrigued by this scrap of what he seems to have regarded as local folklore, but, like all who have had contact with them, he had such respect for the Sherpas, that he included the incident in a report that he sent to Katmandu, capital of Nepal, to be telegraphed on to his representatives in India. And this is where the strange mistakes began. It appears that Colonel Howard-Bury in noting the name given by the Sherpas either mistransliterated it or miswrote it; he also failed to realize that he was dealing with one of several kinds of creatures known to the Sherpas and that they, on this occasion, apparently both in an endeavor to emphasize this and for the sake of clarity used as a generic term for all of them, the name *kang-mi,* which was a word foreign to their language. This is a Tibetan colloquialism in some areas, and is itself partly of foreign origin even there, in that *kang,* is apparently of Chinese origin while *mi* is a form of Nepalese *meh.* The combination thus meant "snow

51

creature." His *metoh* would better have been written *meh-teh*, a name of which we shall hear much, and which turns out to mean the *meh* or man-sized *teh* or wild creature. However, the Indian telegraphist then got in the act and either he dispatched this word as, or it was transcribed in India, as *metch*.

The recipients in India were unfamiliar with any of the languages or dialects of the area but they were impressed by the fact that Howard-Bury had thought whatever it might be important enough to cable a report, so they appealed to a sort of fount of universal wisdom for help. This was a remarkable gentleman named Mr. Henry Newman who has for years written a most fascinating column in the *Calcutta Statesman* on almost every conceivable subject and who has the most incredible fund of information at his finger tips. This gentleman, however, did not really know the local languages or dialects of eastern Tibet and Nepal either, but this did not deter him from giving an immediate translation of this *metch kangmi* which, he stated categorically, was *Tibetan* for an "abominable snowman." The result was like the explosion of an atom bomb.

Nobody, and notably the press, could possibly pass up any such delicious term. They seized upon it with the utmost avidity, and bestowed upon it enormous mileage but almost without anything concrete to report. The British press gulped this up and the public was delighted. Then there came a lull in the storm. During this time, it now transpires, a number of eager persons started a fairly systematic search for previous reports on these abominable creatures, and they came up with sufficient to convince their editors that the story was not just a flash in a pan, but a full-fledged mystery that had actually been going on for years.

Thus, the "birth" of the Abominable Snowman per se may be precisely dated as of 1920. And once it was launched it gathered momentum. As we shall see later when we come to examine the actual reports from the eastern Himalayan region, almost everybody who went there, and notably the mountaineers, reported either seeing "snowmen," their tracks, or hearing them; finding cairns and other objects moved by them; or relating information secondhand that they had gleaned from the native population. The business reached a crescendo in 1939 with the publication of several quite long accounts in books by well-known and much respected explorers such as Ronald

Kaulbach. Then came World War II and the matter faded into limbo. But it did not by any means stop.

No sooner was the war over than the onslaught on Mt. Everest was resumed and along with this came a new approach to the ABSM affair. Everybody appears to have felt it incumbent to at least mention the matter even if he could not contribute anything new or material to the story. Yet, there were very few who did not have something concrete to offer and indeed, I am unable to name one who didn't. What is more, prior to World War II, this was an almost exclusively British affair, though there was a book on the first American Karakoram Expedition, entitled *Five Miles High,* that was most pertinent. It has now become international as a result not only of expeditions going to the area from many nations and of multinational composition, but also because of reports that came to light but which were originally made during the war. Also, for the first time, reports by what may be called native foreigners began to appear.

The whole subject of "natives" is a sorry one and it is rather muddling to Americans because, to them, it has several meanings, none of which is exactly synonymous with the term as developed, and understood among the British. It was the declaration of independence by a number of Asiatic nations that brought confusion, in that, while these peoples were manifestly native to their own countries, they suddenly became no longer "natives" in the precise British sense, so that what they said had to be accepted and assessed in an entirely new light. Whereas, while anything stated by such people prior to the war could be passed off as a mere "native tale" or a story "by some benighted native," it had now to be treated with respect as a statement by a responsible citizen. What is more, an Indian traveling through Nepal to Tibet also became just as much a "foreigner" as any Britisher—and, in some cases, actually more so, because there were places where more Britishers had been living longer than any Indians. This proved extremely awkward to the British at first and it took about a decade even for their phlegmatic genius for compromise along with a fairly genuine common decency and belief in good manners, to gain the upper hand.

Despite the international scramble, it was again the British who attracted world attention to the matter of ABSMs and it was still their mountaineers who did this. The most notable was Mr. Eric Shipton who on still another reconnaissance of the Everest Bloc came upon a long set of tracks—not by any means for the first time in his life—and, after following them for some distance, noting they were definitely bipedal but negotiated almost impossible obstacles that would be hard for even an experienced mountaineer to do, took a series of clear photographs of them. These were published in the much respected *Illustrated London News,* not a publication given to elaboration, irresponsible reportage, or the mounting of international jokes. This time everybody had to take the matter seriously; and they did, but in a variety of ways. The public, as is its pragmatic wont, took it at its face value. The press literally howled. The explorers cheered a bit. But the scientists flew into a positive tantrum; an altogether undignified performance, the effects of which have not yet worn off and will not do so for many years. This was in 1951 and it marked the next turning point in the history of ABSMery.

Up till then the matter had been primarily a "Western" and notably a British prequisite; it had also been a child of the popular press with a sort of minor cold war going on between the mountaineers and the zoologists. Now, however, a new agency entered the picture, a polyglot assortment of people of various bents that can only be termed "The Searchers."

Since the turn of the century there had continued to be outright explorers as well as putterers and sportsmen in the field and not a few of these continued to stumble upon ABSMs, or tracks and other evidence of their pasing. None of these, however, had any prior interest in the matter and, like the mountaineers, had been in the Himalayas primarily for other purposes. On the other hand, the whole affair was, until Eric Shipton published his photographs, really nothing more than a news-gimmick though the press had had to tread warily with the reports made by promiment persons and especially the mountaineers engaged in the attack on Everest, which had official backing. The scientific world had not been quite so circumspect. At the outset, it denounced the whole thing as, first, a fraud, and then a case of mistaken identity, and it stuck to this story: and it still in large part sticks to it today, even to the extent of deliberately ridiculing such men as Shipton and Kaulbach. But after their completely unsuccessful attempt to set Shipton's 1951 findings at nought, which backfired with considerable public impact, a sort of revolution began within the ranks of science.

Some topnotch scientists—not just technicians and self-appointed experts who happened to be employed by scientific organizations—started to investigate the whole matter upon truly scientific principles. What is more, these scientists were primarily anthropologists [as opposed to zoologists] and this was of the utmost significance, for the latter had permanently closed the door on the whole question when they could not prove that it was a hoax, stating flatly that all ABSM tracks were made either by bears or monkeys. Also, there were anthropological expeditions actually going into the field and these too began to report discoveries similar to those of the mountaineers. Notable among the fieldworkers were Dr. Wyss-Dunant of a Swiss expedition, Professor von Fürer-Haimendorff of the School of Oriental and African Studies, and in particular Prof. René von Nebesky-Wojkowitz. Among these not engaged in fieldwork were Dr. W. C. Osman Hill then of the Zoological Society of London in England, Dr. Bernard Heuvelmans, Belgian zoologist, in Paris, and latterly a whole group of Russian scientists led by Prof. B. F. Porshnev.

It was the press, however, that was in the end first in the field with an expedition aimed primarily at the ABSMs. This was organized by the *Daily Mail* of London and went to the Himalayas in 1954. It was a curious outfit and it was not very successful but it initiated a new phase in the history of this mystery. It was led by a reporter Ralph Izzard and had among its members a professional zoologist, Dr. Biswas of Calcutta and also a man named W. M. (Gerald) Russell, whose experience was of great significance though nobody seems to have realized it at that time. However, it was once again directed by mountaineers. The significance of this escaped everybody then and to a very great extent still does. The universal impression had been gained over the years that the Abominable (as then supposed) Snowman, whatever it might be, was a denizen of the snowfields and therefore inhabited the uppermost slopes of the Himalayas. As a result, its pursuit was looked upon primarily as a mountaineering job and was therefore given to the professionals and the experts in that field of sport. The idea of including a scientist and especially a zoologist, had never occurred to anybody previously. The idea of including a man with the particular skills and experience, as well as training, of Gerald Russell has not even yet, it seems, dawned upon anybody.

Russell alone among the whole army of investigators is really the only man qualified to tackle the problem, for he is a professional collector, which is something absolutely different from either hunters or sportsmen on the one hand, or research scientists on the other. Then again, no ABSM is a denizen of any snowfield—naturally; and as should be obvious to any sane person on a moment's consideration, for in such places there is nothing to eat. All turn out to inhabit dense mountain forests. Thus, just about the last persons suited to search for them are mountaineers (who have a positive passion for climbing mountains above all else, it should be pointed out), while sportsmen and hunters are little better for other and even more obvious reasons.

This is a somewhat sensitive question but one of first importance. The techniques developed over the ages for hunting are basically aggressive, be they noisy as in "beating," or silent as in "stalking." Further, the dog—which is not only a domestic but actually an artificial animal—has been extensively used in hunting. These methods obtain the quickest results, in the largest amounts, of what is specifically desired. Collecting, on the other hand, should best be almost entirely passive. Silence is one of its features in certain of its aspects but almost as much noise is permissible as in hunting in certain circumstances. To obtain animals not normally hunted, the less ground covered the better but the longer the collector must sit and wait for the animals to become used to his presence, the noises he makes, and the effluvia he gives off in the normal course of "living." As many artificial things as possible must be eliminated; and most notably dogs, metal (especially metal cleaned with mineral oils), and suchlike that are not indigenous to the wild. Given time, any wild creature, however timid, will come to investigate the collector, whereas it will fly before the hunter long before it is detected.

Even zoologists, unless they have had extensive *collecting* experience in the field, are little better, for they, poor souls, are hustled about by everybody else into and out of the least likely areas for proper investigation, and are in any case supplied in advance with a sort of "book of rules" that goes far to negating the search for anything that is not already known.

The *Daily Mail* expedition did, nonetheless, include among its ranks, and deliberately, a very experienced zoologist with field experience in the form of Dr. Biswas, and, quite fortuitously in the person of Gerald Russell, the first and only man on any ABSM expedition trained to tackle such a collecting problem. It also accomplished something else, in that it publicized the whole matter and served notice on everybody that the press was no longer overawed by what they had termed "scientific opinion," but from then on took the affair for granted as having graduated from the category of the "silly season filler." In fact, it pointed the way to some serious endeavor designed to try to solve the mystery. This challenge was taken up by quite a new type of operator.

The *Daily Mail* expedition returned in 1955, and in that same year an Argentine mountaineering expedition and another British party (of Royal Air Force alpinists) reported having encountered tracks and other evidence of ABSMs. The following year John Keel, already mentioned, made his trip through the country and, as stated in his book published in 1958, tracked and sighted an ABSM. At the same time, the Russians were conducting investigations and getting ready to make a concerted attack upon the problem. There were also quite a number of others in the field, while the few serious students at home began to bring to light all manner of related items from the past.

The busiest of these scientific sleuths and the most open-minded and best-informed was the zoologist, Dr. Bernard Heuvelmans, who had for long specialized in the collection and examination of evidence for the existence of any creatures as yet unknown to and unidentified by zoologists. It was he, moreover, who first brought the findings of the Hollanders in the East Indies, the French in Indo-China, and to a very considerable extent that of the South American explorers to light. The American edition of these findings by Heuvelmans, *On the Track of Unknown Animals,* was published by Hill and Wang of New York, in 1958. However, the most significant personality to enter the field was the prominent Texan, Mr. Thomas B. Slick.

Tom Slick, as he was known to everybody [2] and all over the world, was a most remarkable man. To Americans he is probably best known because of the airline that carries his name, which is itself a natural advertisement with amusing connotations in the English language. Then, in the world of commerce he was widely known for his position in the mysterious world of oil and the very down-to-earth world of beef; but, his international reputation is based on his extraordinary efforts in the cause of world peace. Tom Slick did many other things and was not only a patron of but a driving force in many purely scientific endeavors. He established the second largest privately endowed research unit in the world, in the form of the Southwest Research

[2] Mr. Slick was killed in a plane crash in Montana in 1962.

Institute near his home town of San Antonio, and adjacent to this another large organization for educational promotion. I am often asked to describe this man, and my response is invariably the same; namely, to say simply that, for all his activities and the vastness of his outlook and effort, he is less like the popular conception of a Texan than anybody I have ever met. Tom Slick did things and very fortunately he became intrigued with the business of ABSMs. Despite ridicule, especially among many of those closest to him, he set to work upon it with the determination that he, almost alone in the Western World it seems, was capable of and willing to apply.

I speak of Tom Slick at length because it was he, and he almost alone, who by his quiet persuasion heaved this whole irksome business out of a sort of ten-ring, international circus, into the realm of serious scientific endeavor; while he also stimulated others in England, France, Italy, India, and elsewhere to work on the problem, by means of personal contacts and by the exercise of sympathetic encouragement. Finally, he did one more thing. This was to break out of the confined limits of the Himalayan area of the Oriental Region and direct attention and proper effort to other parts of the world, such as California, which are proving to be every bit as important in regards to ABSMs, if not much more significant than even the uplands of Eurasia. He began his own personal investigations by a trip to the Himalayan region in 1957.

In 1957, Tom Slick, together with F. K. Johnson, mounted the first full-fledged expedition to the Himalayas for the specific and sole purpose of investigating ABSMs. This saw the extremely fortuitous bringing together of Gerald Russell and the brothers Peter and Bryan Byrne, and was the happiest event that had until then happened to ABSMery. For the first time in history the leadership was not given to mountaineers or hunters, but to persons with collecting experience who believed that the quarry was real, was multiple in form, and that, in all its forms, it lived in the forests as opposed to on the upper snowfields. As a result, this expedition came closer to obtaining concrete results than any other before, and produced more straight evidence of the existence of such creatures than all other expeditions put together (for details see Chapter 12).

In the same year, however, the Soviet Academy of Sciences had established a special commission to co-ordinate the findings of several groups who had been working on the problem in countries within the Soviet sphere. These workers had brought to light the astonishing reports of Khakhlov made to the Academy in 1914, but which had been shelved; they had before them the current report of a Dr. Pronin, a hydrologist of Leningrad University who alleged he had seen an ABSM in the Pamirs; they had a wealth of material from the Mongolian Peoples' Republic and a lot from China; and they had decided to mount proper scientific expeditions to investigate. These were four in number and were put into the field in 1958—one to the Caucasus where a creature named the "Wind Man" had been rumored for centuries; one to the north face of the Everest Bloc; one to the Mongolian region; and one to the Pamirs, which, for certain odd reasons they considered to be the breeding ground of the ABSMs. Meantime, they started the publication of their over-all findings in the form of booklets (see Chapters 13 and 14) and concurrently with this, a series of studies on fossil men, and particularly the Neanderthalers. Also, a wealth of previously unpublished material, some historical and some current, appeared in certain Russian magazines—notably, *Tekhnika Molodyozhi.*

These Soviet activities shed an entirely new light on the whole business, and also put it on such an altogether higher plane that Western scientific circles were obliged to change their attitude toward the matter quite drastically. No longer could they simply avoid the issue by saying that it had been explained or that its protagonists were merely a bunch of amateur enthusiasts pursuing a fantasy. At the same time, a certain nervous irritation was to be detected in their pronouncements, because the press just then began harping on the case of the Coelacanth fish discovered off the southeast coast of South Africa. This had at first been called a hoax but had finally had to be accepted as living proof of the fact that not everything about the life of this planet is known. Obviously, creatures confidently thought to have been decently extinct for tens of millions of years can still be around.

Further, it was the Russians who first stressed, though perhaps more by inference, something that those scientists in the West who *had* been taking the matter seriously had been harping on for some time. This was that the whole problem is an anthropological rather than a zoological matter. In other words, all the Sino-Soviet evidence pointed to ABSMs being primitive *Hominids* (i.e. Men) rather than *Pongids* (i.e. Apes) or other nonhuman creatures, thus linking them with known fossil forms such as *Gigantopithecus,* the Pithecanthropines, and especially the Neanderthalers. And, in doing this, they also emphasized another point.

That was the now very obvious but totally ignored fact that there is not just one creature called *The* Abominable Snowman, but a whole raft of creatures distributed almost all over the world, of very considerable variety, and of as many as three distinct types in the Tibetan-Himalayan area alone. This suggestion was of course not merely obnoxious but positively horrific to the orthodox scientists who were still vehemently denying even the possibility of the existence of even *one* such entity. Then, the final bombshell landed. At this point in my narrative I must confess to a considerable embarrassment since I must speak in the first person and I do this with much diffidence.

In 1958, I received a number of reports of an ABSM in California. At first, this sounded quite balmy even to us —and we are used to the most outrageous things—and got itself filed among what we call *forteana,* which is to say those damnable and unacceptable items of the categories collected by the late Charles Fort. However, it so happened that I was privileged to spend the year 1959 touring the North American continent gathering material for a book on its geology, topography, vegetational cover, and wildlife. Before leaving, I had a research specialist—Stanley I. Rowe, with whom I had long been associated— prepare for me from his files, from ours, and from other sources, the details of any and all oddities and enigmas reported from this continent, by states and provinces. These I investigated as a news-reporter as I went along; and when I came to northern California I fell into the most extraordinary state of affairs that I have ever encountered in my life. This was no idle rumor but a full-fledged mystery and a straight down-the-line, hard-boiled news-story.

This I tell in detail in Chapter 6, so suffice it to say here that I found there clear and most convincing evidence of the existence of a form of ABSM of most outstanding qualities. But worse was to follow for, prompted by this astonishing discovery, I went aside in British Columbia to investigate their long-renowned *Sasquatch,* only to find that it was just as definite, and apparently identical to these *Oh-Mahs* (or "Bigfeet") of California. Subsequent research has, what is more, brought to light a mass of other reports of similar things from Quebec, the Canadian Northwest Territories, the Yukon, the Idaho Rockies, Washington, and Oregon.[3]

This brings us up to the date of writing, except to note that a large Japanese expedition went in 1959–60 to the Himalayas specifically to search for ABSMs; while there were other expeditions in that area, in Sumatra, and in California, fitted out for the purpose. Finally, later this year (1960), Sir Edmund Hillary, backed by American sponsors and with Marlin Perkins, Director of the Lincoln Park Zoo of Chicago accompanying him as zoological expert, conducted an expedition to the eastern Himalayas with this pursuit as his second major objective.

[3] These affairs in our Northwest were summarized in two articles in *True Magazine* for October, 1959, and January, 1960, and set a whole new phase of ABSMery in motion.

2. Ubiquitous Woodsmen

REPORTS FROM CANADA (1860 TO 1920)

In my opening remarks in the previous chapter I said that I was going to tell this story to the chronology of discoveries made by the Western World, starting about the year 1860, rather than according to straight historical chronology. Having briefly outlined these discoveries from that date up to this year, I landed up in the northwestern corner of North America. I now find that this is just the place where I have to commence my detailed reporting and for several reasons. By way of explanation I resort to a map (Map I); a procedure that, I am afraid, you will discover I nearly always do.

ABSMs have now been reported from several dozen areas scattered all over five of the continents. At first sight this distribution does not appear to make any sense at all. This is a misconception but to go into the whys and wherefors thereof at this juncture would not only be exhausting but more or less incomprehensible. Nonetheless, one cannot just go barging off all over the world reporting on this and that, both in time and space, without some ordered plan. Skipping around and back and forth over oceans just to point out similarities would be altogether aggravating. Some orderly procedure is therefore called for; and very fortunately there is a ready-made one that will serve many purposes. This is to adopt the travelogue approach, starting out from some specific point, visiting all the other necessary points, and ending up where we began. Doing this in the pursuit of ABSMs just happens to be most convenient, and for a number of reasons. If we take northwestern North America as our starting point, we will be able to dispense with a great deal of verbal garbage and duplication.

I therefore propose to take you on a journey starting

from western Canada, south through the Americas to Patagonia, then back up to the southern edge of the Amazon Basin; then hop over the Atlantic to West Africa, proceed through or rather around the Congo Basin and over the eastern uplands to the forested coastal lands of East Africa. From there, we will jump over the Indian Ocean to the island of Sumatra, proceed from there up the Malay Peninsula to the main body of the great Indo-Chinese peninsula, then turn sharp left in Assam and travel along the Himalayas to the vast Pamirs, and on southwest through Persia to the Caucasus. This will be a turnabout point from which we will return east to the Pamirs, on to the Kunluns, then to the Tien-Shans, Ala-Tau, Altais, and Sayans. From there we will go south through the Khangais and over the Ala-Shan Desert to the Nan-Shans and on to the mountains of Szechwan. Here will be another turnabout point from where we will go north again through the Tsin-lings and the Ordos to the Khingans. In this last lap on our way home we will be following a lot more than ABSMs, and in following these we will cross over the Bering Straits to and through Alaska and the Yukon back to our starting point in British Columbia and specifically to a small place named Yale, on the middle Fraser River (see Map VI).

It was near this place that something frightfully important happened in the year 1884; on the morning of July 3, as a matter of fact. The gorge of the Fraser narrows along this stretch so that rock walls tower on either side. Today, two railroads and the main west-to-east Canadian highway squeeze through this point and the little township of Yale clings to the bank of the river on one side, and is dotted about a narrow meadow on the other. Since I beg to be regarded exclusively as a reporter for the duration of the forthcoming journey, the best thing for me to do is to quote the original report on what happened there on that day. This goes as follows, as taken from the Victoria newspaper, *The Daily British Colonist:*

YALE, B.C., JULY 3, 1884—In the immediate vicinity of No. 4 tunnel, situated some 20 miles above this village, are bluffs of rock which have hitherto been unsurmountable, but on Monday morning last were successfully scaled by Mr. Onderdonk's employees on the regular train from Lytton. Assisted by Mr. Costerton, the British Columbia Express Company's messenger, a number of gentlemen from Lytton and points east of

63

that place, after considerable trouble and perilous climbing captured a creature who may truly be called half man and half beast. "Jacko," as the creature has been called by his capturers, is something of the gorilla type standing about 4 feet 7 inches in height and weighing 127 pounds. He has long, black, strong hair and resembles a human being with one exception, his entire body, excepting his hands (or paws) and feet are covered with glossy hair about one inch long. His fore arm is much longer than a man's fore arm, and he possesses extraordinary strength, as he will take hold of a stick and break it by wrenching or twisting it, which no man living could break in the same way. Since his capture he is very reticent, only occasionally uttering a noise which is half bark and half growl. He is, however, becoming daily more attached to his keeper, Mr. George Telbury, of this place, who proposes shortly starting for London, England, to exhibit him. His favorite food so far is berries, and he drinks fresh milk with evident relish. By advice of Dr. Hannington, raw meats have been withheld from Jacko, as the doctor thinks it would have a tendency to make him savage. The mode of capture was as follows: Ned Austin, the engineer, on coming in sight of the bluff at the eastern end of the No. 4 tunnel saw what he supposed to be a man lying asleep at close proximity to the track, and as quick as thought blew the signal to apply the brakes. The brakes were instantly applied, and in a few seconds the train was brought to a standstill. At this moment the supposed man sprang up, and uttering a sharp quick bark began to climb the steep bluff. Conductor R. J. Craig and Express Messenger Costerton, followed by the baggage man and brakesmen, jumped from the train and knowing they were some 20 minutes ahead of time, immediately gave chase. After 5 minutes of perilous climbing the then supposed demented Indian was corralled on a projecting shelf of rock where he could neither ascend nor descend. The query now was how to capture him alive, which was quickly decided by Mr. Craig, who crawled on his hands and knees until he was about 40 feet above the creature. Taking a small piece of loose rock he let it fall and it had the desired effect of rendering poor Jacko incapable of resistance for a time at least. The bell rope was then brought up and Jacko was now lowered to terra firma. After binding him and placing him in a baggage car, "off brakes" was sounded and the train started for Yale. At the station a large crowd who had heard of the capture by telephone from Spuzzum Flat were assembled, and each one anxious to have the first look at the monstrosity, but they were disappointed, as Jacko had been taken off at the machine shops and placed in charge of his present keeper.

The question naturally arises, how came the creature where it was first seen by Mr. Austin? From bruises about its head and body, and apparent soreness since its capture, it is supposed that Jacko ventured too near the edge of the bluff, slipped, fell and lay where found until the sound of the rushing train aroused him. Mr. Thomas White, and Mr. Gouin, C. B. E., as well as Mr. Major, who kept a small store about half a mile west of the tunnel during the past 2 years, have mentioned having seen a curious creature at different points between Camps 13 and 17, but no attention was paid to their remarks as people came to the conclusion that they had either seen a bear or stray Indian dog. Who can unravel the mystery that now surrounds Jacko? Does he belong to a species hitherto unknown in this part of the continent or is he really what the train men first thought he was, a crazy Indian?

Now, whatever you may think of the press, you cannot just write off anything and everything reported by it that you don't like, don't believe in, and don't want. Further, to a newspaperman, this report is excellent, being factual, giving names that were obviously carefully checked even to titles such as the C. B. E. of Mr. Gouin, and hardly being at all speculative. In fact, it is really a model report and one that some present-day newsmen might well emulate. Then, the persons concerned were not a bunch of citizens with names only to identify them; they were mostly people with responsible positions who must have been widely known at that time throughout the area, for the railroad played a very important part in the opening up and development of lower British Columbia. The reporter, moreover, himself took a very common-sense view of the business when he inquired what manner of creature this might be and stated flatly that it was completely human but for being covered with silky black hair and having exceptional strength in its arms. The asinine opinions of others—such as, that the similar if not identical creature seen before might have been a bear or a "stray Indian dog"

65

—are recorded "straight" and without facetious comment. The whole thing cannot, in fact, be lightly dismissed. It therefore has to be most seriously considered.

The story has been publicized for some 50 years now, so that afficionados of ABSMery can often almost quote it verbatim but, although I must here class myself among these reportorial limpets, I wish to put on record one thought about it that has always stayed with me. This stemmed from a comment made in another paper shortly after the original story was published, and which asked quite without facetiousness also but with a slight air of mystification, how anybody could suggest that this "Jacko" could have been a chimpanzee that had escaped from a circus. This little aside puts the whole affair in a remarkably vivid light, for we tend to forget that it was penned 75 years ago in a country that was then only recently connected with the rest of the world. Also, it was written before palaeontologists had demonstrated that true monkeys and, more so, the apes (i.e. Pongids), never have existed in the Western Hemisphere.

This creature was captured, and it is absolutely sure that it existed in "captivity" for some time (a reporter in 1946 interviewed an old gentleman in Lytton, B.C. who remembered having seen it): it was not human, yet it was more so than it was anything else; it had definitely been captured on the Fraser River; therefore, there had to be some explanation of how it got there and what it was. The standard answers to these questions today would undoubtedly be that it was (1) a hoax, or (2) a "cross"—though between what and what would doubtless not be suggested, (3) a throwback—and probably an "Indian" one, (4) a little boy who had been lost years before on a hunting trip and either managed to survive all on his own or been fed by wolves, (5) a mentally defective glandular case from an "institution," or (6); and most likely of all, an ape escaped from a bankrupt circus. Surprisingly, the locals and even hard-boiled newspapermen of the time did not indulge in any of these latterday foibles: rather, they asked a straight question and poo-poohed any outlander's suggestion that it was a chimp escaped from a circus. They even inquired as to whether it might be a very primitive form of human or an as yet unidentified species of great ape, and in either case indigenous to the area.

I may be properly accused of harping on this case, but I think that of almost all ABSM reports it is perhaps the most cogent. It took place just within the "age of reason" (today, perhaps, rather a misnomer) in a country then inhabited and being opened up by the most extremely pragmatic Westerners of predominantly hard-headed Anglo-Saxon stock, at a time when there was little call for phoney sensationalism. It was not just a report of tracks or other secondary items, nor even of an alleged sighting; it was a clear and definite account of a capture by known people with all the witnesses needed for confirmation. Quite apart from anything else, it alone sets at nought the constant refrain "Well, why haven't we ever caught one?"

This is by no means the only ABSM that has been caught, but it is the only one that I know of that was caught by what we must call for lack of a better phrase "Westerners," and it is this culture that is the most skeptical, the most stubborn, and at the same time the most interested. Of course, the more aggravating part of the business is that there is no proper end to the Jacko story, and no physical evidence of his existence has come down to us—at least as far as anybody so far knows. What actually happened is not recorded; the only inkling that I have traced being a remark by Mr. Stephen Franklin, staff writer of *Weekend* magazine, in his excellent article dated April 4, 1959, in which it is stated (and I quote) that "The editor of the *Inland Sentinel* inopportunely chose this month (the one in which Jacko was captured) to hump his newspaper and his presses up the canyon from Yale to Kamloops, and didn't publish an edition for several weeks."

This statement is itself a kind of *non sequitur* since the original reports come from *The Daily British Colonist,* of Victoria. I made somewhat extensive search for any series on the forlorn Jacko in a Yale paper of old, but was unable to unearth even the morgue of the *Inland Sentinel* which moved to Kamloops. Jacko, sad to tell, just "dropped out of the news" without apparently further comment; perhaps the most enigmatic figure ever to appear in the pages of history and potentially one of the most important.

Would that we could unearth the end of this story and learn what did happen to him, for he must have either (1) escaped, (2) died, or (3) been killed, and in the two last events it is possible that some part of him may have been preserved and be lying either in somebody's attic trunk, or even in a museum. And do not for a moment get the idea that the latter is impossible.

Jacko, however, is not just an isolated imp that suddenly appeared upon the scene and then disappeared. Before his capture either he or one of his species had been reported from the same area by Mr. Alexander Caulfield Anderson, a well-known explorer and an executive of the Hudson's Bay Company, who was doing a "survey" of the newly opened territory and seeking a feasible trade route through it for his company. He reported just such hairy hominids as having hurled rocks down upon him and his surveying party from more than one slope. That was in 1864. Many years later, Mr. J. W. Burns (now retired and living in San Francisco) who had devoted a lifetime to the study of this business, unearthed an old Amerindian woman from Port Douglas at the head of Harrison Lake (see Map VI) who alleged, and brought some seconders to confirm, that she had been kidnapped by one of these creatures in the year 1871, kept by it for a year, but finally returned by it to her tribal homestead because she "aggravated it so much" (though, she said, it had treated her with every consideration). This old lady died in 1940 at the age of 86. When abducted she was 17 years old and was, she stated, forced to swim the Harrison River by the ABSM and then carried by him to a rock shelter where its aged parents dwelt. This account comes from Mr. Burns who had for years enjoyed the confidence of this retiring Amerind. It has been embellished in various ways by others to the effects that the girl had rosin plastered over her eyes by the creature; that she became pregnant by it; and that she subsequently gave birth to a half-breed that either was stillborn, died shortly after birth, or is still hidden by her people from the eyes of the white man. She never said any of these things to Mr. Burns but adhered to her straightforward story till her death.

Nor is this woman's story unique. All the Amerinds of southern British Columbia, Washington State, Oregon, parts of Idaho, and the Yuroks and the Hüppas of northern California not only have similar tales to tell but a history of these creatures so complete and extensive that it would take a volume to tell in itself. The poor Amerinds have always been and still are regarded by Americans and Canadians as "natives," which indeed they are, but in the same light as the British used to regard the inhabitants of all countries other than their own or at least beyond the confines of western Europe. The stories told by, and the traditions of, Amerinds are not, therefore, regarded as of much worth or reliability. Nonetheless and despite the fact that these people did not previously write and have had even today little if any contact among themselves over any distance, their reports upon these local ABSMs are absolutely the same all the way from the Mackenzie Range to Alaska through the Yukons and British Columbia, down through Washington and Oregon to California, and back to the western flank of the Rockies in Idaho. There are traditions and folk-tales spread over an even wider area among these people, but this is another matter. I am here speaking of perfectly straightforward, up-to-date accounts of encounters with such creatures that have been made by them ever since the white man first got to speak with them and which have come in from one source or another annually every year since the capture of Jacko. I will interject some of these as I go along.

Before doing so, however, I must put on record that I do not share the old British or what seems to be the current American opinion of "natives" and never have. Further, as a working reporter, having now been privileged to travel extensively throughout just the five continents with which we are concerned in this story, I would state that I find the so-called "native" in some respects on the whole more reliable than the foreigner, and the white foreigner in particular. First, they seem to me to know their country better; secondly, those of them that are country folk are almost invariably consummate naturalists and know their local fauna inside out (and much better than we do); third, if they like you and feel that you are not going to laugh at everything they say, they are very pragmatic and are willing to tell you, straight, what is what in their opinion; fourth, provided one appreciates the very basic fact that to many non-Europeans there is a nonmaterial world that is just as real as the material one, one can readily distinguish between stories of one and the other, and may even without giving offense ask the teller to which category any story belongs. When my job was collecting animals for scientific institutions in out of the way parts of the world—a profession I pursued for two decades—I always asked the natives for information on their local fauna. While all people may display, and often do so, lapses or gaps in their knowledge, and so just do not know an animal that has always been right under their noses, what they *do* tell has, I found, invariably turned out to be the truth. More than this, some people, such as the Mayas of Yucatan, are absolutely incredible "taxonomists" in that they differentiate, and have names for every type of animal, so that in one case I found out after long and patient recording phonetically that they even had the spiders of their country classified, all in just the same way as does our modern

69

zoology. Then finally, I would also put on record that I have a particular respect for the nonprofessional American "Indian" as he is so incorrectly and lugubriously called.

My wife and I have lived with various of these peoples —and they are as varied a lot as "Europeans" if not more so—off and on for many years; we did so in rather exceptional circumstances in that we were neither their employers nor employees, were not interested specifically in their "culture," art, or anything else, but had several mutual interests with them in their crops, stock, local wildlife, and plants. My wife has an exceptional knack of learning languages by ear and under appropriate circumstances and in local costume she can look like almost any race on earth while I, as a "doctor" or "medicine person" was on the one hand unobtrusive and inoffensive to them while, on the other, having my wife with me I could browse around in the obscurer corners of life without giving concern to the elders or alarm to my male contemporaries. Thus, by simply living alongside these people—and going to their dances only for the fun of it, instead of to study their alleged implications, and so forth—we came to chat around the evening fire of many things. While I have found the African the most enjoyable company at such times of genuine relaxation, and the Malayan peoples the most informed (sometimes terrifyingly so to a European), it has been the Amerinds that I have found to be the most down to earth and pragmatic. Many of these peoples—and they are the first to admit it; roar with laughter at the fact; and will not be offended by a sincere friend saying so—love to drink alcohol and sometimes indulge in stimulants that we class as narcotics, and when they do so they can very readily become uproarious in all manner of ways. At these times they will concoct the most delicious imagery compounded of mysticism, ancient tradition, and personal whim, and, while there may be all manner of historical gems to be gleaned from such outpourings, none of it should be taken as "exact science." When, however, they are stone-cold "sober," in the strictest sense of that loose term, they can give out information of a caliber that would do justice to a Yale professor. Don't ever underestimate the Amerind or his knowledge! I shall not forget a remark made to a partner of mine, who has also lived with these people and likes them very much, so that they seem to like him. He was making exhaustive inquiries into this very matter of ABSMs, when an old gentleman—a doyen of his tribal unit and a pillar of the local church—suddenly burst out with "Oh! Don't tell me the white men have finally gotten around to *that?*"

Let us, nonetheless, ignore the Amerinds for the moment and concentrate on the unfolding of ABSMery in and about British Columbia as reported by "white men" or allegedly witnessed by them. This history is now just about 100 years old, starting with Mr. Anderson of the Hudson's Bay Company. During this period some paleface appears to have reported an ABSM incident almost every year and they are now doing so in droves, to such an exaggerated extent that even Chambers of Commerce (*vide* that of Harrison Lake, the leading resort area of the vast city of Vancouver) have gotten into the act, and one sees large cutouts of the creatures along highways advertising anything from motels and garages to bakeries, cleaning services, and speedboats. Most notable contributions to this tradition have been made in the years 1901, 1904, 1907, 1909, 1910, 1912, 1915, 1924, 1936, 1939, 1941, 1948, 1954, 1955, 1956, and, 1959. And all but two of these were "sightings" or rather personal encounters, but usually confirmed by more than one witness—not just dreary footprints found in snow or mud, hanks of hair, overturned barrels, or piles of excrement. This is really a pretty astonishing picture and makes affairs even in Nepal look somewhat picayune.

All of this centers around the lower Fraser River and notably around Lake Harrison. Therefore, I resort, as usual, to a map (Map VI) in order to cut down verbiage. All of these reports have been published before, and often so many times that there are those who feel that the process has been protracted *ad nauseam*. Nevertheless, I am, as I have said, myself reporting and I do not know of any one place where all of them have been brought together in chronological order. That anything like this could have been going on for a century right in our front yard—it being politically in Canada—is amazing enough but we are to get an even more profound jolt when we come to see that the very same thing has been going on in our own *back yard*—to wit, in Washington, Oregon, California, and, according to none other than Theodore Roosevelt, at one time at least, in Idaho.

The opening gambit was a sworn statement made by a highly respected lumberman who had also been most successful as a timber-cruiser and prospector, named Mike King. This gentleman had had to penetrate an isolated area in the north of Vancouver Island in 1901, alone, because

71

his Amerindian employees refused even to enter it on any account but mostly because they said that it was a territory of the "Wildmen of the Woods." From other accounts of Mr. King it seems that he was not a man to be diverted from essential business routine by such stories, but that he had a profound respect for the local "natives" because they had guided him to a reasonable fortune on more than one occasion simply by their real knowledge of the country and the timber that grew in it. Some days after penetrating this wild area, Mr. King topped a ridge and spotted below a creature squatting by a creek washing some kind of roots and arranging them in two neat piles beside him, or her, on the bank. This should be compared with the specific remarks made by Mr. Ostman (see Chapter 3.) on the same subject. In my interview with Mr. Ostman, he stressed the collection of roots by the creatures and even named the plant most chosen, also the careful washing and stacking of these. Perhaps he got the notion from reading this account, but personally I doubt it. King's natural instinct was to raise his rifle and sight, for the creature was large, covered in reddish brown fur, and thus potentially dangerous. By the time the fact that brown bears don't wash roots and stack them up had penetrated, he realized that he had some kind of hominid in his sights and he lowered the rifle. The creature took off, running like a man and, as Mr. King later reported: "His arms were peculiarly long and used freely in climbing and brush-running [i.e. scrambling on all fours through scrub]." King descended the slope and inspected the spoor left by the departed one, and noted that it was a distinctly "human foot but with phenomenally long and spreading toes." [1]

On reading the original account from an old clipping to a company of easterners some years ago, I heard somebody murmur, "And so endeth the first lesson." And so indeed! For, although that statement has been repeatedly recounted and Mike King has been repeatedly said to have elaborated, no further direct quotes appear to be extant. This is the way that unexpected things happen. I know from the few that I have experienced. You are not prepared for them; by the time you have managed to bring your senses to bear upon them, they are up and away; and you are left gaping, with a blurred impression all around a

[1] This remark, and particularly the word *"long"* used to describe the toes, rather than the whole foot, is most pertinent as we shall see when we come to examine the tracks of the *Oh-Mahs*.

single vivid centerpiece. What more can you add unless you want to be a tattler? Mike King apparently had both the decency and the common sense to say what he had to say and then shut up.

The next lot to have a similar encounter (in 1904) were out hunting near Great Central Lake on Vancouver Island. Their names were J. Kincaid, T. Hutchins, A. Crump, and W. Buss, four citizens of Qualicum. They were apparently beating the bush, and put up what they afterward described as a boy ABSM that was covered with brown hair but had long *head-hair and a beard*. This is a very odd report in that it otherwise crops up only once or twice in all the accounts of ABSMs, and is, categorically, contrary to all the other reports by everybody who has alleged that he or she has seen these creatures at close range.

The third classic report is dated 1907 and was made by the Captain and crew of the coastal steamer *Capilano* on their return from a routine cruise during which they had called at a small landing named Bishop's Cove. There, they said, the entire Amerindian population had come charging aboard begging for asylum or outright emigration due to a huge monkey-like, human-shaped creature that had been clam-digging along their beach for a number of nights in succession, and that gave vent to most disturbing high-pitched howls. These people readily identified the creature but insisted that it had moved into their territory with its family, if not its whole clan, and that it would not brook any interference by a few poorly armed humans. The comments on this report are rather illuminating as they display a curious acknowledgement of the presence of such "Wildmen" and the fact that, while they are accepted as being basically peaceable and known to mind their own business, and while they avoid organized men in masses, they tend to adopt a nasty tone when it comes to hunting and collecting rights, and appear then to regard the Amerinds as interlopers and a nuisance. In 1907, however, the attitude of even the British toward real primitives was going through a peculiar phase; halfway between the concept of the "worthless native" and that of the "noble savage." The Amerinds had proved an unreliable labor force, while certain other non-Europeans had turned out to be far too civilized for rank exploitation. The idea of really primitive creatures had not yet been abandoned and everybody was still undecided just how to behave toward them. The thought that we might be dealing with sub-hominids did not, of course, occur to anybody pro-

73

fessing any education (after all, Darwin was hardly cold as of then) but it remained in no way illogical to the uneducated, and it was played on by the press.

This may in some measure account for the solemnity with which a discovery made in 1912 was greeted. I got this report from Mr. Burns, mentioned above. It came to him from the principal, a Mr. Ernest A. Edwards, who states that he was residing at Shushwap, B.C., at that date, and that he and his wife had unearthed on the small island of Neskain a little way off the coast, a human skeleton that they found protruding from the bank of a river. The location was noted for its abundance of "arrowheads" of Amerindian origin. This skeleton is stated to have measured "from skull to ankel-joints—7 feet 6 inches, so with feet and scalp, the person must have been eight feet tall." Mr. Burns received this information in a letter from Mr. Edwards in 1941, and this included the further comments that "I, together with my wife, examined the jaw. The teeth were of huge size, but in perfect condition—no cavities noticeable. The jawbone was so large that it would span my face easily at the cheek bones. Together with the help of Indians, I crated it and shipped it to Rexham Museum, North Wales, England, where I believe it still is. In his acknowledgement, the Curator of the museum was greatly astonished, remarking among other observations, that it was hard to believe such jaws and teeth 'existed' in human beings."

The receipt of such intelligence as this naturally prompts an almost fiendish "Ho-ho! what is this?" on the part of any reporter, so I wrote to the Curator of the museum specified and got the following reply from the Librarian of the town of Wrexham (not Rexham, there being no such town in Wales or anywhere else in Great Britain): "With regard to your query, I have checked the Minutes of this establishment [i.e. museum and public library] for the years 1912, 1913, and 1914, and there is no mention of the receipt of a skeleton. Yours sincerely, Clifford Harris, F.L.A."

Reports of the discovery of the skeletons of giant humans or humanoids are extremely numerous, and have been coming in from all over this continent for many years. They constitute a subject of their own which I have endeavored to pursue for a long time now but, I regret to have to say, without any success. One and all have just "evaporated" like this, but I must admit, very often within the portals of some museum which had acknowledged receipt of the relic. There is the famous story of the forty mummified giants in Mammoth Cave, Kentucky; of the giants in giant coffins in some unnamed cave in Utah; of others dug up in a peat bog in West Virginia and allegedly shipped to the Smithsonian; and of others "preserved" in sundry small county museums in Nevada. I have voluminous correspondence on file on these items but I have never yet managed to obtain sight of any single bone. This is odd because human giants are not really terribly rare [I have seen it stated that there are several thousand men over 7 feet tall living today in the United States] whereas such persons in the past would probably have been regarded with some awe and might be expected to have been accorded rather special burial, so augmenting our chances of unearthing them.

The matter of skeletal remains of ABSMs is, of course, of first importance and second only to the procurement of a whole living specimen. The chance of unearthing a skeleton of one is not quite so unlikely as one might suppose, for it now transpires that very primitive peoples indeed seem to have performed deliberate interments, if only to clear away refuse from a cannibalistic meal in a cave. Some ABSMs might well be or have once been at such a level of "cultural" development and it is constantly reported by the Amerinds in this area that their particular local variety indulge something akin to hibernation, or at least winter inactivity equivalent to that of the local bears, and that they do this in caves. This presents a dubious aspect of these traditions however, because, in the absence of limestone strata in the area, caves are rarities. Nonetheless, there are caves in volcanic rocks of certain kinds and some have been alleged to have been found in the mountains around Harrison Lake. There is one story of such that pertains to ABSMs. This again I got from Mr. J. W. Burns. It goes as follows and comes from an Amerind named Charley Victor, a resident of Chilliwack on the lower Fraser:

> The first time I came to know about these people [the local ABSMs, now named Sasquatches], I did not see anybody. Three young men and myself were picking salmonberries on a rocky mountain slope 5 or 6 miles from the old town of Yale. In our search for berries we suddenly stumbled upon a large opening in the side of the mountain. This discovery greatly surprised all of us, for we knew every foot of the mountain, and never knew nor heard there was a cave in the vicinity. Outside the

mouth of the cave there was an enormous boulder. We peered into the cavity but couldn't see anything.

We gathered some pitchwood, lighted it and began to explore. But before we got very far from the entrance of the cave, we came upon a sort of stone house or enclosure. It was a crude affair. We couldn't make a thorough examination, for our pitchwood kept going out. We left, intending to return in a couple of days and go on exploring. Old Indians, to whom we told the story of our discovery, warned us not to venture near the cave again, as it was surely occupied by a Sasquatch. That was the first time I heard about the hairy men that inhabit the mountains. We, however, disregarded the advice of the old men and sneaked off to explore the cave, but to our great disappointment found the boulder rolled back into the mouth and fitting it so nicely that you might suppose it had been made for that purpose.

This story seems to me to have a certain ring of truth about it, and the idea of using a boulder as a door, either for protective purposes or for concealment of a breeding-chamber, is not in any way illogical or impossible. There is, however, it should be pointed out, a modern tendency to, as it were, chase anything elusive back into caves, and especially wild men; probably because of all that has been written, from archaeological texts to comic books, about "Cave Men." The majority of primitive hominids did not live in caves; simply, because the number of caves available was, except in a few special areas, very limited. [Further, they may have first entered them to get away from either heat or rain as much as from cold.] Yet, the remains of early men and animals are better and more readily preserved in cave floors than out in the open, while locating open-air camping sites is very chancy. The idea that men went through a cave-living phase, all over the world, has therefore gained wide credence. *Sasquatches* could just as well hole up in ice-caves made by themselves in deep snow, as some bears do. But caves should be searched most diligently for remains or other evidence of their occupation.

It was not too far away from this alleged cave site that the next encounter of which we have record and that is documented, sworn to, and witnessed by more than one person, took place in 1915. A Statutory Declaration of this was sworn to in September of 1957 by one of the participants, Mr. Charles Flood of Westminster, B.C. This goes as follows:

I, **Charles Flood** of New Westminster (formerly of Hope) declare the following story to be true:

I am 75 years of age and spent most of my life prospecting in the local mountains to the south of Hope, toward the American boundary and in the Chilliwack Lake area.

In 1915, Donald McRae and Green Hicks of Agassiz, B.C. and myself, explored an area over an unknown divide, on the way back to Hope, near the Holy Cross Mountains.

Green Hicks, a half-breed Indian, told McRae and me a story, he claimed he had seen alligators at what he called Alligator lake, and wild humans at what he called Cougar Lake. Out of curiosity we went with him; he had been there a week previous looking for a fur trap line. Sure enough, we saw his alligators, but they were black, twice the size of lizards in a small mud lake.

Awhile further up was Cougar Lake. Several years before a fire swept over many square miles of mountains which resulted in large areas of mountain huckle-berry growth. Green Hicks suddenly stopped us and drew our attention to a large, light brown creature about 8 feet high, standing on its hind legs (standing upright) pulling the berry bushes with one hand or paw toward him and putting berries in his mouth with the other hand, or paw.

I stood still wondering, and McRae and Green Hicks were arguing. Hicks said "it is a wild man" and McRae said "it is a bear." As far as I am concerned the strange creature looked more like a human being. We seen several black and brown bear on the trip, but that thing looked altogether different. Huge brown bear are known to be in Alaska, but have never been seen in southern British Columbia.

This document brings up two questions that I should discuss briefly forthwith. The first is the matter of the Law. As I have already said, we in this country do not have much respect for this aspect of human organization and often tend to the observation that "laws are only made to be broken." This is not so in some other countries however, and the Canadians have an intense respect for their laws and for authority in general. Canadians will scoff at the suggestion that one of their countrymen is more likely *not* to lie before a justice of the peace than an American, but it is nonetheless a fact that a Canadian is more likely to make such a deposition if his veracity has been called in question and/or he wants to assert his sincerity. Also, he will think longer and more carefully about his statement if made before established authority because, should anything he say therein be mendacious and thereby cause any distress or harm to others, he will be held fully accountable. Thus, these sworn statements and others that follow have a rather strong implication. The other matter is the introduction of an almost classic red herring.

An inexplicably high percentage of all esoteric investigations turn up other unexpected and apparently unrelated matters that are often just as weird, if not more so, than the original object of pursuit. In this case, the matter of "alligators" is quite extraordinary. Alligators, per se, are only two in number, one species being indigenous to the Mississippi Valley and around the Gulf coast to Florida; the other to the Yangtse-Kiang Valley of China. The term "alligator" has, however, become a colloquialism for all the crocodilians, and it is also applied in some countries to various lizards that spend most of their time in fresh water. Popular names are also very dangerous in that they become displaced in the most outrageous manner, such as the designation of a species of tortoise in Florida as a "gopher," when that is the name for a group of small mammals otherwise called ground-squirrels. Reptiles are, however, cold-blooded, and the existence of an aquatic one in even southern British Columbia would be unlikely, to say the least. Yet, there is a species of salamander [an amphibian named *Batracochoseps*] found in Alaska, and the giant salamander of the mountain streams of Japan is customarily iced in every winter. The mere mention of such a creature as an alligator in this story tends to cast doubt upon its other features, but then who is to say what can or cannot be. There is volcanicity in the area, and there might thus be hot or warm springs and lakes there. Also, at some time, one or other of the present-day species of alligator *must* have gotten either from China to the Mississippi, or vice versa. The only route for such an emigration is over the Bering Straits; thus passing through what is now British Columbia along the way.[2]

This matter of volcanicity and hot springs brings us to

---

[2] Recent discoveries have indicated strongly that there may be a fairly large aquatic lizard indigenous to this area.

another really quite fabulous item of Canadian ABSMery. This is the matter of the lower Nahanni area of the Northwest Territories. If you go to the western part of the Northwest Territories you will sooner or later be told about the place where banana trees have been grown. This sounds quite wacky but, if you pursue the matter diligently, you will learn that in the area of the junction of the Liard and South Nahanni Rivers (see Map V), lying against the vast mountain barrier which cuts our entire continent from the mouth of the Mackenzie River on the Arctic Sea to Vera Cruz on the Gulf of Mexico, abutting on to the central plains like a monstrous wall, there is a volcanic area where hot springs are found. There have been mission stations along the Liard for over a century and it is quite true that at these, magnificent vegetables are grown out in the open in the brief but intense summer. Also, they have been raised indoors, and among the latter have been a number of banana trees. However, this area, which lies at the south end of the vast Mackenzie Range, has long been one of myth and fantasy. The reports emanating from there cannot better be summed up than by quoting a column from a publication named *Doubt,* the periodical of the Fortean Society of New York. It was founded by the late author, Tiffany Thayer, in conjunction with several other notable persons such as Ben Hecht, in memory of, and to carry on the work of Charles Fort, that assiduous collector of borderline reports for so many years. This reads in part, when speaking of an expedition said to have been organized to visit the area:

This Valley, number one legend of the Northlands, has as its background, stories of tropical growth, hot springs, head-hunting mountainmen, caves, pre-historic monsters, wailing winds, and lost gold mines. Actual fact certifies the hot springs, the wailing winds, and some person or persons who delight in lopping off prospectors' heads. As for the pre-historic monsters, Indians have returned from the Nahanni country with fairly accurate drawings of mastodons burned on raw hide. The more recent history began some 40 years ago (circa 1910) when the two MacLeod brothers of Fort Simpson were found dead in the valley, and reportedly decapitated. Already the Indians shunned the place because of its "mammoth grizzlies" and "evil spirits wailing in the canyons."

Canadian police records show that Joe Mulholland of

Minnesota, Bill Espler of Winnipeg, Phil Powers and the MacLeod brothers of Ft. Simpson, Martin Jorgenson, Yukon Fischer, Annie La Ferte, one O'Brien, Edwin Hall, Andy Hays, an unidentified prospector and Ernest Savard have perished in the strange valley since 1910. In 1945 the body of Savard was found in his sleeping bag, head nearly severed from his shoulders. Savard had previously brought rich ore samples out of the Nahanni. In 1946 Prospector John Patterson disappeared in the valley. His partner, Frank Henderson, was to have met him there, but never found him.

The "head-hunting mountain-men" are alleged locally, and for a great distance around, stretching to the limits of the mountain forest toward Alaska,* east to northern Manitoba, and south all the way to the lower Fraser and beyond, to be ABSMs of the *Sasquatch* type and with all its characteristics, such as winter-withdrawal, occasional bursts of carnivorousness, and so forth. I also have reports in the form of private letters of similar creatures from all across the Northwest Territories just south of the tree-line, and again in northern Quebec Province.

This is a somewhat irksome matter as I have been unable to obtain any casts of footprints or other physical evidence from these regions nor even sworn statements as yet. The reports are categoric and specific. Those from northern Manitoba are second hand only, and from Amerindian informants via white men who have hunted there for many years in succession. Those from Quebec have puzzled me for years. I have constantly heard about them but have only three pieces of paper to show for my exhaustive and prolonged inquiries and appeals. These are all letters from American summer visitors on serious hunting and camping trips by canoe, guided by professional Amerindian trappers and hunters. All three are substantially identical and all give somewhat similar accounts of events in widely separated places. One is from a lone man, a business executive from Chicago; one is from a party of four men of

* The dividing line between two major types of vegetation forms a great curve to the north close to this area, and then bends down to the south, and even southeast for a stretch, along the Pacific coast. The southernmost of these is a type of forest that grows far up mountainsides; the northern type grows only in valleys, leaving the upper slopes bare. ABSMs are reported from all over the former in the mountains but not from the latter.

assorted professions who have hunted for years on their annual vacations together; the third is from the father of a family of four—three grown sons and a (then) teenage daughter.

In each case, a tall, very heavily built, man-shaped creature with bullet-head and bull-neck, and clothed all over in long shiny black hair, with very long arms, short legs and big hands, is said suddenly to have appeared on the bank of a river in which the party was quietly fishing. On one occasion, the creature is said to have carried off some fish left on a rock on the bank; on another it chased the Amerindian guide out of the woods and into his canoe and then waded some distance out into the water after him. The family party seem to have become fairly familiar with two of the creatures over a period of several days. They say they constantly prowled around their camp, and showed themselves among the trees whenever they went out in the canoes. One seems to have shown signs of chasing the girl on one occasion but, the father told me, they gained the impression that this seemed to be more through curiosity than menace. Two of the Amerinds are said to have asserted that they and their people knew the creatures quite well and that there were quite a lot of them in those forests. The other guide, who was chased, appeared to be scared almost witless and swore that the big thing was some form of spirit or devil. However, it smashed branches and hurled stones, it is reported.

I am frankly stymied over these reports. Two of the writers asked that I withhold their names in *perpetuo* as they did not want the reports to become known to their business associates. The third man I never traced. It was many months before I could get to the places from where these people wrote and although I traced two of them, they all stopped answering my letters and I am left with nothing to follow up. This is an almost chronic condition of laborers in the vineyards of ABSMery. People almost all just dry up in time. Of course, many probably write in the first place by way of a joke or just to see how gullible the enquirer is; but not all are of this ilk. Many people also, I believe, take fright at the possibility of ridicule, or even become alarmed about their own sanity, after they have once gotten something so unusual off their chests. Others again, either consider the matter explained or just don't want it explained. It takes years of work to get at the facts and this is rendered almost futile when one is dealing with a new locale that is only just being penetrated by civilized people.

The ABSM tradition extends all across Canada but is concentrated in southern British Columbia; probably because that was the first area opened up and is still being probed from all around.

3. Further Sasquatchery

MORE REPORTS FROM CANADA
(1920-1940)

Just because I have skipped over some 60 years by the recounting of only 8 stories, is not to be taken to mean that these were the only reports current during that period. Quite to the contrary, almost every year somebody or some group of people in southern British Columbia stated that they had either run into a *Sasquatch*, been chased by one, shot at one, or seen its foot-tracks. Many of these accounts are from our friends, the Amerinds, and many of them are not specifically dated. They begin "Some years ago . . ." or "Early last year . . ." but fail to state which year, or how many years ago. A lot of these have become garbled because of loose reporting or because they were made to specialists in local languages, each of which has a different name for its local ABSMs. The very name, *Sasquatch*, now so widely disseminated and known in Canada, is actually of partially artificial construction and was first, I understand, coined by Mr. Burns in an effort to obviate some of this muddle and to draw attention to the fact that throughout a very wide area—from the Yukon to California—all the names refer to the same creature. This name is derived from the Salish Amerindian word for "wildmen of the woods" which may be transliterated as *Te Smaï'Etl Soqwaia'm*, also written as *Sami 'Soq' wia'm*, the form used by the Chehalis tribal group. Farther south among the Pugets, the name was *Hoquiam*, now the name of a flourishing small town on the Chehalis River south of the Olympic Mountains in Washington State. However, many of the locals had a habit of prefixing almost everything with a sibilant so that this name also came as *S'oq'wiam*. In the Cascades the name was *See-ah-tik* but down around Mt. Shasta it was *See-oh-mah*. In the Klamaths we note that it is still *Oh-Mah* among the Hüppa, while the Yuroks call them *Toki-mussi*. On Vancouver Island, and north up the inlets of the mainland, the sound changes to something more like "*Sokqueatl*" or "*Soss-q'atl*" and it was from this that Mr. Burns derived the anglicized "*Sasquatch*," or "Susquotch" as Americans have usually written it.

I mentioned above that all these names refer to a single kind of creature. This is so, as far as the Amerinds are concerned; but, you may well ask as you read on, how come these creatures are stated to vary so much in appearance. On analysis, it will be noted that this variation is almost exclusively in two features—length and quality of hair and its disposal about the body, and color of skin and fur. Further analysis will also show that these differences seem to be due to age and sex. The young ones, like Jacko and the one shot by a local hunter and to be described in a moment, are said to have had light faces and yet black, shiny, straight, and apparently orderly hair all over (one imagines like that of a chimpanzee), but the adults are invariably said to have black faces and skin, and reddish-brown fur, often shaggy, and sometimes washed with white or silver-tipped. The matter of long head-hair is variable but most of the close-up sightings speak of very short head-hair, no beard, but a curiously forward, upward, and finally backward curl of longer hair all across the brow like that seen on certain Spider Monkeys (genus *Ateles*).

The growth and rearrangement of body hair with age is absolutely consistent with what is known among other mammals and notably primates and particularly apes. Further, the changes in color are exactly what we would expect and are very similar to those to be noted among gorillas and some gibbons. Baby chimpanzees often start off with faces and hands the color of those of white men but end up with complexions as dark as Dravidians or Wolofs. Some gorillas develop a distinct gingery tinge—the "black" of mammalian hair being only melanin, and really a very dark red—and almost all of them go silvery gray with age. Some gorilla families have bright red topknots just like some human beings. Some gibbons vary in a most bewildering way in coat colors. They may be black, gray, chocolate, white, or beige to start with and throughout life, or they may change from one color to another with age. Different races of the different species do all manner of different things in this respect. It is therefore quite consistent that these large ABSMs should start off with jet

84

black hair and light skins, and end up hoary old black-faced creatures with silver-tipped reddish fur. The females might lack the gray and might be less shaggy. There may also be family likeness to start with.

Let us assume that we are now chronologically at the turn of the year 1920 and 1921 but still in British Columbia. As I said in the brief historical review of world-wide ABSMery, this was a most important date in that it saw the birth of the term "Abominable Snowman" and really kicked off the whole thing. I have often wondered what would have happened if the Squamish word for these creatures in their country, instead, had happened to have been mistranslated as something equally fetching, I suppose we would then, in time, have witnessed a *New York Journal American* Expedition to Harrison Lakes, and Admiral Byrd flying skin-trophies to Chicago from the hamlets of the Alaskan panhandle. It is nothing more than a quirk of history and a series of harmless mistakes that has put Nepal instead of Vancouver Island on the map in this respect; though it has to be admitted that Mt. Everest has played its part.

It was about this time, moreover, that an incident is alleged to have occurred in this area that is in many ways perhaps one of the most fantastic ABSM stories ever told. It only came to light in 1957 but concerns happenings alleged to have taken place in 1924 in the mountains behind Toba Inlet, which is on the coast of British Columbia (see Map VI). It came to light through a letter (written to John Green, owner of *The Advance,* published in Agassiz, a small town near Harrison, some 70 miles from Vancouver) by a retired prospector and lumberman of Swedish origin named Mr. Albert Ostman. This letter was a result of the publication by Mr. Green of an affidavit sworn to by a Mr. William Roe (then of Edmonton, Alberta) concerning certain experiences he had in the year 1955 on Mica Mountain on the Alberta border. (This latter statement is reproduced in full in the next chapter and concerns Mr. Roe's meeting with a female *Sasquatch.*) Reading this, Mr. Ostman apparently decided to break more than a quarter century of silence and relate what had happened to him. Mr. Ostman now lives at Fort Langley outside Chilliwack, and John Green, who for years has gathered information on the *Sasquatches,* sought him out and persuaded him to write his full story. This Mr. Ostman did—painstakingly, and in two large notebooks. Mr. Green published this in his newspaper along with a photostat of a sworn affidavit testifying to its truth by Mr. Ostman.

I had the pleasure of meeting both gentlemen in company with a partner of mine, Robert Christie, who was traveling with me at the time, and a Mr. and Mrs. René Dahinden. He is Swiss; his wife, Swedish, as is Mr. Ostman. As I already had Mr. Ostman's story both on paper and on tape from an interview between him and a reporter from a local radio station, I confined my questions to trying to recall his memory about certain zoological or anthropological details. I fully admit to having loaded these questions with snares and abstruse technical catches, and to having been rather rough in my approach. I know that I thereby incensed John Green and the Dahindens, who not only have a very great affection and respect for Mr. Ostman but feel that, with his still slight language difficulty, outsiders such as I tend to rattle him. I do not agree, in that Mr. Ostman has the wisdom of age as well as long experience, and a sense of humor that cannot be downed; and I don't think that he was annoyed with me then, or will be hurt if he reads this. In fact, I felt that he was twinkling at me all the time; and I fancy that, if he ever thought of me after I left, it was simply as a "very funny fellow," as he might say. This is more the case since I went away a very puzzled reporter.

This story, when read cold, sounds utterly preposterous. If one has read a great deal on ABSMs in general and on the *Sasquatch* in particular it also, at first, appears highly suspicious because it seems to knit together just about everything else that has ever been published on the matter. In fact, given some firsthand experience of the country, I could have written just that story myself. The world is full of good weavers of yarns and some of them, who are not professional writers of fiction, can be so damnably convincing that they have fooled not only the press but governments and even peoples, if not the whole world. Fabrications, if well enough done, consistently adhered to, and big enough lies, can, as has so often been pointed out (e.g. the case of Hitler) be utterly convincing. However, in technical matters, and most notably in the biological sciences, there are subjects that just cannot be imagined or thought up by anybody, unless they have learned of them specifically in advance and, what is much more important, their exact significance relative to a whole host of other technicalities is appreciated. Anybody can read anything that has been published on *Sasquatches* and yet still attribute to them some trivial biological character that really *is impossible*. In the case of ABSMs there are a large number of very abstruse matters of this nature that may be slipped in casually. Only one answer to these can be right, while an endless string of other answers will be wrong, and conclusively so. I put about two dozen of such, directly and unexpectedly, to Mr. Ostman and, of all those for which he had a reply, he did not miss once—not one impossible answer; not a single uncalled-for elaboration; and not one unrequested fact that did not have a possible and quite logical place in the general picture. What is more, when we got off on the sketching of the creature's head, there emerged several points that were *not* then in published *Sasquatch* literature, nor in that of any ABSM, nor even in textbooks of physical anthropology. Yet, subsequent to that interview, some of these points (such as the odd head-shape) *have* appeared in the last type of publication.

This is really rather alarming and has given me many sleepless nights. Some things I just cannot bring myself to take at their face evaluation; and, frankly, Mr. Ostman's story was at first one of these. Besides, he even included some gross fallacies such as that he became poisoned through eating a broody grouse—an old wives' tale, if ever there was one. But then, I have to admit to myself now, that this fact is still believed in parts of his home country —namely, that one does get poisoned by eating birds taken sitting on eggs—and that he probably believed this; while he was in poor enough condition at the time of his adventure to be made sick by almost anything. Also, I ask myself, why tell this story? Mr. Ostman is not an uneducated country bumpkin. He is well read, speaks two languages, has traveled quite a lot, lives very much in the world, and knows quite well what ridicule is, and all about its deadly efficacy. He is retired, owns his own property, has many friends, and does not need publicity; nor does he welcome it, though he is extremely long-suffering and most gracious in discussing his experiences with newsmen and others who call upon him. He never told his story in his youth for fear of ridicule, knowing what effects it might have. He doesn't care now; he is still sincerely puzzled; and he is eager to do anything he can to help clear up the mystery. Mr. Ostman is, in fact, sick and tired of skeptics.

After a strenuous year on a job, he decided to take a part vacation with some prospecting on the side. He chose a wild area at the head of this Toba Inlet which is the first substantial fjord north of Powell River. This is on the mainland opposite the middle of Vancouver Island. There was allegedly a lost gold mine thereabouts and he decided to take a crack at finding it. He hired an old Amerind to take him up the fjord and he says that he first heard from him on that journey of the existence of the giant hairy "Wild Men of the Woods." He had supplies for three weeks plus rifle, sleeping bag, and other basic equipment. The local man left him alone on shore and he proceeded inland and found a good campsite.

This he fixed up very comfortably, making a thick bed of small branches on which to place his sleeping bag, and hung his supply bags well off the ground on a pole. The next morning he, nonetheless, found his things disturbed, though nothing was missing. Being a knowledgeable woodsman, he assumed that a porcupine was responsible, so the following night he loaded his rifle and placed it under his bed flap. The next morning he found, to his dismay, that his packsack still hung from the pole well off the ground but that its contents had been emptied out and some items of food taken. Strangely, his salt had not been touched. This surprised him not a little, because porcupines have an insatiable craving for salt and always go for it first. At the same time, he did not think that it was a bear because, although he admits to having been a very heavy sleeper, bears usually make a great rumpus and smash up everything. Albert Ostman did not like these events one bit, so he stayed rather closely around camp in the hopes of catching the marauder in the act. On the third night he took special precautions; intending to stay awake all night, he did not undress but merely removed his boots and left them at the bottom of his sleeping bag, put his geological pick at hand, and took his loaded rifle into the bag with him. But he did fall asleep.

The next thing he knew he was being picked up like a puppy in a paper bag, and felt himself heaved, as he at first thought, on to a horse's back. Bemused and half awake, he tried to get at his knife to cut his way out of his sleeping bag, but he was wedged down into the bottom in a sitting position and could not reach it. Then he felt his packsack bumping against him with the hard cans within clearly discernible by their sharp impact. As far as I was able to ascertain in my interview with him, he was completely in the bag, as one might say, and its opening was being held shut above his head. How he managed to breathe in such circumstances, and for over an hour, puzzled me until he explained that he was slung over the back of something walking on two legs and that its hand was not big enough to go all around the bag-opening. I never heard Mr. Ostman say that he was scared, but he admits that he was terribly hot in there and that his cramped legs were extremely painful. Don't forget, moreover, that he hadn't a clue at that time as to what was going on or what had got him.

He says that he was carried up hill and down dale, then he was dragged along the ground, and that his carrier even jog-trotted over level places. This is some going for anything carrying a man of Ostman's size plus a knapsack full of supplies and other equipment. But, this is by no means the strangest part of the proceedings; yet it is still at least possible. Another aspect seems quite impossible; namely, that Ostman estimates—and sticks to it—that this trip in the bag took three hours. In an interview with a commentator from a radio station (a tape of which I have), but made, of course, a quarter of a century later, he says thirty miles. Personally, I fail to see how he survived such an ordeal, stuffed up in a bag, but that is not so much the point: what is are the time, the distances, and the speed of travel implied. These are not easy things to estimate at the best of times, and they are among the first to become exaggerated in the mind with the passage of time. I wish that Mr. Ostman had not tried to give any estimates on such a late date since its causes the eyebrows of all who read or hear his story to go up sharply.

Anyhow, at the end of what must have been an ordeal, however brief it really was, he was dumped unceremoniously on the ground. He heard some voices gibbering but not using true speech as far as he could ascertain. He apparently got his head out of the bag for air and then tried to crawl out, but his legs had rather naturally gone numb and it was some time before he could emerge and rescue his boots. It was still dark and starting to rain. He then tells, in various characteristic ways, what happened when it began to dawn and he could see the outlines of four large creatures on two legs around him. I don't know if his native Swedish wit got the better of him, but he says that when he could stand up he asked the somewhat banal question: "What do you chaps want with me?" I find this most refreshing.

He found that his captors consisted of two big ones (a pair), and two youngsters, also a male and a female. He stresses that the two latter seemed thoroughly scared of him, and that the "Old Woman," as he rather delightfully called the elder female, seemed very peeved with her mate for dragging such an object home; but, he then goes on to say—and this I find very interesting, if odd—that the "Old Man" kept gesticulating, and *telling* the others all about it. In other words, their gibbering *was* speech. All of them were hairy and without clothing; and Ostman estimates the "Old Man" to have been between seven and eight feet tall. When the sun was fully up, they all left him.

He says that he found himself in a ten-acre bowl high in the mountains, its edges so steep as to be unscalable, and with only one outlet—a V-shaped cut with walls about twenty feet high and about eight feet wide at the bottom. It is not quite clear why, at this point, he did not try to make a break for this gap, but this was possibly because of his still wobbly legs. Later on, he made several attempts, both frontally at speed and by subtlety, but the "Old Man" kept a weather eye on him and invariably cut off his approach, making "*pushing*" motions with his hands, and a sound that Ostman invariably describes as something like "sooka-sooka." However, when he first arrived, he moved over to the opposite side of the bowl and set up camp under two small trees. I find the inventory that he says he took of his possessions most interesting. Prunes, macaroni, his full box of rifle cartridges, and his matches were missing; so was his pick. Otherwise, all was intact. He had an emergency waterproof box of matches in his pocket but says that there was no dry wood in the valley, which seems to have been open and grassy with a few scattered junipers. All his cooking utensils had also been left, but he opened a coffee-can and went to look for water.

I will now complete the story as best I can from the various versions that I have heard, though I would stress that Mr. Ostman is remarkably consistent however many times he tells his story. Each interviewer, however, manages to ask a new question and elicit from him some scraps of information that the teller had not thought of or mentioned before. As I don't know the sequence in which the various versions were recorded, I have no way of differentiating between inconsistencies and mere additions. It would seem that Ostman made his first attempt to get out on the second day but was driven back by the "Old Man." The young male kept coming closer to him and he finally rolled his empty snuff box to him. The *Sasquatch* grabbed it, showed it to his sister, and then took it to his father. Somehow, Ostman got it back, because he used it later.

During the next five days nothing much seems to have occurred except that the young male gave Ostman some grass with sweet roots to eat and got some snuff in return, which he chewed. The "Old Man" then also developed a liking for snuff; and this finally did the trick.

On the seventh day, as far as I can make out, the boy and the "Old Man" came right up to Ostman and squatted down watching him take a pinch of snuff. Ostman held out the box to him (the "Old Man") who, instead of taking a pinch in imitation, grabbed the box and emptied the whole contents into his mouth and swallowed it. In a few minutes his eyes began to roll, he let out a screech, and grabbed a can half full of cold coffee and coffee-grounds, which he drank. This made him worse; and, after rolling about some more, he charged off to the spring. Ostman gathered up his possessions and made a dash for the opening in the cliff. The "Old Lady" tried to intercept him and was very close on his heels, but he fired a shot at the rock above her head and she fled back again. Ostman found himself in a canyon running south, down which he made record time, as he put it. Then, he climbed a ridge and saw Mount Baker way off to the side, so that he knew which way to go to hit the coast. He was not followed.

He rested for two hours on the ridge, then started down again. That night he camped near heavy timber and shot a grouse sitting on eggs; he roasted and ate the bird. The next morning he was very groggy and stomachically upset, which he attributed to eating the grouse, since it was his belief that a broody bird was poisonous. Finally, he heard a motor running and made for it, coming out at an advance logging operation. The foreman, seeing that he was just about at the end of his tether, took him in and fed him and let him rest up for a couple of days. Ostman then made his way down to a camp on the Salmon Arm Branch of the Sechelt Inlet, where he got a boat back to Vancouver.

This is Mr. Ostman's story and you may make what you will of it. As I have said, there are some curious discrepancies in it but not even these are impossibilities, with the exception of the times and the distances as mentioned above. The grouse, broody or not, could quite well have upset his stomach. Mr. Ostman seems to be a straightforward and honest man. But, it is the facts that he gave me about the ABSMs themselves that go farther than anything else to convince me of the validity of the whole thing—unless, of course, as I have also said above, he read all of these elsewhere.

His descriptions of the creatures are considerably detailed. What is more, the sexual and age differences he describes are very reasonable, and do not in any way insult such variations as found among men or other primates. Of the adult male, he says that he was about eight feet tall, barrel-chested, with powerful shoulders and a very pronounced and large "hump" on his back, causing his head to be carried somewhat forward. This is exactly in accord with the posture of some sub-hominids as deduced from the angle at which the condyles are set to the back of the skull. The biceps were said to be enormous but to taper to the inside of the elbow; the forearm to be disproportionate (to a human) long but well proportioned. The hands were wide but the palm long and curved permanently into "a kind of a scoop"; the fingers short, and the nails flat, broad, and "shaped like chisels." Mr. Ostman mentioned to me quite casually that they were copper-colored. This is most significant, as we shall see later (Chapter 14). He estimated the neck to be about thirty inches around. The whole body was covered in hair, somewhat longer on the head; shorter but thicker in other parts. It covered his ears. Only the palms of the hands and the soles of the feet, which had pronounced pads, were naked and a dirty dark gray in color. The "top" (i.e. bridge) of the nose and eyelids alone were naked. The big male's canine teeth were longer than the others but not sufficiently so to be called tusks.

The adult female he described as being over seven feet tall and weighing between 500 and 600 pounds. He said that she could have been anywhere between forty and seventy years old, using humans as a criterion; but, she was apparently very ugly, with an enormously wide pelvis that caused her to walk like a goose. She had long, large, and pendent breasts.

The young male spent the most time near Ostman and was thus most closely observed. Ostman says that he could have been anywhere from eleven to eighteen years of age, but was already seven feet tall and weighed about 300 pounds. His chest would have measured between fifty and fifty-five inches around and his waist was some twenty-six to thirty-eight inches: and don't forget that Mr. Ostman was a lumberman and better at estimating the girth of things (like trees) than the average person. He had wide jaws and a narrow, sloping forehead. The back of his head, as in all of them, apparently rose some four or five inches above the brow-line, and was pointed. Mr. Ostman went to great pains to explain this, and to get the shape just right. The head-hair was about six inches long; that on the body shorter but much thicker in some areas.

The young female was very shy; she did not approach Ostman closely but kept peeking at him from behind the bushes. He could not estimate her age, but remarks that she was without any visible breast development and was, in fact, quite flat-chested. Like her mother, she had a very pronounced upcurled bang across her brow-ridges. This was continuous from temple to temple. Curiously, no amount of questioning would prompt Mr. Ostman to elaborate any further on this individual, which may in part be psychological since it seems to be his conviction that he had been kidnaped as a potential suitor for her, and I think he has a sort of subconscious and rather touching modesty about her shyness. Mr. Ostman maintains a delightful old-world delicacy about the proprieties and neatly turned aside some purely biological questions with such noncommittal phrases as "I wouldn't know about that." But he did tell us of a few more interesting observations on the behavior of the group.

First and foremost was this gibbering in which they indulged. As his story progresses, it becomes quite clear that he assumed in the end that they were actually communicating intelligently, since they made a variety of noises befitting special situations and seemed to discuss the objects they carried one to the other. There was also the delightful expression "ook" that the young male made on one occasion. Then, almost equally significant, was the fact that the old female and the young male went regularly to gather vegetable foods; the former going out of the gap and returning with armfuls of branches, including fresh spruce and hemlock tips, grasses, and ferns. These, he told me, she washed and stacked up. She also brought quantities of a certain kind of "ground nut" of a kind that Mr. Ostman had often seen in abundance on Vancouver Island. (Shades of Mike King!) Inquiry elicited the fact that this is a root-nodule of a herbaceous plant related to the Hemlock of Europe (not the tree called by that name in this continent), one form of which grows such nutlike growths that are edible and, in fact, delicious. The young male used also to go every day and return with bundles of a kind of grass with a "sweet root."

Mr. Ostman stressed the incredible climbing ability of the male youngster and remarked on the form of his and his father's feet as having an enormous big toe. At one point he states that, in order to get a purchase in climbing, all he would need would be to find a resting place for this toe alone.

One of Mr. Ostman's observations is very peculiar, and is one which can be taken either as evidence that the whole thing is a wild fabrication or as glowing testimony to the recorder's veracity and powers of observation. It brings up some very fundamental matters with regard to the history of culture among early hominids—if it proves to be true, that is. This was that, according to Mr. Ostman, the four creatures slept and lived for the most part under a rock-ledge like the rock-shelters known to have been favored by many Stone Age men. In this, which was some ten feet deep and thirty feet wide, he says that they had regular beds of branches, moss, and dry grass, and that they had coverlets of woven strips of bark, forming great flattened bags, *and stuffed with dry grasses and moss*. However, I could not elicit from Mr. Ostman any facts as to whether he visited the shelter and examined these objects or, if not, how he knew so much about their construction and composition. This worried, and still worries, me.

Should such items have existed, combined with the primitive speech, the collection of food and its washing, we are faced with a pretty problem. Are we to suppose that, prior to the use of bone and horn tools (such as the little very primitive Australopithecines of South Africa are now thought to have used) and the discovery and control of fire, hominids (man or otherwise) went through a prior period of food-gathering but still knew weaving? This would seem not to be unreasonable or illogical, though even crude weaving calls for considerable dexterity. Be it noted at the same time that Orangs, Chimps, and Gorillas on occasion, tie true knots when making their sleeping platforms while some Gorillas do so regularly. Weaving in its most primitive form, moreover, is little further advanced than excessive knot-tying; besides, some birds do the most incredibly accurate jobs of weaving, even with different colored wools, on a piece of small-mesh wire. Also, animals, and particularly the primates, definitely do communicate. (I may say that even I can speak fairly good Rhesus!)

Thus, there is nothing really outrageous about Mr. Ostman's statements about these creatures nor about the whole concept of some of the *Sasquatches* (Neo-Giants, as we shall eventually come to call them) being food-collectors, with a primitive speech but lacking fire, clothes, and tools. And, it is even more interesting to note that Mr. Ostman states clearly that he never saw them bring to their camp, or eat, any animal food. The most primitive sub-hominids were probably, like their close congeners (the apes), fruit- and leaf-eaters. Only when some of them were forced out onto the savannahs, scrublands, and deserts did they have to take up animal-hunting and become partially or wholly carnivorous, as, apparently, did the Australopithecines of South Africa. If the Great Apes, still living today, have continued to be pure vegetarians, there is no reason why some of the most primitive Hominids could not also have so continued to be. This gives us a somewhat new concept of our own background and of the possibilities for ABSMs.

This brings up several questions that, if it were possible, ought to be discussed concurrently with any straight reportage on the ABSMs themselves. The details of a report on any such alleged creature cannot be evaluated properly without prior knowledge or exposition of certain aspects, on the one hand, of vegatology, and, on the other, of palaeanthropology, both physical and cultural (see Maps II and III). Our whole outlook on the last of these fields has undergone a complete revolution in the past two decades. The old idea was that sub-Hominids had bent knees, a stooped gait, ape-like faces and teeth and tiny brains, and no "culture" at all, in that they had no speech, no fire, no tools. Then, it was also previously believed, sub-Men came along that stood more upright and were bigger-brained and less ape-like about the muzzle. These creatures were assumed to have invented tools by bashing at things with stones, which often cracked, giving them cutting edges. The usual idea was that they were hunters and lived in caves, and progressed steadily toward Man, though taking an inordinately long time about it. Finally, some of them developed such big brains and pushed-in faces that they became true Men.

Meantime, their tools got better and better, finer made, and more diversified. Also, the great growth in certain parts of their brains made cogent speech possible. Then, the theory went, they somehow got on to fire and its uses as opposed to its dangers, developed "society," developed the art of pottery, and finally realized that from tiny seeds tall grasses grow, so that they gave up hunting and settled down to agriculture. And, in time, came the wheel, writing, money, and all the other improvements that inevitably contributed to their downfall. Be that as it may, the development of Hominid *mentality,* as opposed to mere brain capacity and structure, was not much considered, being assumed simply to have advanced along with his gray matter, since, it was then believed, you could not be expected to assess the psychology of any extinct creature and especially one with a brain no bigger than an ape's.

The first real break through this massive theoretical structure was really made by a rather dubious antiquarian named Mr. Dawson, who foisted upon science not only the now infamous Piltdown cranium, teeth, and mandible, but also a fraudulent tool that he himself appears to have made from a semi-fossilized bone of some elephantine. Piltdown Man never did look quite right but was fully accepted by physical anthropologists as a very early and primitive man-thing but with a very large brain. Thus, his grotesque tool was also accepted. Then, there was also some suspicion that tools had been found in the same strata in which Dr. DuBois found his genuine "Apeman" in Java, but the matter was rather hurriedly suppressed. Acceptance of tools along with sub-Humans finally came with the diggings in north China that produced Pekin Man. This was rather a rude shock, but did not grossly disturb the neat historical sequence then believed in. It simply meant moving tool-making back some way. The real shocker came with Dr. Raymond Dart's discovery of enormous quantities of bone and tooth tools most obviously and carefully worked, which had to have been made by none other than the little Australopithecines that were at first classed as Apes, and only grudgingly accepted as most primitive sub-Men after the discovery that they walked erect. Worse still, there was a strong plea made for acceptance of the fact that they used fire as well. It then was decided (by most, but not all, anthropologists) that the Hominids went through what is called an odontokeratic, namely "Tooth" and "Horn," tool-making phase before they came to use stones.

This picture has now been considerably muddied by Dr. Leakey's discoveries of early Chellean Man in East Africa, and an appalling-looking chap with positively immense brow ridges, but who made splendid hand-axes of stone. Nevertheless, it is only now slowly dawning on anthropologists that the first tools were more probably sticks, and otherwise wooden; for the earliest Hominids were definitely vegetarians and forest dwellers. The horn-tooth toolmakers were carnivorous. The use of wood implies pulling twigs and branches from trees and the discovery of the many uses of strips of bark. From this to primitive weaving is but a step. Thus, it is quite probable that the earliest Hominids were vegetable gatherers, using sticks and possibly the crudest weaving, and that they so equipped themselves long before they got around to breaking stones, using fire, or even developing a true language. It is therefore most interesting to note, as our story continues, that the only tools ever reported in use by ABSMs have been made of wood.

4· The Appearance of Bigfeet

STILL MORE REPORTS FROM CANADA (1940 TO 1960)

Mr. Ostman's story was related to Queen Elizabeth II when she visited British Columbia in 1959. The story is said to have been submitted to Her Majesty by an official along with other Sasquatchery, in a remote vacation cabin at a lake near Kamloops on August 28. By coincidence, I was on that same day closeted in a small railroad shack with a charming Amerindian couple named Mr. and Mrs. George Chapman, at Jacko's old retreat of Yale, some miles lower down the Fraser River. I also was hearing a story, but firsthand, and in what turned out later to have been rather extraordinary circumstances.

We had crossed the log-filled Fraser in a small boat, rowing first away upstream, then very rapidly a long way downstream broadside, and then finally a long way back upstream again on the other side in the lee of a tall bank. Scrambling to the top of this we struck a railroad along which an Amerindian family were straggling in from the hills. By some strange quirk of fate, this turned out to be the Chapman family for whom we were looking. They hospitably invited us in to the freight office, behind which they had a small house.

That could have been a very tense or even profitless interview for several reasons. Here we were, two palefaces with locally odd accents—Robbie Christie, though born in New Jersey, has ranched in Colorado, wears a Texan-type hat, and has a vaguely British accent; while I talk a sort of bastardized Anglo-Saxon with an American intonation and a British accent, neither of which are popular in Canada—who had met up with a reticent Amerindian couple, apparently quite by chance on a railroad track, and who now had suddenly demanded to hear the facts of a series

98

of incidents that had happened to these good people 18 years before. Somehow, however, and perhaps due mostly to a kind of mild shock, we all got off on the right foot and within a surprisingly short space of time Mrs. Chapman was recounting those terrible hours with complete clarity, only every now and then being mildly corrected by her husband, or having her account augmented by details which she had not witnessed.

We had heard their story from several sources and had read it in several printed versions, but I wanted to get it firsthand and I wanted to be able to shoot my particular glossary of awkward biological questions at the principals, who were alleged eyewitnesses of a living *Sasquatch* in daylight. It is just as well that we crossed the Fraser River just when we did, and so met the Chapmans, because about a month afterward they were drowned crossing at the same spot late one night. The irony and tragedy of this event upset me greatly for, as I have said, I have a great liking and respect for the Amerindian peoples and I not only found this couple graciously natural and friendly but they also impressed me, as very few other people have ever done, with their sincerity and honesty. The Chapman family at the time of the incident consisted of George and Jeannie Chapman and three children. Mr. Chapman worked on the railroad. They lived near a small place called Ruby Creek, 30 miles up the Fraser River from Agassiz. It was about 3 in the afternoon of a cloudless summer day when Jeannie Chapman's eldest son, then aged 9, came running to the house saying that there was a cow coming down out of the woods at the foot of the nearby mountain. The other kids, a boy aged 7, and a little girl of 5, were still playing in a field behind the house bordering on the rail track.

Mrs. Chapman went out to look, since the boy seemed oddly disturbed, and then saw what she at first thought was a very big bear moving about among the bushes bordering the field beyond the railroad tracks. She called the two smaller children who came running immediately. Then the creature moved out onto the tracks and she saw to her horror that it was a gigantic man covered with *hair*, not fur. The hair seemed to be about 4 inches long all over, and of a pale yellow-brown color. To pin down this color Mrs. Chapman pointed out to me a sheet of lightly varnished plywood in the room where we were sitting. This was of a brownish-ochre color.

This creature advanced directly toward the house and

Mrs. Chapman had, as she put it, "much too much time to look at it" because she stood her ground outside while the eldest boy—on her instructions—got a blanket from the house and rounded up the other children. The kids were in a near panic, she told us, and it took 2 or 3 minutes to get the blanket, during which time the creature had reached the near corner of the field only about 100 feet away from her. Mrs. Chapman then spread the blanket and, holding it aloft so that the children could not see the creature or it them, she backed off at the double to the old field and down on to the river beach, out of sight, and ran with the kids downstream to the village.

I asked her a leading question about the blanket. Had her purpose in using it been to prevent the children seeing the creature, in accord with an alleged Amerindian belief that to do so brings bad luck and often death? Her reply was both prompt and surprising. She said that, although she had heard *white men* tell of that belief, she had not heard it from her parents or any other of her people, whose advice regarding the so-called *Sasquatch* had been simply not to go farther than certain points up certain valleys, to run if she saw one, but not to struggle if one caught her, as it might squeeze her to death by mistake.

"No," she said, "I used the blanket because I thought it was after one of the kids and so might go into the house to look for them instead of following me." This seems to have been sound logic as the creature *did* go into the house and also rummaged through an outhouse pretty thoroughly, hauling from it a 55-gallon barrel of salt fish, breaking this open, and scattering its contents about outside. (The tragic irony of it is that all those original three children *did* die within 3 years, while, as I have said, a month after we interviewed them, the Chapmans and their *new* children drowned as well.)

Mrs. Chapman told me that the creature was about 7½ feet tall. She could easily estimate the height by the various fence and line posts standing about the field. It had a rather small head and a very short, thick neck; in fact really no neck at all, a point emphasized by William Roe and by almost all others who claim to have seen one of these creatures. Its body was entirely human in shape except that it was immensely thick through its chest and its arms were exceptionally long. She did not see the feet which were in the grass. Its shoulders were very wide and it had no breasts, from which Mr. Chapman assumed it was a male, though she also did not see any male genitalia due to the long hair covering its groin. She was most definite on one point: the naked parts of its face and its hands were much darker than its hair, and appeared to be almost black.

George Chapman returned home from his work on the railroad that day shortly before 6 in the evening and by a route that bypassed the village, so that he saw no one to tell him what had happened. When he reached his house he immediately saw the woodshed door battered in, and spotted enormous humanoid footprints all over the place. Greatly alarmed—for, like all of his people, he had heard since childhood about the "big wild men of the mountains," though he did not hear the word *Sasquatch* till after this incident—he called for his family and then dashed through the house. Then he spotted the foot-tracks of his wife and kids going off toward the river. He followed these until he picked them up on the sand beside the river and saw them going off downstream *without any giant ones following.*

Somewhat relieved, he was retracing his steps when he stumbled across the giant's foot-tracks on the river bank farther upstream. These came down out of the potato patch, which lay between the house and the river, milled about by the river, and then went back through the old field toward the foot of the mountains where they disappeared in the heavy growth.

Returning to the house, relieved to know that the tracks of all four of his family had gone off downstream to the village, George Chapman went to examine the woodshed. In our interview, after 18 years, he still expressed voluble astonishment that any living thing, even a 7-foot-6-inch man with a barrel-chest could lift a 55-gallon tub of fish out of the narrow door of the shack and break it open without using a tool. He confirmed the creature's height after finding a number of long brown hairs stuck in the slabwood lintel of the doorway, above the level of his head. George Chapman then went off to the village to look for his family, and found them in a state of calm collapse. He gathered them up and invited his father-in-law and two others to return with him, for protection of his family when he was away at work. The foot-tracks returned every night for a week and on two occasions the dogs that the Chapmans had taken with them set up the most awful racket at exactly 2 o'clock in the morning. The Sasquatch did not, however, molest them or, apparently, touch either the house or the woodshed. But the whole business was too unnerving and the family finally moved out. They never went back.

After a long chat about this and other matters, Mrs. Chapman suddenly told us something very significant just as we were leaving. She said: "It made an awful funny noise." I asked her if she could imitate this noise for me but it was her husband who did so, saying that he had heard it at night twice during the week after the first incident. He then proceeded to utter exactly the same strange, gurgling whistle that the men in California, who had told us they had heard an *Oh-Mah* (or "Bigfoot") call, had given. This is a sound I cannot reproduce in print, but I can assure you that it is unlike anything I have ever heard given by man or beast anywhere in the world. To me, this information is of the greatest significance. That an Amerindian couple in British Columbia should give out with exactly the same strange sound in connection with a *Sasquatch* that two highly educated white men did, over 600 miles south in connection with California's Bigfoot, is incredible. If this is all a hoax or a publicity stunt, or mass hallucination, as some people have claimed, how does it happen that this noise—which defies description—always sounds the same no matter who has tried to reproduce it for me?

A somewhat more colorful story was told by a well-known old Amerindian "medicine man" named Frank Dan. (This I reproduce by the kind permission of Mr. J. W. Burns.) This, he says, occurred in July, 1936 along Morris Creek, a small tributary of the Harrison River (see Map VI). J. W. Burns writes of Frank's story:

> It was a lovely day, the clear waters of the creek shimmered in the bright sunshine and reflected the wild surroundings of cliff, trees, and vagrant cloud. A languid breeze wafted across the rocky gullies. Frank's canoe was gliding like a happy vision along the mountain stream. The Indian was busy hooking one fish after another; hungry fish that had been liberated only a few days before from some hatchery. But the Indian was happy as he pulled them in and sang his medicine song. Then, without warning, a rock was hurled from the shelving slope above, falling with a fearful splash within a few feet of his canoe, almost swamping the frail craft. Startled out of his skin, Frank glanced upward, and to his amazement beheld a weird looking creature, covered with hair, leaping from rock to rock down the wild declivity with

102

the agility of a mountain goat. Frank recognized the hairy creature instantly. It was a Sasquatch. He knew it was one of the giants—he had met them on several ocsions in past years, once on his own doorstep. But those were a timid sort and not unruly like the gent he was now facing.

Frank called upon his medicine powers, sula, and similar spirits to protect him. There was an immediate response to his appeal. The air throbbed and some huge boulders slid down the rocky mountain side, making a noise like the crack of doom. This was to frighten away the Sasquatch. But the giant was not to be frightened by falling rocks. Instead he hurried down the declivity carrying a great stone, probably weighing a ton or more [sic], under his great hairy arm, which Frank guessed— just a rough guess—was at least 2 yards in length. Reaching a point of vantage—a jutting ledge that hung far out over the water—he hurled it with all his might, this time missing the canoe by a narrow margin, filling it with water and drenching the poor frightened occupant with a cloud of spray.

Some idea of the size of the boulder may be gained from the fact that its huge bulk blocked the channel. Later it was dredged out by Jack Penny on the authority of the department of hinterland navigation. It may now be seen on the 10th floor of the Vancouver Public Museum in the department of "Curious Rocks." When you're in Vancouver drop in to the museum and T. P. O. Menzies, curator, will gladly show it to you. The giant now posed upon the other ledge in an attitude of wild majesty as if he were monarch of these forboding haunts, shaking a colossal fist at the "great medicine man" who sat awe-struck and shuddering in the canoe, which he was trying to bail out with his shoe. The Indian saw the Sasquatch was in a towering rage, a passion that caused the great man to exude a repugnant odor, which was carried down to the canoe by a wisp of wind. The smell made Frank dizzy and his eyes began to smart and pop. Frank never smelt anything in his whole medicine career like it. It was more repelling than the stench of moccasin oil gone rotten. Indeed, it was so nasty that the fish quitted the pools and nooks and headed in schools for the Harrison River. The Indian, believing the giant was about to dive into the water and attack him, cast off his fishing lines and paddled away as fast as he was able.

I include this story not so much for anything it might add to the general picture of ABSMs in the area—there is ample evidence of that in any case—but to exemplify the type of tale told by the Amerind that causes the white man to doubt his veracity. Frank Dan was an old and respected medicine man living by the precepts and beliefs of his ancestors. Thus, his interpretation of events had to be in accord with his position in the community. I believe that facts colored by these precepts may be readily spotted in his account and just as readily eliminated. If this is done, we are left with a pretty straightforward account; namely, that while fishing, a *Sasquatch* appeared, hurled some rocks at the old gentleman, and stank like hell. The induced landslide and the weight of the second rock hurled, or perhaps merely dislodged into the river, as well as the giant's implied curse, are pure embellishments. Even the mass exodus of the trout might well be perfectly true and due to a cascade of boulders rather than to a stink in the air that they could of course not smell in the water. Besides, Frank Dan's "medicine" came off second best and he had manifestly fled. He couldn't explain this fact away, so he just did the best he could so not to show up in too poor a light. As a matter of fact, Mr. Burns records that he gave up being a medicine man from then on, saying that his powers had been finally defeated. That would seem to be the act of an honest man.

During this decade the Amerinds of this area appear, by all accounts, to have suffered quite a spell with their *Sasquatches*. One by the name of Paull, in company with others returning from a lacrosse game, met one on the main road near Agassiz; another party only a few miles away ran into one on a mountain, and one of the men fired at it in pure fright, whereupon it pursued them to their canoe, in which they just managed to escape. Another local man, when dressing after a swim in a river on a hot summer day was confronted by one near a rock, and was just about to address it in his language when it rose to its full height and nearly scared him out of his wits. Still another group told Mr. Burns that they had watched one fighting a large bear for a long time and finally killing it by strangulation. In another place, an old man said that a party of *Sasquatches* used to watch loggers at work and then, after they had gone home for the evening, come out and imitate their activities as if playing a game. But, perhaps the most curious is an incident told to the same indefatigable investigator, Mr. Burns, by the same Charley

Victor of Chilliwack already mentioned, and which I herewith reproduce with the former's permission. Charley speaks, and says:

I was hunting in the mountains near Hatzic. I had my dog with me. I came out on a plateau where there were several big cedar trees. The dog stood before one of the trees and began to growl and bark at it. On looking up to see what excited him, I noticed a large hole in the tree 7 feet from the ground. The dog pawed and leaped upon the trunk, and looked at me to raise him up, which I did, and he went into the hole. The next moment a muffled cry came from the hole. I said to myself: "The dog is tearing into a bear," and with my rifle ready I urged the dog to drive him out, and out came something I took for a bear. I shot and it fell with a thud to the ground. "Murder! Oh my!" I spoke to myself in surprise and alarm, for the thing I had shot looked to me like a white boy. He was nude. He was about 12 or 14 years of age. [In his description of the boy, the Indian said his hair was black and woolly.] Wounded and bleeding, the poor fellow sprawled upon the ground, but when I drew close to examine the extent of his injury, he let out a wild yell, or, rather a call as if he were appealing for help. From across the mountain a long way off rolled a booming voice. Less than half an hour, out from the depths of the forest came the strangest and wildest creature one could possibly see. I raised my rifle, but not to shoot, but in case I would have to defend myself. The strange creature walked toward me without the slightest fear. The wild person was a woman. Her face was almost negro black and her long straight hair fell to her waist. In height she would be about 6 foot but her chest and shoulders were well above the average breadth.

The old man remarked that he had met several "Wild Persons" in his time but had never seen anyone half so savage in appearance as this woman. This old brave confessed that he was really afraid of her and that he had fled.

This story does add some significant facts to the over-all picture because of the details given of the youngster's fur color compared to that of the female, and the curious statement about the length of her head-hair. The former agrees with the accounts of Jacko and some other reputed

ABSM youngsters: the latter is, as far as I know, a completely unique item. I wonder about this latter because I have noted a distinct tendency, perhaps psychological, for people to assume that the head-hair of wild people would be of the Lady Godiva type. A good friend of mine a well-known artist who has illustrated many scientific works and natural history books, once sent me his "impression" of a Californian *Oh-Mah* which greatly surprised me. Despite this man's extensive knowledge of mammalian anatomy and long experience in drawing animals to the specifications and approval of zoologists, he had depicted just a great big white-type man with long flowing hair and an immense beard. This seems, indeed, to be the popular conception of an ABSM; yet, everybody who claims to have seen one makes special mention of the small pointed heads, small round eyes close together and directed straightforward, extra long arms, and *short* head-hair, a naked face *without* beard and prognathous jaws but no lips (i.e. no eversion of the lips). The picture given of all of them by those who claim to have seen them, is of creatures with several distinctly nonhuman characters, especially about the head and face. However, the same witnesses everywhere and all natives who say they know of the existence of ABSMs—and this goes for the Central Asiatics, as well as Malays, African, and North and South Americans —insist just as vehemently that the creatures are human rather than animal. Quite where various people draw the dividing line between the two presents other puzzles, but the Kazakhs of the U.S.S.R. who caught one of their *Ksy-Giiks,* thought it was a man wearing a disguise, while the Soviet Army medical officer who examined a *Kaptar,* pronounced it so human that it should be released. Even the Hill Batuks of Sumatra, who are themselves just about at the bottom rung of the cultural ladder, call their local *Orang Pendeks* and *Orang Gadangs* by a name that denotes "wild *men.*" The Malays of the same country, however, call even the *Mias* (their great ape), the Orang-utan (i.e. "hutan" *), which simply mean wild (*utan*) man (*orang*). The Amerinds of our Northwest insist that the *Sasquatches* are very lowly forms of men, so lowly that they, Amerinds, do not want to associate with them in any way; preferring not to talk about them and especially about the

---

* This is the correct spelling in Malay, and "orang" really means "person," not "man."—Author.

possibility of mating with them. That would lead to contamination of their race, and, if the very idea got into the white man's head, it would lead to a further degradation of their status by the implication that they might be partly wild themselves.

The basic "humanity" of ABSMs is perhaps understandable as regards the pigmy and the giant types, for both leave what at first sight look exactly like either very small or very large human footprints, as most certainly do the Eurasian *Almasty* (see Chapter 13.) The man-sized *Meh-Teh* type, on the other hand, leave a most unhuman type of footprint. Encounters with *Sasquatches* are really so common that they become boring in the telling. I could give dozens more, all of which were allegedly witnessed by more than two people and occurred between 1930 and 1960, but I shall refrain and confine my concluding remarks to three cases that for some reason created great stirs and which appear to have finally convinced the general public that something was going on.

The first would not appear to have been any more outstanding than dozens of others, but the personalities of the couple concerned played a considerable part in the formulation of public opinion. These were two young people named Adeline August and her boy friend William Point. They happened to be particularly popular and attractive, and were then attending the local high school. They had been on a picnic and were walking home along the Canadian Pacific Railroad track right by Agassiz when a large *Sasquatch* stepped out of the woods ahead of them. Adeline sensibly bolted, but young William stood his ground to cover her flight and grabbed up two rocks with which to defend himself. However the ABSM kept steadily advancing and when it was only 50 feet away William Point decided to retreat. He said that it was about twice the size of an ordinary, large, well-built man, covered with hair, and had arms so long that they almost reached the ground. William Point also said, "It seemed to me that his eyes were very large, and the lower part of his nose was wide, and spread over the greater part of his face." Locally, the account of this young couple was fully believed, and *despite* the fact that they were Amerinds.

This was in 1954. The following year the most outstanding of all Canadian cases occurred. This was related by one William Roe, mentioned above, and is succinctly and amply covered in the following affidavit:

DEPOSITION BY MR. WILLIAM ROE

From the City of Edmonton, Alberta. An affidavit by William Roe. To the Agassiz, Harrison Advance, Printers & Publishers, Drawer O, Agassiz, B.C.; Attention Mr. John W. Green. From the legal Department of Allen F. MacDonald, B.A., L.L.B., City Solicitor., H. F. Wilson, B.A., Asst. City Solicitor and R. N. Saunders, Claims Agent.

Dear Sir:

Re Affidavit of Mr. William Roe, on August 26th, 1957. Mr. Wm. Roe approached the writer requesting the swearing out of An Affidavit in regard to a strange animal he had seen in British Columbia.

The affidavit was drawn up by a member of our legal department and sworn to in the usual manner by the writer.

I cannot state as to the creditability of the story.

We trust the foregoing information will be of assistance.

Yours truly,
(signed)   W. H. Clark
Asst. Claims Agent

WHC:ek.

AFFIDAVIT

I, W. Roe, of the City of Edmonton, in the province of Alberta make oath and say,

(1) That the exhibit A attached to this, my affidavit, is absolutely true and correct in all details.

Sworn before me in the City of Edmonton, Province of Alberta, this 26th day of August, A.D. 1957,

> (signed) Wm. Roe and then
> signed by Clark under a
> numbering D.D. 2822

EXHIBIT A

Ever since I was a small boy back in the forests of Michigan, I have studied the lives and habits of wild animals. Later when I supported my family in northern Alberta by hunting and trapping, I spent many hours just observing the wild things. They fascinated me. The most incredible experience I ever had with a wild creature occurred near a little place called Tete Jaune Cache, B.C., about 80 miles west of Jasper, Alberta.

I had been working on the highway near this place, Tete Jaune Cache, for about 2 years. In October 1955, I decided to climb five miles up Mica Mountain to an old deserted mine, just for something to do. I came in sight of the mine about 3 o'clock in the afternoon after an easy climb. I had just come out of a patch of low brush into a clearing, when I saw what I thought was a grizzly bear in the brush on the other side. I had shot a grizzly near that spot the year before. This one was only about 75 yards away, but I didn't want to shoot it, for I had no way of getting it out. So I sat down on a small rock and watched, with my rifle in my hand.

I could just see part of the animal's head and the top of one shoulder. A moment later it raised up and stepped out into the opening. Then I saw it wasn't a bear.

This to the best of my recollection is what the creature looked like and how it acted as it came across the clearing directly towards me. My first impression was of a huge man about 6 feet tall, almost 3 feet wide, and probably weighing near 300 pounds. It was covered from head to foot with dark brown, silver-tipped hair. But as it came closer I saw by its breasts that it was female.

And yet, its torso was not curved like a female's. Its broad frame was straight from shoulder to hip. Its arms were much thicker than a man's arms and longer, reaching almost to its knees. Its feet were broader proportionately than a man's, about 5 inches wide in the front and tapering to much thinner heels. When it walked it placed the heel of its foot down first, and I could see the grey-brown skin or hide on the soles of its feet.

It came to the edge of the bush I was hiding in, within 20 feet of me, and squatted down on its haunches. Reaching out its hands it pulled the branches of bushes towards it and stripped the leaves with its teeth. Its lips curled flexibly around the leaves as it ate. I was close enough to see that its teeth were white and even. The head was higher at the back than at the front. The nose was broad and flat. The lips and chin protruded farther than its nose. But the hair that covered it, leaving bare only the parts of its face around the mouth, nose and ears, made it resemble an animal as much as a human. None of this hair, even on the back of its head, was longer than an inch, and that on its face much shorter.

Its ears were shaped like a human's ears. But its eyes were small and black like a bear's. And its neck also was unhuman, thicker and shorter than any man's I have ever seen.

As I watched this creature I wondered if some movie company was making a film in this place and that what I saw was an actor made up to look partly human, partly animal. But as I observed it more I decided it would be impossible to fake such a specimen. Anyway, I learned later there was no such company near that area. Nor, in fact, did anyone live up Mica Mountain, according to the people who lived in Tete Jaune Cache.

Finally, the wild thing must have got my scent, for it looked directly at me through an opening in the brush. A look of amazement crossed its face. It looked so comical at that moment I had to grin. Still in a crouched position, it backed up three or four short steps, then straightened up to its full height and started to walk rapidly back the way it had come. For a moment it watched me over its shoulder as it went, not exactly afraid, but as though it wanted no contact with anything strange.

The thought came to me that if I shot it I would possibly have a specimen of great interest to scientists the world over. I had heard stories about the Sasquatch, the giant hairy "Indians" that live in the legend of the Indians of British Columbia and also, many claim are still, in fact, alive today. Maybe this was a Sasquatch, I told myself.

I levelled my rifle. The creature was still walking rapidly away, again turning its head to look in my direction. I lowered the rifle. Although I have called the creature 'it," I felt now that it was a human being, and I knew I would never forgive myself if I killed it.

Just as it came to the other patch of brush it threw its head back and made a peculiar noise that seemed to be half laugh and half language, and which I could only describe as a kind of a whinny. Then it walked from the small brush into a stand of lodge-pole pines.

I stepped out into the opening and looked across a small ridge just beyond the pine to see if I could see it again. It came out on the ridge a couple of hundred yards away from me, tipped its head back again, and again emitted the only sound I had heard it make, but what this half laugh, half language was meant to convey

I do not know. It disappeared then, and I never saw it again.

I wanted to find out if it lived on vegetation entirely or ate meat as well, so I went down and looked for signs. I found it* in five different places, and although I examined it thoroughly, could find no hair or shells or bugs or insects. So I believe it was strictly a vegetarian.

I found one place where it had slept for a couple of nights under a tree. Now, the nights were cool up the mountain, at this time of year especially, and yet it had not used a fire. I found no signs that it possessed even the simplest of tools. Nor did I find any signs that it had a single companion while in this place.

Whether this creature was a Sasquatch I do not know. It will always remain a mystery to me unless another one is found.

I hearby declare the above statement to be in every part true, to the best of my powers of observation and recollection.

Signed William Roe

Witnessed

This priceless document was also unearthed by the indefatigable John Green of the *Agassiz-Harrison Advance,* upon whom the mantle of *Sasquatch* research, nobly worn by Mr. J. W. Burns for so many years, seems to have fallen. He published it in his paper and the results were electric. Not only did it bring Mr. Ostman's story to light; it got the whole neighborhood on its toes, including even the Chamber of Commerce of the resort town of Harrison which made moves to advertise a *Sasquatch* hunt as a come-on for its centenary celebrations! Fortunately, and decently, this idea was dropped but $5000 is said to have been offered for the capture of a *Sasquatch*. This was not, of course, collected but it brought forth another rash of encounter stories. Notable among these—and most noted in the world press—was a story reported by a Mr. Stanley Hunt of Vernon, B.C., a respected and widely known auctioneer, who, when driving at night along the Trans-Canada Highway near a place called Flood on the lower Fraser River south of Yale, on May 17, 1956, had to slow down to permit one of them to cross the road. It was

* [I add here the following note that I presume he is referring there to droppings or faeces of this animal of which he says he found evidence in five different places.]

immense and covered with "gray hair," and, waiting for it on the other side of the road, there was, Mr. Hunt relates, another one "gangly, not stocky like a bear."

According to C. S. Lambert, writing in 1954, the situation changed considerably in 1935 when:

> After a series of alarming reports that these giants were prowling around Harrison Mills, 50 miles east of Vancouver, disturbing the residents by their weird wolf-like howls at night, and destroying property, a band of vigilantes was organized to track the marauders down. However, no specimen of the primitive tribe was captured, and many white people became openly sceptical of the existence of the giants.
>
> According to Allen Roy Evans, in the Montreal Standard ("B.C.'s Hairy Giants"), the Indians are now very sensitive to any imputations cast upon their veracity in this matter. During the 19th century they were ready to tell enquirers all they knew about the Susquatch men; but today they have become more reserved, and talk only to Government agents about the matter. They maintain that the "Wild Indians" are divided into two tribes, whose rivalry with each other keeps their number down and so prevents them becoming a serious menace to others.
>
> Expeditions have been organized to track down the Susquatch men to their lair in the mountains; but the Indians employed to guide these expeditions invariably desert before they reach the danger zone. However, certain large caves have been discovered, with man-made walls of stone inside them, and specially-shaped stones fitted to their mouths, like doors. The difficulty in the way of penetrating to the heart of the Morris Mountains district is very great. The terrain is cut up by deep gorges and almost impassable ravines; it is easy to get lost, and hard to make substantial progress in any one direction for long.

In the fall of the following year large human-like footprints turned up overnight all over the place in this area. Throughout a hundred years of *Sasquatchery*, footprints are often mentioned casually, but nobody seems to have been particularly impressed by them or to have done anything about them. Suddenly they took over the front pages.

5. Footprints on the Sands of . . .

ABOMINABLE AFFAIRS IN THE U.S.

If you look out of your window one morning to find that it has snowed during the night, you may be happy or you may be sad. If then, while contemplating this quite natural phenomenon, you perceive upon its pristine surface a number of marks of regular shape, forming a set of tracks, the sundry relays, feedbacks, and synapses in your brain may snap open or shut in ordered patterns, causing you to register almost subconsciously such concrete items as man, dog, car, snowplow, or suchlike. You may even go so far as actually to think, saying to yourself "That's funny, Mary went out already." Foot-tracks are commonplace, and quite logical, and we consider them as objects. Yet they are not even quasi-objects; they are entirely negative physically; are purely subjective concepts; and in almost all cases are ephemeral things. Nevertheless, they are quite acceptable, provided we have a ready-made answer for them, ranging from vague terms such as "dog," all the way to "Mary wearing a particular pair of shoes." When, however, a set of foot-tracks turns up on snow, or any other surface for that matter, to which people cannot immediately put a label, they become quite hysterical, and in their frantic efforts to explain this appalling thing, they will indulge in the most terrifyingly illogical actions. They also say the silliest things.

Simple logic demands that a foot or any other print must have been made by something, and something which must have been at the point where the imprint was made. But sometimes, unfortunately for humanity, matters don't always work out that way, in either one or both of these respects. The second class of problems is the less awful. For instance, "How on earth did Mary get up on the barn roof?" may jolt you but can have all sorts of logical explanations. If one is sufficiently concerned about Mary's welfare, it is the common practice to investigate these in order of likelihood, starting by asking Mary, if she is around; and ending by calling in the long-suffering police if she has disappeared. Even in this class, however, there can be nasty ones. We once found a set of what looked like our tame porcupine's tracks, inside an empty cage, which was constructed of heavy wire in the form of a cube on all six sides, and had a firmly locked door. That took some investigation and it reduced a number of normally sane citizens to gibbering idiots in the meantime.

(Said porcupine had once been housed in that cage for an hour or so, while its own cage was cleaned and repaired, by an assistant who was not present when the bizarre discovery was made. The earth floor inside the cage had been wet at the time and the animal had left deep tracks in the claylike mud. This dried solid. The assistant had then, in accord with his routine duties, put a 2-inch covering of fresh earth over this. The night before the uproar there had been about 15 minutes of torrential rain, which had washed all this top layer exactly off the old hardened one and the tracks had appeared looking just as if they were fresh and, of course, once again in damp earth.)

The more abominable class is that of individual prints or sets of tracks—and the two items are quite different and should be at all times most carefully defined by the use of the appropriate term—for which there is not a ready-made explanation. A *print* (or imprint) is an individual item such as that of one foot. A set of *tracks* (or a track) is, on the other hand, a series of prints, either interrupted as in animals, or continuous as made by wheeled machines, left by some moving object. There are quite a lot of reports of single prints being found both in such positions as may be explained—as in a small patch of mud on a rocky path—but on occasion in places that cannot be explained. These last are, of course, very unnerving.

Sasquatch imprints and tracks, along with those of their relatives or congeners, by whatever name they were known, were perfectly all right by the Amerinds because they had just such a ready-made answer, all of them, as they readily tell one, knowing perfectly well that they were made by the big, wild, hairy men of the woods: or by their wives and children. As the Amerinds gave up being Americans and started to become, or were forced to become sort of bogus Europeans, they forgot to tell their own children about these personages. The result was that in time we even have

Amerinds becoming for a time slightly disturbed.
[Amerinds *never* under any conditions become "hysterical."] When, however, white men first saw these large
ABSM tracks they invariably went into a fairly advanced
trauma. This habit was apparently universal among Europeans and people of European origin, right up until the
time when a ready-made answer become disseminated—
namely, *Sasquatches, Oh-Mahs,* etc.—whereupon a happy
reaction set in. This was simply to say: "Oh, those!
Don't worry, they're made by runaway Indians; they have
huge feet, you know, and sometimes grow hair to keep out
the cold." (Amerinds, I should point out here, are either
wholly or substantially of Mongoloid ancestry, the group
of the human race that is defined as being the most gla-
brous [almost without body hair], and having particularly
small, neat feet.)

It is rather interesting to note in passing that persons of
African ancestry have behaved quite otherwise throughout. They possess ancestors who have always recognized a
non-material world just as widespread and as real as the
material one. This is probably why they are such great
pragmatists. What is more, according to them, entities in
both worlds customarily muck about in the other, so that
men's souls can range around "elsewhere" and *chumbis*
—or what we in our innocence call ghosts, poltergeists,
and spirits—can, in their estimation, quite well leave imprints and foot-tracks. Africans of the Negroid branch of
humanity and their descendants are, therefore, the greatest
skeptics throughout our story, they have never really been
interested in or even much surprised about the matter,
for they have a sort of built-in answer; and while they
have always thought Europeans to be stupid for not carrying on with disembodied entities, they usually think the
Amerinds quite batty for needing an embodied entity to
explain these tracks. The few people of African origin
whom I have met in the course of this business in North
America, as well as in Africa appear, furthermore, to have
accepted the physical appearance of ABSMs that they
themselves have witnessed, with the utmost equanimity
and simply as lucky or dangerous happenstances.

I bring all this up now because it has to be aired in any
case sooner or later, and because from now on we are
going to have all three major branches of the human race
involved in the matter. Their reactions are indeed different, whatever anybody may say about generalizations. All
three "races" are present in the United States, where our

story now takes us, and since we are going to follow the foot-tracks of the ABSMs, clear through this country to tropical America, we are going to have to be prepared for some real surprises—both ways. You will see what I mean by this in a minute.

At this point I would ask you to glance at Maps II and IV before proceeding, because, without some idea of the facts of vegetational distribution, very little of what I have to say in this and the next chapter will make much sense. I know by experience that it is quite all right for me or anybody else to say almost anything about foreign lands, and the farther away and thus foreign they are, the more outrageous the claims may be. This is the reason why such a high percentage of "explorers" are found, on proper investigation (if that is possible, which it seldom is), to be phonies, even if only mildly and innocuously so. When, on the other hand, anybody makes even slightly unusual remarks about the country *in* which he is speaking and to citizens *of* that country, he is almost certain to be disbelieved, probably ridiculed, and oftimes harassed for his pains. This applies to statements as innocent as "You know, the hillbillies down there don't wear shoes." Try it sometime, *down there,* but don't wait to see what happens, for you'll have the local State Department on your back if you have published your statement, and you'll find yourself excluded from private swimming pools if you have merely said it in family circles.

Since I have a private swimming (duck) pond of my own, and seldom wear shoes indoors in winter or either in- or out-of-doors throughout the whole summer and early fall as well as, for other reasons that I will not go into, I have made a profession of saying things about the country I am in. I am, in fact and as I said at the outset, a reporter and as I don't give a damn whether anybody wears shoes or not, nor what their opinions are on that or any other subject, and am interested only in facts, I am constantly saying things that annoy people. What I have to say now is going to annoy some types very much. Moreover, if you haven't as yet glanced at these maps, you may be so annoyed that you will just stop reading. I don't want you to do this, but for purely altruistic reasons—namely that these facts are such fun. To keep you reading, therefore, let me just tell you that, if you do so, you are going to get a really good laugh, specifically at the expense of just those people whom you have always thought were idiots in any case. [Admittedly, this includes almost everybody other than yourself, which makes it all the more pleasant.]

Animals (and ABSMs) take no account of political boundaries even when they are physically erected by people in the form of barbed-wire fences or iron curtains. They do, on the other hand, not only take into account but conform absolutely to certain boundaries and dividing lines set up by Nature. No animal ever, it seems, transgresses such a boundary and these boundaries may often be so precise that you can stand with one foot in one great natural province and the other foot in another. There are animals that range over more than one and sometimes over half a dozen provinces. These are called *catholic* species; but most animals stay within the confines of just one province. Within the provinces, moreover, there are a number of natural niches or environments. Nature abhors a vacuum (as we have been repeatedly told) and she fills all her niches with an appropriate animal species. If any one dies out or is exterminated, some other animal will come in to inhabit its niche. As an example, the South American aquatic porcupine called the Coypu (*Myopotamus coypu*) the fur of which is called *nutria,* was introduced into North America 50 years ago and immediately started to fill up the niche previously occupied by the Beaver which had, at that time, been largely exterminated in this country by fur trappers.

Sometimes a species of animal will introduce itself into an area and do battle with the established occupants of the particular niche that it likes. Then again, men have introduced animals from one country to another and started virtual animal wars, usually with fatal consequences to one or the other party. In Australia introduced European animals, like the dog, cat, fox, and rabbit, have committed mass mayhem on the indigenous fauna: on the other hand, attempts to introduce the pheasant in certain parts of North America have repeatedly failed. The whys and the wherefores of these results have proved very puzzling in that there seemed to be no rhyme or reason for them. There is, nonetheless, a law governing the matter, and a very precise one. This is a botanical matter.

The whole earth is portioned out into different types of plant growth—different in the way the vegetation grows (in height, density, and so forth) rather than in what particular types of plants it contains—and these form great belts around the earth regardless of oceans, seas, and mountains. These belts, which meander about and broaden out or wither down sometimes almost to nothing, are also subdivided into blocks or provinces going from east to west, like the cross-stripes on a banded snake. Each one of these provinces has its own history, climate, weather, soils, flora, and fauna. What is more, it has now been discovered that all faunas are wholly dependent upon vegetation but not so much upon the constitution of that vegetation as upon *the way in which it grows*. Human beings are animals and they conform to these general principles too, even down to national types. So it seems, do ABSMs (see Map II).

Man, however, is what is called an adaptable animal. He is also incredibly tough, and can survive in more types of vegetation and in a wider variety of environments than most animals, being surpassed in this ability by only a few other animals, such as the spiders and their allies, which live in water and in air, and range from icecaps to still hot lava flows, and to the tops of mountains where even plants give up. Nevertheless, when man comes to settle down and try to earn a living and breed, even he conforms to the old pattern. Hollanders gyrate to coastal flats, and Norwegians to warm, wet fiords. However, man *can* survive an ousting from his natural environment and he has often done so. The Neanderthalers appear to have been driven back into the hills by the folk of Cromagnon-culture; and the Hebrews of the desert were blasted all over the lot, and have survived.

ABSMs, it seems, have also been driven back into certain environments. By the time my story is told, you will see why I say this and why it happened. There is nothing mysterious about it. It is simply that ABSMs are Hominids or, just as every benighted native has always asserted, *human* rather than animal, and thus are endowed in one degree or another with human attributes, and most notably their powers of survival, their adaptability, their toughness, and their acuteness. The Pongids, or apes, on the other hand, though looking so like humans, are the lousiest adapters, are completely stuck with their special environments and in their particular provinces. They can hardly breed outside them, even with the very best and most modern human medical assistance—as witness the tiny number of gorillas born in captivity. In other words, about 50 million years ago, Nature started an experiment with a couple of Primate types now called the Hominid and the Pongid. The first made the grade, and mostly through the efforts and discoveries of ABSMs; the latter failed, and are doomed.

If there are ABSMs in North America, as well as Central and South America (as would appear from what follows), and they are Hominids, they must have come here from somewhere else, for we can say with almost absolute certainty that neither Man nor the Hominids was evolved in the New World. What is more, not so much as a single bone or other indication has ever been discovered suggesting that either the Pongids or any of the true Monkeys ever even got here. On the other hand, men got here, and at a rather early date. Bones of the animals he brought back from hunting forays have been dated certainly back to before the last ice-advance; some are claimed to be more than 40,000 years old. We have not yet obtained the bones of the earliest of these men themselves, but, if some anthropologists are right, there are some extremely old and quite primitive stone implements at the lowest levels, and we now know that a creature (such as East Africa's *Zinjanthropus*) was a toolmaker but most certainly would be called an ABSM if he were found running around today. Failure to find the bones of ABSMs is no cause for stating that they never existed. Tools of the types known as Chellean and Acheulean have been known from all over southern Europe and Africa since men started collecting such items, but it was not until the last decade that we found a single bone of the men who made them—if we have yet done so, as a matter of fact.

However, ABSMs seem once to have roamed much of North America. Why, then, should those alleged still to do so, although really very hominoid in form, appear to be without tools, fire, or speech? We have to look at it this way. They were probably here in the purely "animal" stage of their development, and they kept coming in waves [over the Bering Straits, if you like] at ever increasingly efficient levels of toolmaking and development, until they were replaced by their cousins who were so *"something-or-other"* that we, upon digging up their remains, call them Men. [Lots of these came too, making ever better tools, until the misguided Amerinds made the mistake of tagging along. At this point we enter history and the domain of other specialities.] As brighter and better ABSMs turned up, however, the previous occupants had to move out into less desirable environments—nasty places like deserts and mountains—and by the time proper Men arrived, these places were getting quite crowded. At that point another factor became operative.

ABSMs, both here and all over the world, had been getting "better"—which is another way of saying more complicated or mixed up—and, thus, in certain ways less efficient again. The more complex their culture became —and don't think that they didn't have a culture for Nutcracker-Man (*Zinjanthropus*) of 600,000 years ago in East Africa made splendid tools but had a brain somewhat more paltry than the average chimp—the more dependent they were upon an easy environment, which means one where it was easy to obtain a living. Chased out into a rough one by still more cultured chaps, they began to find the going very hard. In fact, the more "cultured" they were, the worse they fared when pushed up into the mountains; and the more advanced they were, the more easily and rapidly they gave up and became extinct. Thus, we have the extraordinary spectacle of the more primitive surviving and the more advanced wilting away. Today, only the most primitive have apparently survived, and in the remotest and ruggedest places where any other ABSM less rugged could not get along; where Man, however tough, failed; and where even Modern Man, who has really got somewhere with his culture, finds it hard going. And just where is this?

The answer is very simple and absolutely definitive. It is what is called by botanists *The Montane Forest*. This is why I suggested that you take a look at the maps and see where such forests are, especially today, on our continent. From these you will note that their distribution coincides exactly with that of the reports of our ABSMs; as it does on all the other continents with *their* ABSMs. There is only one exception, from the botanical point of view, and this I would like to dispose of forthwith.

The last retreat on land of anything is a forest. In North America between those latitudes occupied by the United States, most lowland forests are woodlands, and anything unwanted in them has long ago been eliminated. [One can't speak of feral dogs because we introduced them.] In Canada, of course, such forests are still virtually impenetrable. There remain then the montane forests [which are not quite the same thing as mere forests on mountains] and one other type of vegetational growth. This is what are called technically the Bottomlands. By this is meant swamps at low level but mostly in river valleys and deltas, that are covered with a closed-canopy forest of some kind however short in stature, and which are either flooded all the time, seasonally, or from time to time, so that they are unpleasant for man to live in and a lost cause to try and clear, drain, and farm. It so happens that we have a very great acreage of just such country in the United States that is tacitly ignored by everybody and frankly unknown to most. This is concentrated along the Mississippi Valley and up the valleys of the tributaries of that great river.

The best road maps of the states that straddle these Bottomlands look perfectly OK at first sight, being covered with roads of various grades, having names of counties, townships, and so forth scattered all over them and seeming, when viewed individually, to be quite consistent with all other road maps of our country. If, however, you look more carefully at them, take a pair of dividers, consult the scale at the foot of the map, and then select your areas carefully you can isolate almost endless parts of the map that look like this:

==== = secondary roads
---- = dirt roads
o = settlements with names

1050 square miles in northern Louisiana.

This you will not, of course, believe. It will also probably make you very annoyed. You might therefore assuage your

121

fury by going out and buying, or writing to one of the oil companies to obtain, maps of such states as Missouri, Illinois, Kentucky, Tennessee, Arkansas, Alabama, Mississippi, and Louisiana, and spend a moment or two with a rectangle of the dimensions and the scale of the above. It will probably make you even more angry, but I said that I would name names, even if I am "down there."

The reason I bring this obnoxious subject up at this time is that, before we can get back to the main road of our travelogue, there is something that is really unpleasant that has to be taken care of. This is the "Little Red Men of the Trees." How aggravating can I get; and how far out on what limb can I wriggle? You would be surprised indeed; but I warn you in the most friendly fashion, please don't forget that I am a reporter and, as of now, nothing else. It is therefore my duty to report to you; so here goes:

> **Dear Sir,**
> My name is James Meacham, I read the article that you wrote for True Magazine.* I have been planning on going to California in the same area that your article was about. I was a little surprised to read about such a creature as an abominable Snowman living so close to where I intended to visit. I have always liked to explore places that other people care little about. I would like to know all you can tell me about this creature if you can tell anything more than you did in the article. I am sure a man of your standing must have more information about this subject than was in those few pages. I will gladly pay the postage on the information you can send. I cannot offer more because I am not working at the present.
> I have met a few strange things in my life; as I am still young, there are many more I will probably see. I would like to know if you can tell me anything about a creature that looks like a small ape or a large monkey that has hair the color of fur a reddish orange color. I saw such a creature when I was 15. A friend was with me but did not see it. Whatever it was did not have a tail like a monkey but it did swing like one by its arms. This may sound like something that I thought I saw but really didn't which I would believe except for a few details.

* *"The Strange Story of America's Abominable Snowman,"* True, The Man's Magazine, Vol. 40, December, 1959.

I had a .22 calibre semi-automatic with me. I watched this thing for about 5 minutes so I have to believe it. I put fourteen .22 long-rifle shells into whatever it was. From where I was standing I couldn't have missed. We found 1 bullet in the tree trunk so 13 of them hit it. The part that sounds more impossible is that whatever it was, did not even move while 13 bullets went into it. If I had missed all 14 bullets would have gone into the tree trunk.

I have told many people about this but nobody believes it. We found a few hairs where I had shot, but nothing else except the bullet. There was not a trace of blood. My partner thinks it was a squirrel but no squirrel grows that big. If it had been one, 2 of those bullets would have stopped it dead. Whatever it was did not even move till I headed for the tree. It traveled through those trees like an express train. I could hear the leaves rattle but could not see it.

I searched for it for a long time after that but never saw it again. No one in that area knows anything about it or has ever seen it. It had a cry that was enough to drive a person crazy. That was almost 3 years ago [1957] and I still wake up in my sleep sometimes when that sound comes back to me. If you can give me any advice as to what it could have been I will greatly appreciate it. If I had not shot it myself I would not believe it, not being able to find any blood. I know you must receive a lot of letters about this sort of thing, but all I want to know is what animal in a marsh near Jackson, Tenn. could hold 13 long-rifle shells without even moving till you start to come after it? That is what started me looking for things most people think cannot possibly exist.

> Yours truly,
> James M. Meacham

In 1954 a young Orang-utan escaped from a shipment of apes to a well-known Florida organization, took off into the woods, and has never been seen again. I refrain from giving further details because the valuable ape was paid for, but reported as DOA, a trade term for "dead on arrival," and someone still might get in trouble. The incident is fairly widely known in certain circles, and has been a perfect nuisance because when anything like the above is reported, even as far away as Tennessee, it is immediately dredged up by way of explanation. I suppose it is just possible that a healthy young *Mia* [a better name for what we call the Orang-utan] could survive a succession of mild Southern winters and it could travel an enormous distance by trees alone, but what it would eat during most of the year I don't know. Much more important is that a lost ape that has once been in captivity for even a short period would be almost certain to head for the nearest human habitation the moment it got hungry or saw anything novel that frightened it. In all the years that I had a zoo, I never knew an escaped animal [apart from local fauna, and even many of those] *not* to return voluntarily to its own cage during the night. Of course this "ape" might have escaped from some zoo much nearer the place where this correspondent said he saw it, but the loss of a $5000 specimen from a zoo would not go unnoticed; though, it must be admitted, it might well go unreported—to the Directors, that is. There is as much hanky-panky in the animal business as in any other. An escaped Mia is, however, I rather think, itself merely an escape mechanism as it is called, especially when we come to contemplate the following.

From *Hoosier Folklore,* Vol. 5, p. 19, March 1946:

Another type of story that is of much more concern to us here in Southern Illinois nowadays is the "strange beast" legend. . . . Every few years some community reports the presence of a mysterious beast over in the local creek bottom.

Although it is difficult to determine just where a story of this sort has its beginning, this one seems to have originated in the Gum Creek bottom near Mt. Vernon. During the summer of 1941, a preacher was hunting squirrels in the woods along the creek when a large animal that looked something like a baboon jumped out of a tree near him. The preacher struck at the beast with his gun barrel when it walked toward him in an upright position. He finally frightened it away by firing a couple of shots into the air.

Later the beast began to alarm rural people by uttering terrorizing screams mostly at night in the wooded bottom lands along the creeks. School children in the rural districts sometimes heard it, too, and hunters saw its tracks. . . . By early spring of 1942, the animal had local people aroused to a fighting pitch. About that time, a farmer near Bonnie reported that the beast had killed his dog. A call went out for volunteers to join a mass hunt to round up the animal.

The beast must have got news of the big hunt, for reports started coming in of its appearance in other creek bottoms, some as much as 40 or 50 miles from the original site. A man driving near the Big Muddy River, in Jackson County, one night saw the beast bound across the road. Some hunters saw evidence of its presence away over in Okaw. Its rapid changing from place to place must have been aided considerably by its ability to jump, for, by this time, reports had it jumping along at from 20 to 40 feet per leap.

It is impossible to say how many hunters and parties of hunters, armed with everything from shotguns to ropes and nets, went out to look for the strange beast in the various creek bottoms where it had been seen, or its tracks had been seen, or its piercing screams had been heard. Those taking nets and ropes were intent on bringing the creature back alive.

Usually* this strange beast can't be found, and interest in it dies as mysteriously as it arose in the beginning. . . . About 25 years ago, a 'coon hunter from Hecker one night heard a strange beast screaming up ahead on Prairie du Long Creek. Hunters chased this phantom from time to time all one winter. Their dogs would get the trail, then lose it, and they would hear it screaming down the creek in the opposite direction. It was that kind of creature: you'd hear it up creek, but when you set out in that direction you'd hear it a mile down creek.

And again:

Dear Mr. Sanderson,

I listened to you on Long John Nebel's program last Thursday and was very much surprised that you talked about such things as Abominable Snowmen in America. I am a housewife but I majored in biology, attended our state university and have an M.A. in plain zoology. My husband is an experimental chemist employed by . . . [company name withheld for obvious reasons: Author.] and my eldest son is a technician in the Air Force. I came from Mississippi but we have resided here (in Kentucky) for ten years now.

I wonder if you have ever heard of the Little Red

* This is a funny word. Does it imply that sometimes it *can* be found?

Men of the Delta? Nobody thought anything much of them where I was raised except that one had better be careful of shooting one because it might be murder, or so the sheriff might think if anything came of it, but I was surprised to find that the folks hereabout know it too though they took some years to talk about it to me. My husband is a New Englander and these folks don't talk much. They are [the Little Red Men of the Delta] said to be about the size of a ten year old kid and able to climb like monkeys and to live back from the bayous. They talk a lot but keep out of gunshot range and mostly go into the water. They are people and the musk-rat trappers say they often wear scraps of discarded lines [linens?] old jeans and such.

If you have heard about them will you talk about them on the air as it puzzles me that nobody has ever talked about them but everybody in some places seems to know about them. There was sure nothing in my biology course about them but there's a lot folks don't know or don't talk about . . .

Yours, etc.,
Mrs. V. K.

And you can say that again! Plain ordinary citizens just don't talk; they are born with too much sense. Ridicule is the most dastardly thing and can ruin one's whole life in one small jump. It takes real guts to come right out and say you've seen the Loch Ness Monster; and you'd better have private means, if you do. Otherwise, humanity at large will round on you and jump in unison, and they have a collective memory that can last for a century. Don't do it, brethren and sistren! [That's why I always ask specifically whether I may publish a name.]

I could go on quoting tidbits like the above for quite a long time and give transcripts of some tape recordings that I have but what, frankly, is the use? No one will believe either the stories or me. Nonetheless, I would be failing in my duty—which, incidentally, I take very seriously; and please make no mistake about that—if I did not put this outrageous matter before the public. Like many other things "reported" it needs, and can stand, a good airing. I am not saying that there is even so much as a word of truth in any of it but there it is, and it is no good just ignoring it. If people "down there" will persist in penning such tripe, we had better get on with the job of showing it up for what it really is. But just what is it? You tell me: I am merely reporting, and I have not yet had the time, money, nor opportunity to go to those particular places to investigate the matter. Since others apparently have not either, perhaps it would be better that everyone shut up. Meanwhile, however, I refuse to just discount everything anybody from the states listed above says. That would be tantamount to calling them all liars and idiots; and I know for a fact that they are usually neither. What is more, that is their country, and I am prepared to accept the fact that they know more about it than all of us, however whacky what they say may sound. And then there is the matter of the road maps. Just what is anyone prepared to swear under oath he knows about the Bottomlands? I have been a little way into some for brief periods and I must say that I am not prepared to give out much about them at all—they are far too vast, complex, and incomprehensible to any "foreigner." The geodeticists have surveyed them; let them tell us. Their maps are excellent—they are made from points 60 miles apart and from the air. They show everything!

As a sort of parting shot, I quote a newspaper clipping of recent date:

MONSTER AROUND

REFORM, ALA.—A mysterious creature is still roaming the woods around nearby Clanton. It eats peaches, makes sounds like an elephant, and leaves footprints like an ape.

This whole bit is really becoming very difficult because little squibs like this should not include so many splendid possibilities. Of course it would eat peaches, who wouldn't? And I must admit that a herd of elephants in a forest can sound exactly like a troop of chimpanzees having a ball. But who in Reform, Alabama [I like that name] is that good on the ichnology of the *Anthropoidea*? There is a sort of chatty approach about this story, giving the impression that among the citizens of Reform and Clanton there is a considerable understanding about this beast, and there is definite indication that its presence is not a new event. In fact then, are the Bottomlands full of runaway apes or do we have an indigenous and most particular abomination thereabouts? I could give an opinion but I shall refrain, for it would be even more loathesome.

Now, and with a certain sense of relief I may say, we can get back on the straight and narrow path, and pick up our foot-tracks again. These we first stumbled upon in southern

British Columbia at the end of the *Sasquatch* trail. Thence, they went south over the border and, willy-nilly we have had to follow. This is going to get us into a most unpleasant labyrinth. It is, actually, a maze with several alternate correct routes, all of which cross each other and land us up in seemingly impossible predicaments. I follow the foot-tracks first.

In progressing in space we have first to retrace our tracks in time to even earlier than before—to the "49ers," in fact. It was about that date (1849) that Anglo-Saxon type Americans first descended upon the West in any substantial masses. It was, of course, the gold that did it. Actually, this area was the first to be penetrated and colonized by Europeans on this continent; the Spaniards having made some really astonishing advances north through it from Mexico. Few people realize that these intrepid savages in their clanking armor carrying little more than their lovely and holy crosses, actually got into what is now Canada through the mountainous third of our country. This area is still giving our bulldozer operators trouble in crossing from east to west. But, here again, is another story. The point is that the Spaniards later, and very sensibly, contracted into the more fertile and pleasant areas and just left the rest to the benighted Amerinds.

During this long period of some 300 years no less, things went along much as they had done since the last ice-advance in this area—outside the Spanish Missions. There were, however, some most agile-minded priests who interested themselves enormously in the land and took the Amerinds quite seriously. They left records of some of the legends of their flocks that make most interesting reading. I have to mention the fact of the existence of these now because they constitute the earliest sight of our trail, leading, as always, from the Northlands on toward the salubrious climes of tropical America. They [the records] speak of great wild men of the dry upland arroyos and massed piñon forests, that tramped lugubriously about at night scaring adolescent Amerinds and leaving monstrous footprints on the sands of that time all over the region. But, after these ecclesiastical indiscretions, there is a complete blank as far as I know until the 1849 Gold Rush. Then things began to happen in typically Yankee fashion.

This particular facet or phase of ABSMery has, like the overall picture, to be tackled in retrospect and in the order of its rediscovery. The alleged incidents in some cases occurred over a century ago but the records came to light only in the last few years. They had been lying buried in newspaper morgues. What actually happened—and this is quite apart from the reports on individual incidents—is that a whole mass of Easterners, unacquainted with the Far West, suddenly appeared on the scene and went barging off into the outlands looking for gold. Prior to their arrival there had been plenty of people along the coast and idly dotted about the inner belt of the West, but they had stayed literally around the water holes in the latter, while they had not gone back inland from the coast in the more northern and better watered areas—that is from the north end of the Sacramento Valley to Puget Sound. It was when the Easterners tried to penetrate these lands of mighty forests and seemingly everlasting mountain ranges, one behind the other, that things began to happen. Sometimes, they got a bit out of hand.

We are now back in the montane forests of which we have spoken so firmly, and we are going to stay in them for a very long time. Before we go any farther into them, though, I should state a few basic facts. Such types of forest—and there are actually about a couple of dozen of them between Alaska and Tierra del Fuego—are well-nigh impenetrable. That is why not only just substantial parts, but the greater part of them, even in our own country, are not yet "opened up." This is a loose term; so, to be more precise, let me give one example of the state of current affairs in what is just about the *most* accessible of all of them today. This is the 17,000 square-mile block of territory centered around the Klamath River area in northern California.

The extent, position, and boundaries of this area may be seen on Maps V and VII. You may calculate its dimensions for yourself. This I beg of you to do, rather than writing to me about it.* Please note also that it starts at the bottom about Clear Lake which is just 70 miles north of San Francisco, and it continues on north into Oregon. Actually it is confluent with a much vaster block in the Cascades, and is nowhere completely cut off (by farmland or nonforested land) from other lesser blocks in Oregon and thence on to

* In the article mentioned above in *True Magazine*, an extra zero unfortunately became attached to the area given, a mistake that started with my typing but went clean through to the published story. This resulted in a deluge of several thousand letters. But, when it had been corrected, just as many people wrote scoffing at the true figure. Many of these were Californians; and some even from the counties concerned!

Washington. I should explain that in delineating these wilderness blocks I do not consider a road, even a main blacktop, to be a boundary, for it does not deter any living thing that I know of from passing from one side to the other, provided there is cover on both sides right up to its edges. This great area has been surveyed and there are maps of it down to very large scale in conformity with the best series published by the Coast and Geodetic Survey, National Forests, and other official agencies. There are neat county maps covered with names and a grid on a scale of 4/10 of an inch to the mile, that look perfectly splendid at first sight. However, I ran into a Federal agency surveying party when I was deep in the middle of this block in 1959, and spent several evenings with the Chief Surveying Officer who told me things and demonstrated certain facts that, metaphorically speaking, caused myself and my two traveling partners to lose our eyebrows—upward.

It transpired that this area had only once been "surveyed" and that was by unofficial surveyors under contract to the U.S. Government, *in the year 1859!* Further, the survey was ostensibly made on a 1-mile grid; that is to say the surveyor was supposed to walk a mile north, south, east, or west, take a fix and drive a stake, and continue doing this till he reached some previously selected line at the other end that linked up with the next survey. The original notebooks carried by these surveyors of 1859, and in which they recorded the facts and figures of their surveys in the field, a page to a mile, are on file in the Lands Office in San Francisco. They are a revelation. The surveyor whom we met told us that in one notebook he had found no less than 23 pages absolutely blank and without so much as a thumbmark on them, and he told us that all the books covering this area were like that. He stressed that this is no deprecation of the early surveyors as, he said, they actually did a remarkable job on the whole, managing to join up the surveys to the 60-mile triangulation made from mountaintops (and now corrected from aerial photography), but he pointed out that the greater part of the resultant maps are pure conjecture and most of them made by what surveyors call "camp-surveying." What, of course, happened was that the country was so rugged and impassable that the surveyors just went in as far as they could, then came back out, went around to the next possible entrance, and tried again. When they had enough fixes around the edges, they just ruled lines connecting what they had, adjusted a bit for error, and then ruled in the rest of the grid. And this, combined with names given to visible mountains, ranges, Amerindian settlements in accessible valleys, and logging operations, filled the whole thing out nicely, so that on paper it looks almost like the outskirts of San Francisco.

Actually, this great block of territory is quite unknown. Nobody goes into it much except a short way from its edges, and practically nobody has gone through it. I interviewed one experienced locally bred woodsman who took a 3-week summer vacation to attempt this. He did cut across the southwest corner of the square but was a week late getting back to work. A friend of mine working in there at the time of writing did come upon a lone and unknown prospector of the old school some distance in, and he had *a mule* in there. One "scientist" from a "university" in California wrote a furious letter after I had published my report on the ABSMery of this area, stating that he had "collected animals all over every bit of the area during several seasons" and adding gratuitously that "its entire fauna has for decades been well known." This is a point at which I find it very hard to remain civil.

The whole of this country is clothed in a particular kind of montane, closed-canopy, mixed deciduous-coniferous forest, of magnificent proportions and containing some of the finest timber in the world. It grows in three tiers with an undergrowth. The tallest trees such as Sitka Spruce, and Douglas Fir, run up to 150 to 200 feet and stand pretty close together. Under them on the upper reaches there is a closed-canopy of smaller conifers, in the valleys of deciduous trees such as maples, madroñes, etc., and beneath both of these there is usually another closed-canopy of large saplings and smaller trees of mixed constitution. Beneath this again is another layer that is almost impenetrable, being composed of bushes and the dead branches of the spruces and firs which are as strong as spring steel even when leafless, and which persist right down to the ground like a barbed-wire entanglement. It took me half an hour with a sharp machete to get far enough from the one road in the country not to be able to talk to my companions left on that road. I am a fair bushwacker, having been at it all my life, and I am pencil-thin and thus highly suitable for going through and under things.

But this is not by any means all. The whole of this country is constructed like a freshly plowed field on a monstrous scale. While its mountains and peaks are not high by Western standards they are immensely steep, and closely packed

131

so that there is practically no horizontal ground throughout the whole country. The whole thing is a nightmare even to experienced woodsmen, and something much worse to road builders.

This is the real state of affairs throughout a huge block of territory within a hundred miles of one of our greatest cities, although almost everybody in that city would deny it positively, and even the majority of citizens of Eureka, a large and prosperous community right on its edge, have no idea of its true nature. Conditions are even more difficult in other montane areas but from now on I shall simply be saying of them, as we approach them, that they are either better or worse than the Klamath. This is going to relieve me of the necessity for a lot of verbiage. Readers may also find this useful in arguments; while it will give some sort of key to assess other forests in other lands. Actually, though, this Klamath forest is just about as difficult as I have ever run into, and that goes for the tropics too, but it, of course, pales before the British Columbian vegetation on the grounds of topography for, whereas we have here to deal only with little mountains, there they have enormous ones.

It was such topography, moreover, that was tackled by the greenhorns from the East looking for gold. They didn't get very far, but they did, according to the older Amerinds still living, and who got it from their fathers and grandfathers, cause the ABSMs to make a sudden mass withdrawal into the inner recesses of each of the blocks, at that time. This interesting information was first given to me by a Mr. Oscar Mack, doyen of the Yurok clans of the upper Hoopa Valley. The same statement has cropped up again and again during my investigations all over the Puget Sound to California area. If, moreover, you look at Map V, you will note an extremely odd fact. This is that early reports (and of various types) came also from what is now Idaho in what is called more technically the North Montane Province. Some very funny things happened there in early days and they seem still to be happening. Most of them center round the real wilderness area about the upper Salmon River which flows into the Snake River as shown on that map. It was in Idaho also that the first foot-track scare took place.

This is an interesting story in several ways, and has naturally been received with whoops of joy by the skeptics. The story is from the *Humboldt Times* of January 3, 1959, and reads:

STORY OF CENTURY OLD BIGFOOT IN IDAHO ADDS COLOR TO LEGEND: by Betty Allen, Times Correspondent: Willow Creek—Mrs. Alvin Bortles, Boise, Idaho, discussed an account of a "Big Foot" who lived prior to 1868 in the wilderness of Idaho.

The mother of Kenneth Bortles, vice principal of the Hoopa valley high school, Mrs. Bortles said that mysterious tracks of a tremendous size and human shape stirred the residents of Idaho in the early days. Just as with the "Big Foot" tracks of Northern California's Bluff Creek area, some believed they were genuine, others saw in them a clever hoax.

The "Big Foot" lived in the remote wilderness of Reynold's Canyon now known as Reynold's Creek. A thousand dollars was offered for him, dead or alive. Here the likeness to the local "Big Foot" ended for the "Gigantic Monster," as he was called in Idaho, was a killer. The full extent of the depredations of this Big Foot were never known, for many robberies and murders were attributed to him which he probably did not commit. The sometimes wanton killings that were the work of almost superhuman strength both with stock and humans, brought about his downfall. A thousand dollars was offered for Big Foot dead or alive.

John Wheeler, a former army man, set out to collect the reward. In the year 1868, he came upon Big Foot and shot him 16 times. Both legs and one arm were broken before he fell to the ground. As he lay there he asked for a drink of water and, because of his great fear, Wheeler shot him, breaking his other arm before giving the water to the creature. Before he died, he told Wheeler that his real name was Starr Wilkerson and he had been born in the Cherokee nation of a white father. His mother was part Cherokee and part Negro. Even as a very small boy everyone had called him "Big Foot" and made fun of him. At the age of 19 the white girl he loved jilted him for another. Gathering a small band of men about him he killed then, for the sheer love of killing. Later he killed the girl that he had loved.

The foot length of this great giant of a man was 17½ inches and 18 inches around the ball of the foot. His height was 6 feet, 8 inches, with a chest measurement of 59 inches, and his weight was estimated at 300 pounds. He was all bone and sinew, no surplus flesh. He was

133

known to have traveled as far as 60 or 75 miles in a 24-hour period.

Adelaide Hawes gives an account of Starr Wilkerson or "Big Foot" in her book, The Valley of the Tall Grass, written in 1950.

I have other old stories from Idaho, mostly of sheep being torn apart and monstrous human-like footprints by water holes, but nothing ever came of them. There is one story, however, that has always impressed me. This is told by none other than Theodore Roosevelt in a book he published in 1892 entitled *Wilderness Hunter*. Teddy was not a boy to be taken in by anybody much, and he was a great skeptic and debunker, especially in the field of wildlife, being the originator of that most excellent expression of opprobrium, "Nature-Faker." This story seems to have impressed him not a little and mostly because of the still noticeable terror of the teller, half a lifetime later. He was an old man when he talked to Roosevelt and the incident had happened when he was young. His name was Bauman and he was born in the area on the then frontier, and had spent all his life as a hunter and trapper. Roosevelt's account goes as follows:

It was told [to me] by a grizzled, weather-beaten old mountain hunter, named Bauman, who was born and had passed all his life on the frontier. He must have believed what he said, for he could hardly repress a shudder at certain points of the tale.

When the event occurred Bauman was still a young man, and was trapping with a partner among the mountains dividing the forks of the Salmon from the head of Wisdom river. Not having had much luck, he and his partner determined to go up into a particularly wild and lonely pass through which ran a small stream said to contain many beaver. The pass had an evil reputation because the year before a solitary hunter who had wandered into it was there slain, seemingly by a wild beast, the half-eaten remains being afterwards found by some mining prospectors who had passed his camp only the night before.

The memory of this event, however, weighed very lightly with the two trappers, who were as adventurous and hardy as others of their kind. . . . They then struck out on foot through the vast, gloomy forest, and in

134

about 4 hours reached a little open glade where they concluded to camp, as signs of game were plenty.

There was still an hour or two of daylight left, and after building a brush lean-to and throwing down and opening their packs, they started up stream. . . .

At dusk they again reached camp. . . .

They were surprised to find that during their absence something, apparently a bear, had visited camp, and had rummaged about among their things, scattering the contents of their packs, and in sheer wantonness destroying their lean-to. The footprints of the beast were quite plain, but at first they paid no particular heed to them, busying themselves with rebuilding the lean-to, laying out their beds and stores, and lighting the fire.

While Bauman was making ready supper, it being already dark, his companion began to examine the tracks more closely, and soon took a brand from the fire to follow them up, where the intruder had walked along a game trail after leaving the camp. . . . Coming back to the fire, he stood by it a minute or two, peering out into the darkness, and suddenly remarked: "Bauman, that bear has been walking on two legs." Bauman laughed at this, but his partner insisted that he was right, and upon again examining the tracks with a torch, they certainly did seem to be made by but two paws, or feet. However, it was too dark to make sure. After discussing whether the footprints could possibly be those of a human being, and coming to the conclusion that they could not be, the two men rolled up in their blankets, and went to sleep under the lean-to.

At midnight Bauman was awakened by some noise, and sat up in his blankets. As he did so his nostrils were struck by a strong, wild-beast odor, and he caught the loom of a great body in the darkness at the mouth of the lean-to. Grasping his rifle, he fired at the vague, threatening shadow, but must have missed, for immediately afterwards he heard the smashing of the underwood as the thing, whatever it was, rushed off into the impenetrable blackness of the forest and the night.

After this the two men slept but little, sitting up by the rekindled fire, but they heard nothing more. In the morning they started out to look at the few traps they had set the previous evening and put out new ones. By an unspoken agreement they kept together all day, and returned to camp towards evening.

On nearing it they saw, hardly to their astonishment, that the lean-to had been again torn down. The visitor of the preceding day had returned, and in wanton malice had tossed about their camp kit and bedding, and destroyed the shanty. The ground was marked up by its tracks, and on leaving the camp it had gone along the soft earth by the brook, where the footprints were as plain as if on snow, and, after a careful scrutiny of the trail, it certainly did seem as if, whatever the thing was, it had walked off on but two legs.

The men thoroughly uneasy, gathered a great heap of dead logs, and kept up a roaring fire throughout the night, one or the other sitting on guard most of the time. About midnight the thing came down through the forest opposite, across the brook, and stayed there on the hill-side for nearly an hour. They could hear the branches crackle as it moved about, and several times it uttered a harsh, grating, long-drawn moan, a peculiarly sinister sound. Yet it did not venture near the fire.

In the morning the two trappers, after discussing the strange events of the last 36 hours, decided that they would shoulder their packs and leave the valley that afternoon. . . .

All the morning they kept together, picking up trap after trap, each one empty. On first leaving camp they had the disagreeable sensation of being followed. In the dense spruce thickets they occasionally heard a branch snap after they had passed; and now and then there were slight rustling noises among the small pines to one side of them.

At noon they were back within a couple of miles of camp. In the high, bright sunlight their fears seemed absurd to the two armed men, accustomed as they were, through long years of lonely wandering in the wilderness to face every kind of danger from man, brute, or element. There were still three beaver traps to collect from a little pond in a wide ravine near by. Bauman volunteered to gather these and bring them in, while his companion went ahead to camp and made ready the packs.

On reaching the pond Bauman found 3 beavers in the traps, one of which had been pulled loose and carried into a beaver house. He took several hours in securing and preparing the beaver, and when he started homewards he marked, with some uneasiness how low the sun was getting. . . .

At last he came to the edge of the little glade where the camp lay, and shouted as he approached it, but got no answer. The camp fire had gone out, though the thin blue smoke was still curling upwards. Near it lay the packs wrapped and arranged. At first Bauman could see nobody; nor did he receive an answer to his call. Stepping forward he again shouted, and as he did so his eye fell on the body of his friend, stretched beside the trunk of a great fallen spruce. Rushing towards it the horrified trapper found that the body was still warm, but that the neck was broken, while there were four great fang marks in the throat.

The footprints of the unknown beast-creature, printed deep in the soft soil, told the whole story.

The unfortunate man, having finished his packing, had sat down on the spruce log with his face to the fire, and his back to the dense woods, to wait for his companion. . . . It had not eaten the body, but apparently had romped and gambolled round it in uncouth, ferocious glee, occasionally rolling over and over it; and had then fled back into the soundless depths of the woods.

Bauman, utterly unnerved, and believing that the creature with which he had to deal was something either half human or half devil, some great goblin-beast, abandoned everything but his rifle and struck off at speed down the pass, not halting until he reached the beaver meadows where the hobbled ponies were still grazing. Mounting, he rode onwards through the night, until far beyond the reach of pursuit.

Judged by the time of publication of this story and what the old man said, this must have taken place in the early 1800's. Conditions changed radically about those parts in the 1850's, but then, strangely, they lapsed once more into a form of oblivion and, despite the incredible advance of civilization and the complete opening up of the whole West, until it stands today as second to no other area in the Union, parts of it are really less known now than they were a hundred years ago. I have observed this strange progress of progress in action in other lands, notably in the Republic of Haiti. The population of that small Caribbean country is so enormous that the whole of it, and right up its towering mountains, is virtually one great garden-city. You can stand anywhere and spit in three directions and be sure to hit somebody's compound. When the troubles took place in the 1920's and the American Marines took over, they built motorable roads in a network all over the country. Then they left; but at the same time there came the commercial airplane. By 1940 you just couldn't find any of the roads made by the Marines, while a new network was being built that went roaring straight through the country from one important center to another. All in between had gone right back to conditions pertaining before the advent of the Marines, and in some large areas apparently to those pertaining before Columbus. So also with great pieces of our own country.

It is during this initial period of lapse, or collapse, that we once again pick up our tracks. The strangest story is that of Capt. Joseph Walker, an account of which lies in the files of a paper called the *Eureka Daily Leader,* dated February 14, 1879. This recounts that this gentleman, who was then a most renowned mountaineer, trapper, and guide, due to his many exploits in the Rockies, had recently returned from investigating a newly opened territory near the mouth of New York Canyon and had brought to the office of the *Leader* a slab of sandstone about 20 inches long and 41 inches wide and some 3 inches thick. "On the surface of this slab of sandstone was imprinted the clear form of a gigantic footprint [I am quoting here], perfect except for the tip of the great toe. The footprint measured 14½ inches from the end of the heel to the tip of the toe and was 6 inches wide across the ball of the foot. Captain Walker related how he had found the slab of sandstone formation under about 2 feet of sand."

This story has sundry rather odd features. First, a foot 14½ inches by 6 inches across the ball is hardly a gigantic foot compared to what is coming in a moment, but it has a plantar index of 2.42 which is much wider than a human foot and would give an impression of great size. The fact that it was impressed in a slab of sandstone might at first sound more than just suspicious because you can't impress anything into solid rock—you have to chip it out. However, and this should be borne in mind, sandstone can form in a matter of days under certain conditions. A surface of argillaceous sand may dry out under a hot sun and remain baked to the consistency of pottery for months. If then a flood brings down a layer of sand or other material and deposits this on top of it and also immediately dries out, you may get conditions similar to those that pertained in our Porcupine cage at my zoo. More drying, compression and the solution and percolation of, say, lime from the covering layer may then, in only a few years, solidify the bottom layer and turn it to a sandstone. I have seen car tire tracks in sandstone so solid you needed a cold chisel to chip it.

Captain Walker was not a man to be fooled either and he retained a high reputation so that Walker River was named after him by the Federal Government. He was, in fact, solidly on the right track!

6. In Our Own Back Yard

Now that we are squarely back on the tracks, we might as well stay on them and skip, for the moment, all chronology. There is a business about giant, humanoid-appearing foottracks that has been going on in this country for far too long. It needs examination, and either exposition or debunking. It centers around the Great Basin, which is mostly now the state of Nevada, but it slops over in all directions and, in the form of giants capable of making such tracks, it reaches from Canada to Mexico, from the Pacific coast to Pennsylvania, and right on into the portals of the Smithsonian Institution in Washington, D.C.

As will be seen from the discussion of what I euphemistically call Myth, Legend, and Folklore such things are linked up all over a wide area from New Mexico to Puget Sound but center round the Sierra Nevada. They are linked by both traditional, early, and even recent accounts of a giant race of wild people, who inhabited this area in bygone days, and who not only were there before the Amerinds arrived, but persisted for a very long time after they had done so and, it is alleged, still linger on today. In tradition, these personages are not overly exaggerated. They are consistently reported as having been on an average about 7 to 8 feet tall (or its equivalent), but to have included outsized individuals, to boot, that were especially reverenced.

We have seen a record of a skeleton fitting these dimensions allegedly found in British Columbia. There are plenty of others but we just don't talk about them. Unfortunately, I have not had the opportunity to follow up the notes given to me some time ago on this subject, regarding Nevada, by a good friend, a man with a genius for bibliographical research, a very wide and real knowledge of American pre-history and folklore, of Amerindian history, and of colonial tradition. It is a voluminous and very startling file, containing what seem to me to be endless references to what are classed as "giant burials" from all over the place. Many of these are said to be housed in small county and city museums dotted about the West, and most seem to have been lodged therein during the 19th century. A few are said to have gone to the Smithsonian, yet all have been totally ignored ever since. The reason for this ig-*nor*-ance, as well as a notable ignorance of the subject, is stated by this indefatigable literary groundhog to be the really abominable story of the foot-tracks of Carson City jail, a most odd affair. It goes as follows:

The business was a cause célèbre **80 years ago. It could have passed almost unnoticed but for two facts; first, that said tracks were found in sandstone at a depth of some 25 feet below the surface in the jail compound of Carson City, Nevada. The second thing that stimulated such wide interest was not that some scientists said that some of these tracks were made by giant men of over a** million [sic] **years ago, but that Mark Twain wrote a positively hilarious story with the discovery as its main theme or** raison d'etre. **These facts have been quoted, misquoted, and just mentioned over and over again. The true story represents one of the finest examples of scientific skullduggery—and vagueness—on record.**

First, some of the tracks—there were others of elephantines, deer, cats, and "giant birds"—looked like those of a giant humanoid. This fact was published by Dr. Harkness of San Francisco through the California Academy of Sciences. In his report, the author gave some sketches of said tracks but stated that he had "filled out those areas not clearly shown in the originals." These areas happen very conveniently to go right around the front of the imprints and down their inner sides. As a result they look generally much more human than they would otherwise have done; at the same time just such areas would have cut out any imprints of toes (human or otherwise). Dr. LeConte, of California, agreed in print.

The result of these communications was an immediate response [as was almost invariable in that decade] from (Professors) O. K. Marsh and E. D. Cope. Marsh, of Yale, blasted the idea in his own inimitable style: he did

not even bother to refute the matter; he simply stated that the tracks were those of a ground-sloth—either Mylodon or what he called Morotherium [sic]. No animal has received such a name, but there is, of course, the really giant Ground-Sloth (Megatherium); a detail of such a trifling nature would of course not hinder this palaeontological free-booter. The most interesting part of this pat pontification is that he appears to have accepted Harkness' quite illegitimate touching up of the tracks, and then to have stated that they were manifestly those of a ground-sloth. Thus, he was, ipso facto, wrong in that, as touched up, they were not those of such an animal. He seems to have completely missed the further point that before touching up they could well have been so. However, he pulled still another boner.

Ground-Sloths—which were actually enormous kinds of shaggy, short-tailed, neotropical anteaters more closely related to the Giant Anteater (Myrmecophaga) than to the living Tree-Sloths—could apparently stand on their hind legs but they used their immensely thick short tails as a third prong of a tripod to do so. If they waddled along on their hind legs, their tails must have gouged a deep channel between the tracks of their feet. There were no such channels in the Carson City tracks. Marsh seems to have appreciated this fact so he conjured up some "smaller imprints, obviously those of front feet somewhat outside the main tracks." No such tracks were ever recorded, or sketched. [Cope, Marsh's most implacable foe, simply implied that Marsh was wrong, and that anyone else (LeConte and Harkness) was more reliable.] They probably never existed! This is the way awkward "scientific" discoveries are handled: if they don't fit into the already approved scheme, you make them do so—and by any lie your reputation can get away with. For all one knows, the original tracks may have been those of a good old Oh-Mah.

There is an official wind-up to this but it is almost as extraordinary and inexplicable as the facts themselves. For some reason serious-minded scientists—by which I mean those who still have open minds—*have* concluded that these beastly things are the tracks of one of the Giant Ground-Sloths. We have radiocarbon dated bones of some of these creatures killed and eaten by men of a pretty advanced culture in the Southwest—but I cannot understand how any paleontologist, let alone zoologist, could ever conceive of any form of such a creature [of which we *have* a foot] having ever either walked on its hind legs alone or left a footprint anything like those of Carson City jail. This identification, however, led to all the other large humanoid tracks being dismissed as "just those of fossil animals."

Would that we might pursue the matter of giant skeletons but at this juncture it would be inappropriate. It is (as of now) really a separate subject, and until we obtain a fresh skeleton of one of the large or giant ABSMs, or some competent, trustworthy, and really informed physical anthropologist happens to stumble upon one in a museum, it must be left dangling. So, again, we jump back onto the tracks.

This would be in the year 1890 at a place on the Chetco River about the border between California and Oregon. It appears that about that date and thereabouts, the citizenry had been bothered for some time by really gigantic foot-tracks that looked, according to the contemporary records, just like those that would be left by enormous naked human feet, which passed back and forth from the forests to the seashore. Then things began to happen at a mining camp some 50 miles inland. Large objects were moved at night and there were unpleasant noises, all naturally attributed to marauding bears, until one fine morning when, after a particularly rambunctious night, during which somebody fired at something, two sets of large human-type tracks showed up all around the camp. A posse was organized and tracked these for a long way into the forest but eventually gave up. A short time later, however, a man was chased into camp by something very large, the looks of which he did not wait to investigate. A watch was set; two men at a time, for a few hours each. Then it happened.

One couple going to relieve a watch found their two companions dead and really grossly mutilated. They had in fact been literally smashed and apparently by being picked up and slammed repeatedly onto the ground so that they looked as if they had fallen off a high cliff onto rocks. The account particularly specifies that there was nothing anywhere near off which they could have fallen. The wretched men had emptied their rifles and there was both spoor and a large blood-trail leading off into the bush. This the whole camp personnel followed with the aid of Amerindian trackers. It led into the Siskiyou complex of mountains to a point far beyond that which any even of the Amerinds had previously penetrated. There, the men are said to have come upon a fresh lava flow. This is an astonishing item. There is volcanicity in the area and there had been an account 14 years before of a great quake and the sound of a far distant explosion, heard on the coast of Oregon, and of a dull glow said to have been seen in the sky for two nights but nothing definite about a volcanic eruption was even suggested at the time. What is more, this report by a party of ABSM hunters was also ignored and it was not till after World War II that lava beds, now re-vegetated but nonetheless of very recent vintage, were located in the area, although they had shown up on aerial maps as irregular patches of some unique form of ground-cover.

This rather gruesome incident appears to have satisfied even local curiosity for some time as nothing much is reported for quite a few years, though a very old Amerindian patriot told me with a whimsical smile of one Chester Johnny of his tribal group who in the year 1905 spent a happy hour watching a large papa *Toké-Mussi* (as the local giant ABSM or *Sasquatch* is called) trying to teach his two youngsters to swim in a river, and to spike fish with sticks.

The records I have—though they are, of course, very, very far from complete—are almost blank until 1924 when a bunch of hardboiled loggers came literally roaring into the small town of Kelso, Washington, from their advanced camp in the Cascades, and absolutely refused to go back nor anywhere else in the region out of sight of a highway. They said that their camp had been attacked by a number of enormous hairy wild men who had pelted them with stones and other debris. In view of their tough characters and stubborn attitude, a posse was formed and, well armed, went to investigate. No ABSMs were seen but they had left their enormous tracks everywhere and the cabin of the loggers was not just a shambles but in great part destroyed. That year there had been terrible man-induced forest fires in the region for the first time. I have often wondered if the ABSMs decided to give little "human" men a peremptory lesson in conservation—the best and only really satisfactory approach to which is the total eradication of said little men from the entire locality.

Now, here we are back again at the date 1924. Wherever we go, it seems, and it will recur, there was a marked turning point in ABSM history in the demi-decade 1920 to 1925. I think there must have been a great world-wide historical break at that time which perhaps will not become apparent to historians for many generations. What it was I can only conjecture but more and more I am coming to think that this was the real time of change-over from all that went

144

before to what we call modern times, or the new world. Most of the things that have really affected the outlook of humanity, like the invention of the typewriter, electrical power—and especially light and radio—, internal combustion engines, flying machines, and so forth, had taken place before this, but then came the social upheavals of the post-war era. Not even these things had really taken hold before the 1920's, and they took a few years to do so even after that. Man's outlook on life then changed radically everywhere, and he also took a completely new look at his environment. A great number of the shibboleths he had previously held most precious just collapsed, while a whole lot that he had previously considered worthless or redundant suddenly acquired entirely new status. The change was technologically induced but it did not greatly affect basic science—funnily enough—but rather sociological attitudes. It was not that new things began to happen all at once so much as that people began to treat the old ones in an entirely different light. On the one hand, *real* exploration began: on the other, just plain, go-have-a-look exploration came to an end.

Things like abominable foot-tracks went into limbo. The age of "the Curiosity" was over and people were no longer curious. They demanded the facts and in some respects they got them. In others they got falsehood or nothing at all. ABSMs became definitely *de trop,* and staunch souls like Prof. Khakhlov, and others, no longer went barging about the world recording curiosities and writing about them. This initiated the age of skepticism par excellence.

During the 35-year period subsequent to this strange historical turning point, a lot went on nonetheless, and this, due perhaps to its suppression, gradually built up a veritable explosion at the end of the 1950's. It is hard enough to suppress anything, but suppressing truth (i.e. facts) entails its own special hazards. People are more suspicious of truth than they are of falsehood and they almost invariably downgrade it if it clashes with belief or faiths. But "truth will out" seems not to be an altogether valueless cliché. Then again, both false facts, and the suppression of unpleasant facts is apt to be extremely costly; and, if you really want to get at the truth of anything, reach first for a pocketbook. I seem to be full of clichés, but it is also perfectly true that if you hit anybody through his pocketbook you are more likely to loosen him up than by hitting him anywhere else. And, as I am in this rut, I might as well add that, while love of money may be the root of all evil, it is still by far the best invention yet for getting at the facts. The moment anything, however curious (or unpleasant) it is considered generally, develops a value, it automatically develops a potential, and when it is founded on fact, it cannot forever be suppressed.

In our case, also, the facts have several special connotations. They impinge directly upon our most basic precepts, such as religion, ethics, politics, and science. A live ABSM would be the greatest propaganda weapon possible; at one fell swoop it would prove Darwinism, and set at nought a great part of religious belief and dogma, while it would also confound a great deal of that which science has written into *its* dogma. Quite apart from all of these high and mighty matters, plain ordinary people have finally become fed up with being called fools, liars, and idiots. The world is full of crackpots but it is rapidly becoming manifest that most of these make a speciality of pursuing beliefs, prejudices, and faiths rather than the facts of everyday life. If you walk into a truck and stagger home bleeding to death, it is quite useless anybody telling you that you are imagining things, that there is no such thing as a truck, or that you ought to be confined. It doesn't help your feelings (or matters as a whole) if somebody suggests that it was undoubtedly a bus and not a truck, or perhaps even a motorcycle. Either the damned thing was there or it wasn't, skeptics notwithstanding; and the average citizen becomes peeved when he is told that he, who saw the thing, is lying, especially by a person who was *not* present. During the last 40 years, plain, solid citizens have been getting pretty peeved.

During this period, ABSMery in the United States contracted in upon itself and became concentrated in and around this Klamath district in northern California, which I described as an example of a virgin montane forest area. It now transpires that somebody has reported something about the matter every year since 1938 in this area while, of course, the Amerinds thereabouts just went steadily and stoically on living with the business and keeping their mouths shut. I won't go into all of these items because they are so exactly alike, and they are all just like the descriptions given of the *Sasquatches*. Hereabouts they are called, as I have said, *Toké-Mussis* by one Amerindian group, the Yurok or Yurock, and *Oh-Mahs* by the Hŭppas; there are endless other names for the big ones in accordance with the number of tribes, sub-tribes, and familial dialects of the Amerinds. The name *Oh-Mah*, which is rapidly coming into universal acceptance, actually means something very close to "Devil" as used by our ancestors—a sort of large chap with nasty habits who is dangerous, bestial, potentially carnivorous, and smelly but definitely rather human. *Non*-Amerinds in the area have come to call them "Bigfoot" having the usually mistaken idea that there is just *one* giant of some kind loose in the countryside—just as people speak of *The* Loch Ness Monster, as if it were a lone individual that has been paddling about therein since Cretaceous times, mateless and possibly even parentless. But there is a complication here.

I would have had to come to this sooner or later in any case so I might as well introduce it now, even if it is not the place to go into it in full. To jump ahead, let me say that there are now some hundred separate and isolated areas in the world where or from which ABSMs have been reported —and this is apart from Myth, Legend, and Folklore. The creatures described vary considerably but, with a few notable exceptions, they appear to fall very clearly into four main types—a large (or giant, to us), a medium or man-sized, a small or pigmy, and an excessively bestial creature known as the *Meh-Teh*. These types are not set or patterned, and there is considerable variety in the actual sizes of each as reported. However, they would each seem to form a fairly well defined animal form, having certain particulars, characters, characteristics, and other perquisites all their own.

The giant ones are inhabitants of higher elevations and do actually go around in snow when needs be. They seem to be more carnivorous, at least in winter, like many Primates; they have very human-type feet; and they are clothed in short, thick, hairy fur. The medium-sized are very manlike but clothed in longer, darker hair, have very pointed heads, and very short, broad feet with large toes, the first being extra large and widely separated. They are vegetarian or omnivorous and live in upper montane forests but seldom go up above the tree-line. The little pigmies are also forest dwellers, but in the valleys and bottoms, or at lower levels, and where it is much warmer. They have little manlike feet but with very pointed heels, are clothed in fur but have much longer head-hair that forms a mane down the midback. They are excellent tree-climbers and will take to water. They go about in small family parties and have a sort of primitive language and they may even carry palm leaves or bits of anything that will afford shade from sunlight. They are just about as nocturnal as chimps which move about and feed at night in fine moonlight weather. The giants seem to be almost wholly nocturnal; the me-

147

dium jobs more diurnal or crepuscular. The *Meh-Tehs* are quite another matter.

Again and again and again, these four types will crop up. In Canada I have so far heard only of the giants, and I thought that the same went for the Puget Sound to California area, but I am afraid that I have now to bring up the unruly suggestion that some reports from this area seem definitely to be, or try to be, speaking of both the man-sized and pigmy types. This, you may well think, is going a bit too far, in that it is bad enough to be asked to stomach the possibility of a bunch of giant "ape-men" running around half a dozen of our most up-to-date and worthy states, without being asked to accept also Neanderthalers and "Little People." [1] I would have preferred, as I say, not to have brought this up just yet but, as a reporter, what can I do? The very definite footprints left near Roseburg, Oregon, during the night of October 23, 1959, were definitely of the man-sized type, while literally thousands of the little pigmy type are alleged to have started turning up along— perhaps appropriately—the Mad River Valley, about 1950. Thus, as we go along, you must brace yourself for casual asides to the effect that such little ones were seen hither and yon. The Roseburg case is happily so far unique, so that we won't be bothered herein with others of its ilk and so, when I speak of ABSMs hereabouts from now on, it will be of the giant *Oh-Mahs* unless I clearly specify otherwise.

The outburst came in August, 1958.

There was, as usual, an unreported and steady build-up before the event, and there was the usual red herring almost at the outset. This latter was such a bizarre report and was given such wide publicity that it has both diverted public attention and caused many, who might otherwise have investigated the main stream of events with diligence and an open mind, simply to throw up their hands in horror at anything so impertinent. The case is very peculiar, has no precedent and no conclusion. It occurred 3 months after the outbreak of true ABSMery in northern California in August, and it took place 600 miles away from that area, near Riverside in San Bernardino Valley of southern California. Nothing of a similar nature has ever been recorded from anywhere near this place,[2] while all the mountains

[1] The general concensus now is that these are merely the tracks of the youngsters of a single giant type.
[2] Subsequent discoveries render this statement invalid, as of 1968.

from the Sierra Nevada south into Baja California may really be said now to have been explored and combed. [At the same time, we might note the proximity of Hollywood and several large mental institutions.] The following is an account from the *Los Angeles Examiner* which speaks for itself, though very facetiously, and says everything that there is to be said about the business.

MONSTROUS! Driver Tells of "Thing" that Clawed at His Car

RIVERSIDE, NOV. 9 (UP). Funny thing happened to Charlie Wetzel on the way home last night.

A Monster jumped out at him. That's what he told authorities who planned to continue an investigation of the incredible story today.

Wetzel, 24, a resident of nearby Bloomington, reported soberly that he was driving on a street near Riverside when a frightening creature jumped in front of his car.

"It had a round, scare-crowish head," he said, "like something out of Halloween.

"It wasn't human. It had a longer arm than anything I'd ever seen. When it saw me in the car it reached all the way back to the windshield and began clawing at me.

"It didn't have any ears. The face was all round. The eyes were shining like something fluorescent and it had a protuberant mouth. It was scaly, like leaves."

Wetzel said he became terrified when the creature reached over the hood of his car and began clawing at the windshield. He said he reached for a .22 pistol he had in the car.

"I held that pistol and stomped on the gas," he said. "The thing fell back from the car and it gurgled.

"The noise it made didn't sound human. I think I hit it. I heard something hit the pan under the car."

Sheriff's officers said Wetzel pointed at some thin, sweeping marks he said the creature made on his windshield. They went to the scene of the claimed apparition but said they could find nothing to prove or disprove Wetzel's story.

The scene is at a point where North Main Street dips and crosses the Santa Ana River bed, which is usually almost dry. Wetzel said he told the story to his wife and she induced him to phone authorities.

"I kept saying no one would believe a story like this," he said.

Sheriff's Sgt. E. R. Holmes said he thought perhaps a large vulture might have flopped on the hood of Wetzel's car—"sometimes cars hit them when they're in the road eating rabbits cars have killed," he said.

So he searched the area himself today. "But," said Holmes, "I didn't even find a feather."

The build-up to the really valid events may be left till later, for it consists once again of accounts of all the same old things, though, withal, highly confirmatory, and showing that what happened at a place called Bluff Creek in August of that year was neither an isolated case nor anything novel. I will mention these more fully when I come to tell of the aftermath of the Bluff Creek affair.

Before giving the facts of this business I must just hark back for a minute to my description of this country. On Map VII you will see the main roads marked by their route numbers. Apart from the four that surround the area—Nos. 101, 299, 99, and the east-west route over Grant's Pass, there is really only one road through this block of territory. This runs from Willow Creek, diagonally northeast to join Route 99, via Happy Camp. Immediately north of Willow Creek it follows the Hoopa (Hŭppa) Valley and then forks, one small road going back to 101 at the coast, the other major route going into the hills. About 10 miles along this route a new road is being pushed north up a tight valley named Bluff Creek. This road was begun in 1957. I visited the road end in 1959 and it had only gotten in 23 miles, so rough is the country. From this area, the following matters came to light.

In August of 1958—on the morning of the 27th to be precise—a very sane and sober citizen by the name of Mr. Jerald Crew, of Salyer township, Humboldt County, northwest California, an active member of the Baptist Church, a teetotaler, and a man with a reputation in his community that can only be described as heroic in face of certain almost unique personal tragedy, went to his work with heavy-duty equipment at the head of this new lumber access road being pushed into uninhabited and only roughly surveyed territory near the borders of Humboldt and Del Norte Counties. This huge block of territory is crossed kitty-corner from the south at Willow Creek to the northeast by a winding blacktop road, and from east to west by only four other roads of lower grade. Logging trails and some "jeep-roads" now finger into it from these roads and from the main arteries that enclose it to north, west, south, and east, but these are of very limited extent and are hardly used at all. "Jerry" Crew's crawler-tractor had been left overnight at the head of the new road, about 20 miles north of its digression from the narrow blacktop that runs north through the Hoopa [as it is on maps] Amerindian Reservation from Willow Creek to a place with the delightful name of Happy Camp up near the Oregon border.

Jerry was an older member of a crew bulldozing this new road into virtually unexplored territory for one Mr. Ray Wallace, subcontractor to Messrs. Block and Company who had, in turn, contracted with the National Parks Service to carry out the work. He is a local man. His fellow workers were for the most part also local men and included a nephew, James Crew, a very level-headed young chap, others whom I shall mention by name in a minute, and two experienced loggers of Hŭppa Indian origin. The crew had considerable heavy equipment at the scene of operations and had started work in late May as soon as what little snow there is in this area had melted and the much more deadly mud had firmed up. The road had been under construction for two seasons already. The country is mountainous; though this is the understatement of the year, being to most intents and everywhere almost vertical so that you can only go up on all fours or down on your bottom. Unless you make an exaggerated and exhausting climb you cannot see more than about four square miles of the country because you are always on the side of something going either straight up or almost straight down and unless a tree has fallen or been cut out, you can't see *anything* because bare rock is confined to the uppermost summits of the peaks and ridges. The road crawls laboriously up the face of the western wall that encloses a stream known as Bluff Creek. It is still unsurfaced and when I visited it in 1959 was ankle-deep in ultra-fine dust that surpasses anything the deserts of Arizona can produce at their damnedest. All along this mountainous trail there are the stumps of vast trees cut and hauled out, and great slides of friable shales, gray, brown, blue, or even green that have been sliced out of the sheer valley side. The great dozers and crawlers clank and roar in the hot summer sunlight as they gnaw their relentless way into this timeless land. The great trees seem to recoil a little from their mechanical jangling and screeching, but day by day these bright yellow and red monsters munch away ever deeper into one of the last of America's real wildernesses.

Those employed on this work lived during the work-

week in camp near this road-head. They had trailers or
tents or prefabricated houses and some of them had their
families with them and stayed there all week. Others with
families resident in nearby communities normally went
home on Friday night and returned on the following Monday morning. The younger fellows usually did likewise, for
the drive to Willow Creek took only about 2 hours for those
who knew the road. Jerry Crew's practice was to return to
his family over the week-end, leaving his machine parked
at the scene of current operations. He had been on this job
for 3 months that year before the eventful morning which
blew up the storm that literally rocked Humboldt County,
California and made the pages of the world press but
which then sort of folded in upon itself and was heard of no
more for a year.

What Jerry Crew discovered when he went to start up
his "cat" was that somebody had inspected it rather thoroughly during the previous night, as could be plainly seen
by a series of footprints that formed a track to, all around,
and then away from the machine. Such tracks would not
have aroused his curiosity under normal circumstances because there were three dozen men at that road-head and
the newly scraped roadbed was covered with soft mud areas
alternating with patches of loose shale. What did startle
him was that these footprints were of a shoeless or naked
foot of distinctly human shape and proportions but by actual measurement just 17 inches long!

Of these, Jerry Crew took an extremely dim view. He
had heard tell of similar tracks having been seen by another road gang working 8 miles north of a place called
Korbel on the Mad River earlier that year and his nephew,
Jim Crew, had also mentioned having come across something similar in this area. Being a pragmatic family man
he felt, he told me, some considerable annoyance that
some "outsider" should try to pull such a silly stunt on him.
He at first stressed an outsider because, although his fellow
workers liked a harmless joke as much as any man, he
knew they were far too tired to go clomping around in the
dark after the sort of working day they put in on that job,
making silly footprints around the equipment. Then, he
tells me, he got to thinking about this outsider and wondered just how he had got there without passing the camps
farther down the road and being spotted, and how he had
gotten out again, or where he had gone over these precipitous mountains clothed in tangled undergrowth. He

152

followed the tracks up. And that is where he got his second shock.

Going backward he found that they came almost straight down an incline of about 75 degrees on to the road ahead of the parked "cat," then proceeded down the road on one side, circled the machine, and then went on down the road toward the camp. Before getting there, however, they cut across the road and went straight down an even steeper incline and continued into the forest with measured stride varying only when an obstacle had to be stepped over or the bank was so steep, purchase could be obtained only by digging in the heels. The stride was enormous and proved on measurement to be from 46 to 60 inches and to average about 50 inches or almost twice that of his own. Jerald Crew was not only mystified; he was considerably peeved. He went to fetch some of his colleagues. Then he received his third shock that morning.

The majority of them, stout fellows and good friends that they were, refused to even go and look at this preposterous phenomenon that he told them he had found, and he had a hard time persuading any of them even that the tracks were there. Eventually, some of the men, who had in any case to go that way to their work, agreed to go along with him and take a look. Then they got their shocks and, Jerry told me, some of them "looked at me real queer." But there were others who reacted differently, and it then transpired that all of them had either seen something similar thereabouts or elsewhere, or had heard of them from friends and acquaintances whom they regarded as totally reliable. The only Amerinds present said nothing at that time. Then they all went back to work.

Nothing further happened for almost a month; then once again these monstrous Bigfeet appeared again overnight around the equipment and farther down the road toward the valley, notably around a spring. About that time, Mr. Ray Wallace, the contractor, returned from a business trip. He had heard rumors on his way in that either his men were pulling some kind of stunt up in the hills or that some "outsider" was pulling one on them. He paid little attention to these reports but he was, he told me, somewhat apprehensive because the job was a tough one, skilled and reliable workers were not plentiful, and the location was not conducive to the staying power of anyone. When he reached the camp and heard the details of the Bigfeet he was more than just skeptical. He was downright angry. Moreover, all he encountered was more talk which he at that time suspected

153

was some sort of prank but just possibly one prompted by more than mere high spirits or boredom.

The matter was until then and for a further three weeks a purely local affair known only to the men working on the road, and their immediate families for they did not care to speak about it to casual acquaintances or even friends. Then in the middle of September a Mrs. Jess Bemis, wife of one of the men working on the road and one of the skeptics among the crew, wrote a letter to the leading local newspaper, the *Humboldt Times* of Eureka, which said in part "A rumor started among the men, at once, of the existence of a Wild Man. We regarded it as a joke. It was only yesterday that my husband became convinced that the existence of such a person (?) is a fact. Have you heard of this wild man?" Mr. Andrew Genzoli of that paper told me that he regarded this letter with a thoroughly jaundiced eye but that the longer he saw it about his desk the brighter grew the clear blue light of his built-in news-sense, until he could restrain himself no longer and ran the letter in a daily column that he then wrote.

There was little response where he had expected a near storm of derision; instead, a trickle of tentatively confirmatory correspondence began to come in from the Willow Creek area. This was continuing sub rosa when, on October 2, the maker of the tracks appeared again on his apparently rather regular round, leaving tracks for 3 nights in succession and then vanishing again for about 5 days. This time Jerry Crew had prepared for his advent with a supply of plaster of Paris and made a series of casts of both right and left feet early one morning. Two days later he took a couple of days off to drive to Eureka on personal business and carried the casts along with him to show to a friend. While there, somebody mentioned to Andrew Genzoli that a man was in town who had made casts of the prints and he was persuaded to go and fetch Jerry. Andrew Genzoli is an old newshand but of the new school; he can sense a good story as fast as any man but he is properly averse to too good a story. When he met Jerry Crew and saw his trophies he realized he had some real live news, not just a "story," on his hands, and he ran a front-pager on it with photographs the next day. Then the balloon went up.

The wire services picked it up and almost every paper in the country printed it while cables of inquiry flooded in from abroad. The first I heard of it was a cable from a friend in London: he seemed to be slightly hysterical. I get a lot of esoteric cables during the year about sea monsters,

154

two-headed calves, reincarnated Indian girls, and so forth, the majority of which I am constrained to do something about because the world is, after all, a large place and we don't know much about a lot of it as yet, but this one I frankly refused to accept mostly because I rather naturally assumed that the location as given (California) must be a complete error or a misquote. I wracked my brains for any place name in Eurasia or Africa that might have nine letters, begin with "K" and end in "ia." The best we could come up with was Corinthia but this was even more unlikely. Then somebody suggested Carpathia, the country of Dracula and other humanoid unpleasantnesses, and we actually spent 6 dollars on a follow-up. There are few people interested enough in such abstruse matters as to spend that sum in pursuit of truth but I fancy there were many on the morning of October 6, 1958 who doubted what they read in their morning papers just as fervently as I did this cable.

The point I want to make is that this whole bit did sound quite absurd even to us, who became immune to such shocks years ago. It is all very well for abominable creatures to be pounding over snow-covered passes in Nepal and Tibet; after all, giant pandas and yaks, and an antelope with a nose like Jimmy Durante, and other unlikely things come from thereabouts; and it is even conceivable that there might be little hairy men in the vast forests of Mozambique in view of the almost equally unlikely more or less hairless pigmies of the eastern Congo which are there for all tourists to see, but a wild man with a 17-inch foot and a 50-inch stride tromping around California was then a little too much to ask even us to stomach, especially as we had not yet got the news-stories. The amazing thing in this case was that the world press took it seriously enough even to carry it as a news-item.

Not so the rest of humanity. One and all, apart from a few ardent mystics and professional crackpots, and including even the citizens of Humboldt County itself rose up in one concerted howl of righteous indignation. Everybody connected with the business, and notably poor Mr. Genzoli, was immediately almost smothered in brickbats. In the meantime, however, a number of other things had happened. Most notable among these was the reappearance of "Bigfoot" one night before Ray Wallace returned to his operations. Now it so happened that a brother of the contractor, Wilbur Wallace, was working on this job and he, besides seeing the foot-tracks many times, witnessed three other annoying and to him most startling occurrences which he had reported to his brother. I will repeat these roughly in his own words which appeared to me not only straightforward but most convincing.

First, it was reported to him by one of his men that a nearly full 55-gallon drum of diesel fuel which had been left standing beside the road was missing and that Bigfoot tracks led down the road from a steep bank to this spot where it had stood, then crossed the road, continued on down the hill and finally went over the lower bank and away into the bush. Wilbur Wallace went to inspect and found the tracks exactly as the men had stated. He also found the oil drum at the bottom of a steep bank about 175 feet from the road. It had rolled down this bank and had apparently been thrown from the top. What is more, it had been lifted from its original resting place and apparently carried to this point, for there were no marks in the soft mud of its having been either rolled or dragged all that distance. Second, a length of 18-inch galvanized steel culvert disappeared from a dump overnight and was found at the bottom of another bank some distance away. Third, he reported a wheel with tire for a "carry-all" earth-mover, weighing over 700 pounds, had likewise been in part lifted and in part rolled a quarter of a mile down the road and hurled into a deep ravine. Ray Wallace, however, still remained skeptical even after hearing this from his own brother. However, on his first morning at the location he stopped for a drink at a spring on the way down the hill and stepped right into a mass of the big prints in the soft mud around the outflow. Then, I gather from him, though he is a man with a wonderfully good humor, he got "good and mad." There was for him no longer any question about the existence of these monstrous human-like tracks but there remained the question as to who was perpetrating them, and why. Ray Wallace appeared to be a hard-boiled and pragmatic man and he was already experiencing trouble keeping men on the job. Handpicked as they were, not a few had just *had* to leave for one apparently good reason or another. Only later did he learn that almost all of them did so not because they were scared by the Bigfoot, but either because their wives were or because of the ribbing they had to take when they went back to civilization, even for the evening to nearby Willow Creek.

Ray Wallace said he at first thought somebody was deliberately trying to wreck his contract and he was not

156

alone. However, the local representative of the *Humboldt Times,* Mrs. Elizabeth (Betty) Allen, set about to investigate the possibility on her own, and discovered beyond a doubt that neither good nor bad publicity, nor any kind of "scare" actually made any difference to Mr. Wallace's contract. First he was a sub-contractor; second, he was more than up to schedule; third there was no time set on the job; and fourth, it was basically contracted by Messrs. Block and Company, with the Forest Service on a performance, not a time, basis. Ray Wallace got so angry he brought in a man named Ray Kerr, who had read of the matter in the press and asked for a job in order to be able to spend his spare time trying to track the culprit. Kerr brought with him a friend by the name of Bob Breazele, who had hunted professionally in Mexico, owned four good dogs, and a British-made gun of enormous caliber which considerably impressed the locals. Kerr, an experienced equipment operator, did a full daily job: Breazele did not take a job but hunted.

Tracks were seen and followed by them. Then one night in late October, these two were driving down the new road after dark and state that they came upon a gigantic humanoid or human-shaped creature, covered with 6-inch brown fur, squatting by the road. They said it sprang up in their headlights and crossed the road in two strides to vanish into the undergrowth. They went after it with a flashlight but the underbrush was too thick to see anything. They measured the road and found it to be exactly 20 feet wide from the place where the creature had squatted to the little ditch where it had landed after those two strides. Spurred by this encounter they redoubled their hunting forays but their dogs disappeared a few days later when they were following Bigfoot's tracks some distance from the road-head. They were never seen again though a story was told—but later denied by its teller—that their skins and bones were found spattered about some trees. Though this story was denied, there is as much reason to believe that this was done to obviate ridicule as to clear a conscience.

All this was, of course, taken with hoots of derision by everybody even in Willow Creek who had not seen any tracks—but with one notable exception. This was Andrew Genzoli and he sent his newspaper's senior staff photographer to Bluff Creek. The party saw fresh tracks at night and photographed them. They also found something else; as did Ray Wallace later. [I have this first hand from these professional skeptics.] At first, the photographer told me, he was more than just skeptical but when he found the tracks and inspected them he not only was convinced that they were not a hoax or a publicity stunt but, as he put it, "I got the most awful feeling that I can't really describe, but it was nearer fright than anything I ever felt when in service." But worse was in store for the newsmen for, in following the tracks down the road, they came across a pile of faeces of typically human form but, as they put it, "of absolutely monumental proportions." He then added, "I can only describe it as a 2-ton bear with chronic constipation." They contemplated going to fetch a shovel and some container and taking this back to Eureka for analysis but it was a very hot night and a 5-hour drive over a dangerous road and also, as they readily admitted, that strange laziness that so often intervenes in offbeat and rather alarming cases of this nature, took over and cast the die. Press coverage had gone far enough, and they were not ecologists. Later, Ray Wallace says he stumbled upon a similar enormous mass of human-shaped droppings. He shoveled them into a can and found that they occupied exactly the same volume as a single evacuation of a 1200-pound horse.

Further foot-tracks and other incidents continued all that fall and throughout the winter until the spring of 1959 ending in February. However, later in the spring, two fliers, a husband and wife in a private plane, were flying over the Bluff Creek area. It was April and there was still snow on the mountaintops some of which are bare of trees. It is alleged that they spotted great tracks in the snow and that on following them up they sighted the creature that had made them. It was enormous, humanoid, and covered with brown fur, according to secondhand accounts. I tried to locate this couple, with the co-operation of local fliers, several of them having heard of the report, but despite the praiseworthy clannishness of fliers and their willing offers to help, I have not at the time of writing been able to identify this couple. The story may be a rumor or wishful thinking. So also may three other recent and a whole host of past, old, and even ancient reports of actual meetings with one or more Bigfeet in this area.

Among these are alleged statements by two doctors of having met one on Route 299 earlier in 1958; and of a lady of much probity who with her daughter saw two, one smaller by far than the other, feeding on a hillside above the Hoopa Valley. This lady, to whom a partner of mine talked but who does not wish her name publicized, also stated that when she was a young girl, people used to see these creatures from time to time when they went fishing up certain creeks, and she once saw one swimming Bluff Creek when it was in flood. She also stated that in the olden days people did not go above certain points up the side valleys, due to the presence of these creatures.

More important was a positive flood of further alleged discoveries of similar foot-tracks by all manner of local citizenry over a wide area and extending back for many years that came to light as soon as the local press began to take this whole matter seriously. But as these came in, public resentment and ridicule mounted so that the reporters became ever more cagey. Finally, Betty Allen, who as an old-time resident and with experience as an Assistant U.S. Commissioner in Alaska, started talking to the Hŭppa and Yurok Amerinds about these matters and, little by little, an amazing picture emerged.

7. Late North Americans

HYPERBOLE FROM OUR NORTHWEST

You can take the title of this chapter any way you like. Late is a useful word: it has two completely opposite meanings that imply novelty or extinction. There is also a connotation of tardiness about a late-comer. This serves my purpose well.

When Betty Allen started browsing around among her Amerindian friends she brought to light two sets of surprising facts. The first was simply that said friends, one and all, had always known about the *Toké-Mussis* and *Oh-Mahs,* completely accepted them as being quite real, and regarded them as in no wise bizarre. They had, however, and quite rightly, long since decided that they were not a suitable topic for conversation with white men since it seemed to annoy them, while their even mentioning their beliefs about the matter only augmented the general contempt in which all their other ideas were already held. There were those among the Amerinds, even of the older generation who just brushed the business aside or referred to it as folklore. Surprisingly, though, there proved to be not a few among the younger generation who met the white man's skepticism with a deep-rooted scorn of their own, and who affirmed that there was absolutely no doubt that these manlike creatures still exist; and not in too few numbers either, not only all over this territory but over other wide areas. I had the privilege of talking to some of these young people myself and was much impressed—I might almost say startled—not only by their sincerity but also by the matter-of-fact way in which they discussed it, *and* their reasons for not previously discussing it with any outsiders. Though I have the permission of some of these new friends to mention their names, I will refrain from doing so, because they would undoubtedly be subjected to ridicule and an unmerciful ribbing, even in their own community.

I will not report in full what they told me, nor all that Betty Allen learned because it is highly repetitious, is little different from all the other accounts I have given of observations of the creatures, and does not really add any new details. One and all of that category of account of which I speak were firsthand (I have some two dozen on file), alleged encounters with the creatures in and about this block of montane forest which I call the Klamath. The interesting thing is that these reports go back to the 1930's but become increasingly more frequent up till 1958. Since then they have formed a positive flood. My interpretation of this is that, while the age of the tellers naturally showed up statistically, another factor is much more important. This factor is that it is only comparatively recently that roads have been started into these large areas of national forest. The jeep caused the first move in this activity, being one better than a mule in this country, but needing at least a clear path of a certain width that might loosely be called a road. Next, the government decided to open up these national forests to timber-cruising, it having been demonstrated that one of the best ways to conserve timberlands is to cut out the oversized and overage trees which retard new growth. The road-building program for the first time took large numbers of people into areas not previously penetrated, or into which people found it hard to go even to hunt. These are the retreats of the *Oh-Mah*.

The other thing that Betty Allen brought to light was the much more surprising fact that this was not by any means only an Amerindian folk-tale. She began to hear the names of white men and others who, it was said, had also met or seen these creatures. She went after these persons too, and found out in due course that it was so, and that they, in turn, had not been saying anything for fear of ridicule. I withhold their names too, as I do not have the permission of any to publish them and I would no more wish to embarrass them than I would my Amerindian friends. Most of these had also been employed on road construction, but there were others, including two doctors of medicine returning from a mass emergency late one night along Route 299 going east from Willow Creek, who said they had nearly run into one, although they had slowed down, thinking it to be somebody signaling for a lift. They said that it was at least 7 feet tall when it stood up, had straight legs but very long arms, and was clothed in thick lightish brown fur; and who better than (even tired) medical men ought to know? Some of these local stories went back 30 years.

Then, there was the extremely unsavory (to me) interjection of the business of "little people." It is a particularly odd one in this neighborhood for several reasons. First, the Amerinds will not, as far as I have been able to determine, come right out and either assert or deny their existence. Unlike the giants, of which they speak quite factually, they seem to regard these pigmies with a high degree of superstition, and their folk-tales are rife with stories of such little people playing with their children on riverbanks; but, while being visible to youngsters, being invisible to adults. This is a very widespread myth that crops up all over the world about fairies, pixies, and suchlike little folk. However, some white people of higher education, and resident on the outskirts of fully opened-up and settled areas, have told the same story, and perfectly straight, but have also, in several cases, implied that they had assumed, or had definite grounds for supposing that these little hairy ones were the young of the *Oh-Mahs!*

Simultaneously, this dearth of direct claims that these midgets have been *seen* is in marked contrast to reports that their little foot-tracks have actually been found both in snow and mud much more often than those of the giants. I have seen sketches of these drawn to scale, but so far no photographs or plaster casts. Many times they are said to crowd around pools or depressions in snow and to trail into and out of the undergrowth in all directions. They are very funny little imprints, averaging only about 4 inches long and do, for the life of me, look very like those of tiny men but with very pointed heels.

I frankly don't like this: I don't like it one bit: and it also upsets me. All of us almost automatically become annoyed with anything new, and especially when it appears to conflict with our logic and the orderly tenor of our lives. Perhaps you will say that if I can accept the possibility of the presence of giants I ought to be able to take little people in my stride. So I should, but I am afraid that I am a very pragmatic person, and there is something unsubstantial about these little footprints. Perhaps it is that I have not seen them in the fresh state myself. In fact, I find myself performing all the mental gyrations of the most advanced skeptics and debunkers in this case, and I know full well that I am doing my damnedest to explain them away.

The first thing one thinks of—just like the zoologists confronted with the Himalayan *yetis*—is any kind of local animal that might produce these tracks and, by Jove, there certainly is one. This is the large western porcupine. This animal has an astonishingly human-looking hind foot when seen from below, apart from large claws. It has a somewhat pointed heel. But there *is* the problem of its claws; and then there is another objection. The porcupine can waddle along on its hind feet quite well but, like the ground-sloths, it has a thick, stubby tail that is directed downward and which forms a tripod with the hind legs when the animal is standing up. However, it can be raised somewhat and could possibly be carried off the ground. At the same time, the claws on the back feet of really large porcupines are actually raised well off the ground so that the swollen pads under the feet can sink into soft substances quite a way before the claws leave imprints. Yet these tracks clearly show 5 toes—not sharply incised claw marks—all of about the same size and arranged almost straight across the front of the feet. In an endeavor to overcome this fact, an ingenious naturalist friend of mine has suggested that the claws of animals sometimes acquire globular encrustations of ice in winter when they are tramping about in wet snow and when a frost is coming on, and that these might produce the impression of toes. But what then of the tracks in mud, all over, and by thousands? As I say, I don't like this business; but, I also don't like leaving it up in the air; yet, I have nothing to add to it as of now. Until and unless I can go and find some of the tracks in mud myself, and carry out my own particular kind of investigation thereupon, I shall refrain from further comment. Then there has been another most peculiar business in this area. It transpired that nearby, certain persons who are free, white, family folk, live in rather expensive houses sometimes of the split-level ranch type, on blacktop roads around which school buses parade daily to take their offspring to be educated. In many cases they own houses which stand in several acres of land backed up against solid forest that has not been touched except for logging of large timber a century ago. They had something most unpleasant to report. These people live not more than 30 miles from a large and bustling modern city. They stated, in confidence and off the record, to certain locals for whose veracity I will vouch, that they had for long experienced a problem. This was simply that their kids—i.e. under 7-year-olds—had been found to be playing in the back fields up by the borders of the forest with certain fairly small hairy ones, who, when alarmed by the approach of human adults, allegedly took to the trees.

Said human kids, on reaching the age of reason, turned out not to want to talk about this abomination, while their parents most definitely did not and do not want it talked about. Nonetheless, they have talked a bit, and I pass it on to you for what it is worth. This is the kind of thing that gets people really riled: it also seems to me to slop over into the realm of "Little People" that only kids can see. Let us just suppose for a moment that *Oh-Mah* mothers permit their kids to play with ours (up to about the age of 7) but tell them to cut out the moment one of our adult appears over the fence! Naturally it would be only the kids who see the little hairy ones. There is no better playmate for a child than a 2-year-old chimpanzee.

There are other items connected with ABSMery generally in this area and to the north of it, which I also do not like but which should be presented and also without comment. This comes from, of all places, Albany in Oregon, which is in the Willamette Valley at the foot of Mt. Jefferson, and concerns a certain Lake Conser. A brief notice of this was published in *Fate* Magazine's issue for January, 1961 and read:

> **ALBANY, ORE.—The monster of Conser Lake is still on the loose. The creature reportedly stands on two** *webbed* **[italics mine] feet, is 7 to 8 feet high [tall], and with its shaggy white hair somewhat resembles a gorilla. It has kept pace with a truck going 35 m.p.h. Never harmed anyone though.**

This is a nasty one, but let me give you some further details. These were contained in a letter to a friend of mine, dated October 27, 1960.

> **Creatures (several) last report, being sighted on farmer's farm. An attempt is being made to contact farmer whom to date wants his name and address held secret. Have made 5 investigation trips and have for evidence a finger print lifted off a house window including a plaster cast of a foot print (right). Have personal taped accounts of this creature plus many interviews, this includes photographs. He is all of 7' tall, 400 lbs.,**

can move at tremendous speeds, jump tremendous distances. No news items concerning this being have been printed in the Portland Papers. He displays extreme cunning, walks and runs erect, appears frustrated, acts as if would like to communicate. He makes extremely high pitched sounds. His hair or fur has a slight glow in the dark and is 3 to 4 inches long. He walks with feet 19 inches long that make a sqeeshy sound. Has been seen in daylight and at night and seen to disappear once into the lake. Will send you complete report as soon as I can.

Creature first sighted several miles north of Albany, Oregon in a dense land area approximately 3 sq. miles. Open land extends all around this area & dotted with farms. Have any ideas how he got there?

Sorry for the delay for there has been new developments. A farmer who wishes to remain anonymous has sighted several on his farm. He is attempting to make friends with them. One is brown and one is white. At times they imitate his voice when he talks to them. Mr. farmer is an animal trainer and at the last report steady progress is being made. Hal Starr was contacted by this farmer and has promised that the location and that his name not be revealed. I would like to investigate further but am handicapped. They are up to 7′ height covered with long hair which hangs over their faces. They walk erect and with all fours. They have taken a shine to the horses but the horses were frightened of them. Lots of foot prints around and are cloven.

Two weeks ago a sheriff of Salem told me that he heard on the radio KBZY that a person had called in saying that he had seen a creature near Hwy. 99. I talked to the announcer in Salem and verified this event. I am busy writing you a complete report. Hope this will suffice for a while.

I am afraid this did not "hold me" even for a little while because it is altogether one of the most shocking reports that has yet come into my hands. I have been pursuing the matter diligently with, however, no result whatsoever.

This remark about going into water on the part of an ABSM is fairly common and causes me to think furiously on two counts. First, it is really a very bizarre thing for anybody who is making a good story out of a series of lies, to think up. Into a cave, or even into a swamp, yes: but into water, per se, just as if it were an aquatic or at least semi-aquatic creature, is very weird. At the same time, one just has to take into account the perfectly astonishing theory put forward by Professor, Sir Alistair Hardy of Oxford early in 1960 and which, utterly bizarre as it at first sounds, has been most seriously considered by scientists and fully accepted as at least possible by many.

This suggests that one branch of the general Anthropoid stock—and, although Sir Alistair calls them "apes," I think we should surely name them Hominids, or at least as already being on the *Man* branch of that stock rather than on the Pongid or ape branch—about a million years ago took to semi-aquatic life and especially along seacoasts. But let this bold savant state his case in his own words: *

> **"Many apes were driven to hunt in the sea by fierce competition for food in the forests. At first they waded and groped in the water, but gradually learned how to swim. Over a period of several hundred thousand years, the species lost its hair as it carried on its marine life. The only hair left was on the very top of the head to help protect the creature from the sun.**
>
> **"The sea ape learned to stand upright because water helped support the body. It developed longer legs than its land-based brother ape for swimming. Its hands became sensitively shaped to allow it to feel along the sea bed for shellfish and open crabs. It learned to use tools by picking up stones to crack open sea urchins. It would be only a step for man to discover that flints chipped into sharper and more useful tools, knives, and arrows. Then, armed with such equipment and his erect posture, he was all set for the chase. He could now reconquer the continents, running and hunting the animals of the plains. I estimate that apes were driven into shallow sea waters a million years ago. They emerged as men about 500,000 years ago."**

He said he had discussed his theory with many other scientists and they had been unable to find a flaw in it. (A.P.)

Footnote: The story behind this story is even more fascinating than the theory itself, and will be told in a forthcoming sequel to this book. *Author*.

*Quoted from a story in the *New York Herald Tribune*, of March 7, 1960, from a March 6, verbatim, A.P. report on a conference of "Marine Scientists" at Brighton, England.

If in the sea, why not also, or even previously in rivers, lakes, and ponds, more especially as swamps and marshes were much more prevalent in the past than they are now, particularly in the pluvial periods following the ice-advances and retreats of the past million years. Then again, there is another most convincing aspect of this idea, as follows. If at the beginning of the Pleistocene there were a variety of primitive anthropoids of the Hominid branch scattered about the earth, and if all of these were hairy, but did not all become extinct, as we have until now supposed, we have some ready-made characters for our ABSMs.

Let us suppose that several of these started going into water after food, and that one (or perhaps several) types did very well at it; lost their body hair; learned to crack stones and all the rest; and then came back to conquer the land as *Men,* just as Professor Hardy suggests. This still need not presuppose that *all* of them did so. Some of the types that started the practice may never have gotten farther than ducking into inland lakes and, while they did not keep at it fervently enough to lose their body hair, they did develop very long toes with an almost complete web between them. Do not forget that *we* still have two half-webbed toes ourselves—our third and fourth—and please don't fail to take a look at the California "Bigfeet," in which the second "ball" appears to be an enlarged basal big-toe joint. (see Page 333) All the toes of this type must then be *very* long and be webbed because the mud or snow does not squish up between them but forms (and always forms) a tall angular ridge running at right angles to the direction of travel, just where it would be bunched up if the foot were webbed. We might therefore legitimately conceive of the *Sasquatch—Oh-Mah* type of ABSMs at least being relics of early hominids with semi-aquatic habits.

However, to interject at this point, I recently received a report from a neighboring area which would seem to indicate something of the same nature. This came to me from a young man in our Air Force whose wife is part Amerind. He lived until recently on the Makah Indian Reservation at Neah Bay, Washington. This young man got in touch with me through a magazine publisher, stating that he had some information that might interest me. I wrote him, and in reply received some very charming and highly informative letters, the contents of which I see no reason to question. Among these he wrote:

In my letter to you I mentioned the 18½ inch foot prints that were found out on the beach. I know these weren't made by any man going around with a foot cut out of a piece of wood. This beach is about 8 miles in the back woods and is a very hard spot to get to.

On another occasion last summer one of the fishermen out here was going to bed and heard a lot of splashing going on in a swamp in his back yard. From what he told me, he got a flashlight and went out there to take a look around and seen this huge creature tearing back into the woods after the light hit him. Up to this date there has been nothing more seen of it. Altho many people are waiting for it to come back. The day this person told me of what happened I took a gun and went into the swamp to look around. I actually found huge hunks of hair that must have been pulled loose when he ran back into the woods that night.

I have hunted and killed quite a few bears around here but that hair that I found that day was definitely not hair from a bear. For one thing, there was a couple of hairs that I measured to be close to 14 inches long and these hunks had a very strong odor unlike any bear that I have killed.

There is also one other occasion that makes me think that the Abominable Snowman is up around this neck of the woods. This happened to me some time before I read your articles in the True Magazine. One evening I went up this unused logging road to hunt bear. I was some 13 miles up this road and there is not one person living for about 20 miles around. On this occasion I happened to be alone. Well anyway I was sitting on a stump and was sitting there for about an hour when I heard this high pitched scream like a baby but this went on for almost an hour and the more I listened to it the more I decided that it wasn't a mountain lion. Then after a while it stopped and I never heard it again and I left without looking around. Then after I read your article I thought it might have been a Snowman up there. I went up there quite a few times after that but never heard or seen anything.

Once again, I have received nothing more from this source!

It has always been my firm belief, as a reporter, that children don't lie. By this, I mean that, while real kids (say, under seven) live in a world of their own, peopled by many things that are not of our world but which are still most real to them, and while young persons from seven to the age of puberty delight in pulling the legs of their elders with tall tales, all young persons are much more basically honest than grownups. More, important, I do not believe that a young person can carry a lie forced upon him or her by an elder for any length of time; and, especially, under sympathetic questioning. I am therefore always interested in what young people have to say, provided that they know that I am sincerely interested, have an open mind, and am not critical of their age. Young people are also extremely keen observers, perhaps because they take a more nearly worm's-eye view of life and because their senses are more acute. Thus, when somebody tells me something that happened to them when they were young, I like to listen. This then from a young person about an incident when she was still younger:

Dear Mr. Sanderson:

I have just finished reading your story concerning the abominable [sic] man of Northern California. Before I write any further I would like to say that what I am about to say is positively true and I have never told anyone this story before for fear that they would think that I was half cracked and out of my mind.

I have seen this man-monster and can give you a detailed description of him. He is far from being pretty and I still wake up nights dreaming of him.

When: About 9 years ago, at about 10 o'clock in the morning. Where: Near the Eel River above Eureka, California. At the edge of a meadow near the river's edge. Under what circumstances: My family and I were fishing on the Eel River. We had been camped in the vicinity for about 2 weeks and had had poor luck when it came to fishing. I used to go for a short walk before breakfast because there was a very pretty meadow about a mile or two from our camp and I used to love to see the mist rise off the grass. I was only about 10 years old at the time and the world of nature was something which both fascinated and enthralled me. I entered the meadow and proceeded to cross it in order to reach a small knoll at the other side. When I approached the foot of the knoll I heard a sound. It was the sound of someone walking and I thought perhaps my little brother had followed me and was going to jump out and try to scare me. I hollered, "All right, stinker, I know you're there." Needless to say it was not my brother that appeared. Instead it was a creature that I will never forget as long as I live. He stepped out of the bushes and I froze like a statue. He or "it" was about 7½ to 8 feet tall. He was covered with brown stuff that looked more like a soft down than fur. He had small eyes set close together and had a red look about them. His nose was very large and flat against his face. He had a large mouth with the strangest looking fangs that I have ever seen. . . . His form was that of a human and he had hands and feet of enormous size, but very human looking. However, there was one thing that I have not mentioned, the strangest and most frightening thing of all. He had on clothes! Yes, that's right. They were tattered and torn and barely covered him but they were still there. He made a horrible growling sound that I don't think could be imitated by any living thing. Believe me I turned and ran as fast as I could. I reached camp winded and stayed scared all while we were there.

I have often thought that perhaps it was a mutation of some kind. I think this thing is highly dangerous and something should definitely be done about it.

I would be willing to testify to anything I have stated in this letter. I am not a crackpot and am completely sound of mind and body. I just thought you might be interested to know what your man-monster really looks like. Believe me if you saw him he would scare the wits out of you. I know!

Yours truly,

(signed)   (Miss) B. C.*

It is not perhaps quite proper to interject the following comments at this point, but, I contend, a reporter has the right to indulge some speculation upon matters that he has investigated firsthand. This may be an infringement upon editorial rights but can be fobbed off as background information. It seems to me that there is something to this whole bit in California, Oregon, and Washington, and that it is pretty fatuous to try and put it all down to any of the standard explanations such as the hoax, the publicity stunt, the Indian folk-tale, mass hypnotization, mass cases of mistaken identity (of known animals), or other suggestions of that nature. We are all pretty odd, but we are not all liars or crackpots. Further, I do not feel it to be

* Name and address on file, but for release in special circumstances only.—Author.

either right or justified to dub all Washingtonians, Oregonians, and North Californians as either just because they say something we don't like, or which does not fit into our orderly pattern of what is or is not supposed to be. At the same time, I don't give a hang what any "expert" actually says. There are enormous areas in those three states about which nobody—not even the majority of their inhabitants—knows anything. I really cannot see why some new things should not turn up in those states.

If you could read all the reports that I have; and, much more; if you could listen to my recordings or have been with me when I interviewed and got to know the good people who had the guts to tell these stories, I think everyone interested would be not just amazed but somewhat shamed. It is so easy to sit back in one's own home, surrounded by all the normal, known things of modern life, and say "Phui"; but, get out in the woods and get hungry. A person will begin to see a lot of things he never saw before, and would never have seen if he had not got lost and run out of food. Thus, when a teen-ager writes to me from the delightfully named Happy Camp at the edge of the Klamath area and says: "Reading your story of America's abominable snowman, I find very interesting. But I think they've only found the baby. Here, in Happy Camp, our cars are turned over and rolled into the river, 6-foot trees uprooted, slides in the mountains, and when it snows 10 feet deep, 1-inch power lines are snapped in two. The daddy must cause this." I do not yell for Paul Bunyan and go into gales of laughter. Maybe there *was* no flood that shifted the cars, and the trees *were* 6 feet tall, not thick.

If things as bizarre can happen, or be alleged to happen, right in our own back yard, we should be doubly careful of criticizing things that are reported to happen beyond our borders. And when these form a logical concomitant to happenings in our own bailiwick, we ought to listen most carefully. Of course, there is the damnable, added frustration in dealing with foreign matters inherent in their very foreignness—one can't often go and look into them firsthand, and if one does, one has language and other difficulties. Moreover, if we doubt our own citizens, how much more so may we not those of other countries? This is all a pity but nonetheless the way things are. From now on, therefore, I won't expect anyone to believe what I report at all. We go first over the border south to our sister republic of Mexico.

171

8. On the Tracks of . . .

AFFAIRS IN CENTRAL AND
SOUTH AMERICA

The title of this chapter is an acknowledgement of a good friend and fellow zoologist. He, Dr. Bernard Heuvelmans, Consultant to the Musée Royal D'Histoire Naturelle de Belgique, but resident in Paris, is the author of the only book that covers the ABSM problem world-wide. It covers also many other items of a crypto-zoological nature, and is entitled in its English version, *On the Track of Unknown Animals*.* I shall be leaning very heavily upon this work from now on, with its author's more than generous permission. Bernard and I have been on these tracks separately for many years now but, as we have constantly exchanged information and discoveries, a considerable amount of what we have to say has similar origins. However, there is much that both of us have unearthed [either firsthand or by burrowing assiduously through published material], that the other has missed. Frankly, neither of us knows any longer, in many cases, exactly just which items came from which in the first place; and, as constant acknowledgments in the text would be irksome, Bernard has given me permission just to barge ahead and gobble up anything that may seem to me to be pertinent. However, while we were both once professional zoologists, we specialized in different aspects of the science. I started out as and always really remained a field ecologist but have specialized in the major distribution of animals in accordance with that of vegetational types, and therefore approach most, if not all, matters from that angle. Thus, there may be times when I disagree with my good friend Bernard and, since I have never then failed to say so to

* Published in England by Rupert Hart-Davis, 1958; published in the United States by Hill & Wang, 1959.

172

him, I shall also be mentioning the fact in this text as I go along, if occasion arises. It was on a framework of vegetalogy that I tackled ABSMery in North America. From now on, and especially in the tropics, it becomes the main theme of my story.

At this point I have to revert to type and refer to maps, notably No. IV at this point. I have also to ask the reader to plunge once again into botanical geography. In addition to being all of the other unpleasant things that we have accused them of, people are very chauvinistic and, from a national point of view, frankly bucolic. This shows up in various ways, like wars and tariffs, but most noticeably on maps. It is almost impossible to buy a map of any country, *in* that country, that shows anything starting immediately beyond the borders of that country. Thus, not only road maps but even our school atlases have a habit of going along splendidly to the Rio Grande and to some arbitrary, somewhat jiggly, and quite nonexistent line from a point about El Paso, Texas, west and just north of the upper end of the Bay of Baja California and thence to the Pacific coast a few miles south of San Diego, California. Beyond that, southward, there is a great white blank. While the United Staters of North America are outstandingly obtuse in this respect, we cannot really exonerate the other United Staters of this same continent—the United States of Mexico—from indulgence in the same idiocy. Their maps customarily run *up* to that same ridiculous line; above which a ghostly "Pais de los Gringos" may be seen—in strong light.*

The American Geographical Society of New York has published some most excellent maps that show the whole of North America and especially the overlap between our country and Mexico. These are very revealing in that one learns from them—as one does if one actually travels through that strip of territory—that practically everything

---

* Sometimes things get much worse, as when Guatemala published a map of her country which included the whole of British Honduras, because they "claim" it; and then the Mexicans countered with a map of their southern states from the Isthmus of Tehuantepec that showed the northern half of that hapless little independent colony as being a part of their Territory of Quintana Roo. Happily, the Republica de Honduras, being between governments, only issued a pamphlet which claimed all the cays and islands off British Honduras. (There are *five* United States in all America—ours, Mexico, Venezuela, Brazil, and the Argentine.

goes on just the same right across the border. The Tularosa Basin just flows on south into the great Bolson (basin) of Mapimi; the Rockies pass on through the Sacramento and Guadalupe Mountains, via the Chisos, straight into the Sierra Madre Oriental; and the endless semi-parallel ranges that bestrew southern Arizona go right on to become the Sierra Madre Occidental, while the mountains of southern California march on stolidly to become those of Baja California. Nothing much else changes either: even a parrot (a Conure) and the jaguar get on to the north side, and millions of tourists on to the south. The only things that change abruptly are the brands of beer and the length of the women's skirts—there is a strong European influence even just over the border. [Money is interchangeable for a time but the gasoline does, I must admit, seem to be of quite a different substance on the two sides of this otherwise arbitrary border.]

The really funny thing is that practically nobody knows anything about the first great belt just south of our border. There are four major roads and three major railroads to get south and that is all; and all of them roar across a variably unpleasant and dreary desert for a long way before they come to anything important. Mexico lies on its side, so that what we call its west coast is really its south coast. It consists of a central core of enormous volcanic mountains from which two great tines of mountain ranges extend toward the United States, like a pair of giant scissors. Behind, or to the southeast of the core, there is a narrow neck of lowlands, the Tehuantepec Isthmus, and then what is really quite another country named Chiapas that stands up like a large flat salad bowl on a footstool, or actually more like a flamingo's nest.

To the northeast of this is still another Mexican country called Yucatan, which is a low plateau formed of limestone marl, riddled with caves, and separated from Chiapas by a great swath of swamps more or less at sea level and clothed in an awful, low, tangled, spiny growth called *akalché*. Yucatan, which includes the state of that name, as well as the Territory of Quintana Roo, and the states of Campeche, and Tabasco, is the land of the Mayas. Behind Chiapas, on the south side, lies Guatemala; an arbitrary hunk of volcanos and aggressive mountains that really forms part of a much larger mountain block that extends to the great lakes district of Nicaragua.

The Sierra Madre Oriental, along with her many associated ranges, are still not much known, though they are

—and have been for countless centuries—well inhabited. Among them are some valleys filled with a truly tropical type of vegetation. The Sierra Madre Occidental, on the other hand, is almost entirely unknown. There are people living in it but they don't have anything to do with anybody and, least of all and if possible, with Mexicans, whom their inhabitants call "guachés" [which is a slang expression for a very old bus more or less held together with bits of string]. Among these people are the Yaquis who played a great part in modern Mexican history; who still write in hieroglyphs; and who were alleged to have been scalping on the main Pacific Highway in the early days of World War II. They are very splendid people—everything an Amerind should be, both in fact and in fancy. This southern (i.e. to us, western) block of mountains runs for 800 miles southeast till it hits the comparative lowland break of Guadalajara. It is crossed by only one road, from Durango to Mazatlan; it has a canyon in it that has been estimated to be two hundred times the size of the Grand Canyon when all its measurements are taken into consideration, though you may console yourself about this, because nobody has ever explored it. I have seen one end of it and very impressive it is. Most of its bottom is choked with forest and there are said to be "people" in there—at least my Yaqui Indian friends told me so. These are said never to come out, to be very big, and to be *hairy* all over!

The rest of Mexico down to the northern escarpment of Chiapas is charming and much more civilized than any of us northerners realize or like to think. They had universities down there 200 years before our country was founded, and some of their modern ones are carrying on studies that are so far ahead of anything being prosecuted in ours that it makes us look a little silly. [That may be why we don't hear about them.] The best work that I have seen on vegetational distribution, not excluding Soviet Russia, has been done at, and published recently by, the University of San Luis Potosi. The indigenes—for we can hardly call them natives—of this main, central area are too busy even to turn up any folklore about ABSMs, but they have dug up some awfully funny-looking statuettes. But, this is another subject that I cannot get involved in here.

Now, while the plateau of Chiapas is rather an unpleasant, dusty, cactus-strewn place, and looks not unlike one of our lesser deserts (due to its altitude), it is ringed by well forested mountains with gorges that are filled with real "jungle." Also, it flows back into the uplands of the main Central American block; and it is really part of that block. Were it nearer sea level, it would be properly tropical, and it is in any case only just "North" American. The true dividing line between the two continents of *Erica* and *Columbia* (see Map I) is a very complicated line that meanders about all over the place on its way from the Pacific to the Caribbean. Plants and animals respect this line mightily. In fact, you are hard put to it to catch one of the party in the first part in the territory of the second part; and vice versa. Possibly certain ABSMs show the same respect for Nature here, too.

There is nothing like the wealth of material on the subject of ABSMs in the tropics, and notably in South America, that there is in North America, in the Himalayas, and in central Eurasia. What is more, what there is, looks extremely spotty and lacks any pattern unless it be *mapped:* and mapped on vegetalogical grounds at that. When this is done, however, it begins to make a great deal of sense. Despite an enormous volume of literature on the geography and the distribution of plants and animals in South America, there are still many widely held misconceptions about the constitution and history of that continent—held by profound students of the matter as well as by the general (and not technically interested) public. The general impression of the continent is that it is a vast tropical jungle all over but, while a lot of it is covered with closed-canopy forests—whether you should call them jungles or not is a matter of much controversy in any case —the major part of it is *not;* and, a large portion down at the bottom has a temperate climate tailing off to a subpolar one. Then, there are the great Andean uplands and mountain ranges that occupy its whole western side. Least understood of all, however, is the area which is occupied by Brazil.

Looking at Map IX, you will perceive that, in addition to the two mountain blocks in Central America, and the three arbitrary divisions of the Andean ridge, there are three other upland massifs on this continent. These are the Guianese, the Matto Grosso, and the enormous Caãtinga. The last is the most puzzling to foreigners, because one's impression of Brazil has been gained from the periphery of this grim sloping plateau, and this periphery is almost everywhere a lush lowland belt of forests and other massed vegetation. The appalling aridity of this still so-called "Terra Incognita" which reaches its climax in the northeastern bulge of the continent, is not generally known. If you want to get a clear picture of it, you should read a book entitled *Tukani* by Helmut Sick, a scientist who accompanied the first official expedition to cut right across this terrible territory to the Amazon Basin. In this, you will very soon see the complete difference between these uplands, their vegetation, climate and fauna, and that of the equatorial forests of the Amazon. The two are abruptly different worlds and, as one approaches the latter from the former, one comes up against an actual *wall* formed by tall evergreen vegetation.

If one raises the subject of animal life in South America, everybody invariably yells "Green Hell," and thinks of the Amazon Basin. It is a funny thing, but there is nothing hellish about any jungle and rather especially about that of the Amazon. It is, like all equatorial forests, never too hot or too cold, singularly free of noxious insects, completely free from disease [provided you keep away from human beings and don't carry any pestilence in with you when you enter], is well supplied with food that is easy to obtain, has plenty of good water, and is not too badly infested with indigenous people who resent one's presence. There are poisonous snakes and jaguars but you really have to look for them, and they are absolutely harmless as long as you look where you are going and don't molest them. [I once persuaded a jaguar to leave the ridgepole of our bush-home in which my wife was sleeping, one night, simply by saying "Boo" at it.] Then there is this Amazon bit.

It so happens that the basin of this name, which contains the greatest river, and river system, in the world, was, until not long ago geologically speaking, an arm of the South Atlantic—a great inland sea. Further, there is evidence that long since it became land it may have been completely flooded again for briefer periods off and on, and some Brazilian scientists claim that they have evidence that the last time this happened was only about the year 1200 B.C. It is indeed today a sort of enormous botanical cum zoological garden but, actually, its flora and fauna in no way compares in diversity with that of all the surrounding areas combined. In fact, it has manifestly been repopulated quite recently by several streams of animals and plants *from* those areas, which must have remained above sea level either as great islands or massive peninsulas attached to the rest of the continent. Moreover, there were jungles and other wet forests on those blocks as well as the vegetation and appropriate wildlife of their drier uplands. Many of those areas are also extremely ancient; meaning, that they have remained above sea level for a particularly long time. The most isolated and perhaps the oldest is the Guiana Massif, but seniority may be claimed for the Colombian Massif. This was certainly there before the Andes were pushed up. The Andes themselves are really comparatively recent, and they might be *very* new. This is not of our story but it is germane to it, in that the age of the montane forests of the Andes has a very important bearing on the recently past history of ABSMs and their possible distribution there.

The point I am trying to make here is that if I were asked to go find an ABSM, or any other as yet uncaught kind of animal, in South America, the last place that I would go would be the Amazon Basin itself. I would tackle the Guianese Massif first, next the Colombian Massif, and then move on to the uplands surrounding the Matto Grosso. After that I would do what I could about the Caātinga, and then Patagonia, and then the Andes, but would leave the Amazon till last. As a matter of fact, I would do a thorough job on the northern Central American Block before even going to South America at all, and this is just what I now propose to do.

The limits of this last block are very clear on Map IX, and are confined between the Isthmus of Tehuantepec on the west and the gutter filled by the great lakes of Nicaragua on the east. The smaller southern block, running from the latter line to the valley of the Atrato River, that cuts the Panamanian isthmus off from the Colombian Massif, will not concern us. There are some exceedingly strange small animals in that block, and there is some odd folklore but I have nothing concrete upon our subject from it. The main or western block is enormously mountainous, and constitutes one of the major areas of volcanicity in the world. The number of volcanos you can count from a point above Guatemala City is variously estimated and often grossly exaggerated but it is nonetheless quite remarkable. The southern edge of this block drops abruptly to a narrow, catcus-covered, dry, coastal plain; but the northern face steps down through ever-decreasing banks of mountains and hills to a wide forest-covered coastal fringe. Its real border is the valley of the River Usumacinta in Campeche, but north of this there are some ancient low hills in the Peten, and these mount up to the east into what is probably the most remarkable little mountain massif in the whole of Central America. This is called the Maya Mountains and lies in southern British Honduras.

I have been carrying on a very long-distance correspondence with an American lady for long resident in what is really the outer periphery of the Mexican state of Chiapas. She was introduced to me by a man in the publishing field with the very highest reputation and whom I most greatly respect. Were it not for this, I simply could not bring myself to record the following even in a purely reportorial way. As of going to press I have not received a reply to my written request—and letters have to be paddled up a river to her, taking several days—to enter this information over her name.

However, I heard from her that a form of ABSM is not *quite* but *very* well-known in the forests nearby where she lives. [This, incidentally, is a continuation of those montane forests about which my friend Cal Brown writes (see below).] This she tells me is known locally by various names such as *Salvaje, Cax-vinic,* or simply *fantasma humano.* She then goes on, deadpan, to write: "I have seen this creature on various occasions and heard it frequently —the last time was about a year ago however. Some of the things I know about [it] coincide with your information [from other areas] but I can't reconcile the cry described with mine. I don't think I have ever heard anything so disturbing—not frightening but more dreadful and haunting, and full of threat I couldn't imagine. I suspect that from this cry alone men living in this jungle could assume it to be a 'fantasma humano.'" As a friend of mine remarked on reading this, "And I suppose she rides one of the mastodons that the locals use for plowing."

This almost casual letter is somehow quite shocking to me, though knowing what I do of this matter in other much more settled areas, and in view of the fact that it is hard by Cal Brown's pinpointed area for something very similar-sounding, there is really no need to be upset.

As I remarked in a previous passage, Chiapas of Mexico is shaped like a salad bowl held on high. Its eastern rim abuts on to the mountains of Guatemala and these tumble down into the Peten in a tremendous jumble of tall, tight peaks and ridges with deep narrow valleys and gorges in between. The whole is choked with wet tropical forest, is unmapped, unexplored, and just plain not known. I had a group of young associates under the leadership of this Kenneth (Cal) Brown, who worked for some years in

179

this area, collecting scientific specimens for botanical, zoological, and petrological studies, and I once lived for several years in that area myself, flew over almost all of it repeatedly during the war and have walked all about it. Comparing notes (after 20 years of this) Cal and I have come to the conclusion that this is one of the oddest areas on earth, made the more strange, almost eerie in fact, by the presence of many ancient Mayan ruins therein, which one stumbles across everywhere. There is something uncanny about these gigantic artificial hills, with their endless, writhing carvings, courts, passages, mighty flat-roofed halls, now filled only with the chitterings of bats; utterly abandoned in vast uninhabited jungles that just breathe silently in the noonday tropical sun. There are many strange things in these jungles and some of these pertain to our quest (see Map VIII).

Cal Brown has pinpointed for me a valley to which his party once attained and where some of those odd incidents occurred that so often crop up when actually exploring. You can't really put your finger on them, and often one misses even recording them. It may be plants freshly broken in a way that is just not right; or very strange calls; or a certain reluctance by any native people around to go any farther or even to talk much. So powerful was this atmosphere at this place that one of Cal's partners—Wendell Skousen, a geologist, and one of the most pragmatic men I have ever met—corralled the locals almost by force and demanded to know what was going on. Then it came out. The locals explained:

There live in the mountain forest very big, wild men, completely clothed in short, thick, brown, hairy fur, with no necks, small eyes, long arms and huge hands. They leave footprints twice the length of a man's.

The area in question was in Baja Verapaz, around the town of Cubulco. Cubulco is the last vestige of civilization, the road ends there, and for all intents and purposes so does everything. The range of mountains in question is the Sierra de Chuacus, whose greatest peak is Mt. (Cerro) Sanché, 8500 feet elevation. Depending on which direction you're coming from, there are between 5 and 7 ridges from the floor of the Cubulco Valley [Rio Cubulco, which eventualy joins the Rio Negro to the north roughly 20 kilometers] to C. Sanché. Further than this, I would not want to speculate as to range of this alleged creature. I have coloured in a patch on the en-

180

closed map which depicts the approximate range according to what the natives told me, which means it would range into the departmento of El Quiché (see Map VIII).

Cubulco itself, at about 4200 feet, is really "tierra templada," and the area in question ranges up to "tierra fria." The vegetation is open pine and oak forests on the slopes, and many high plateau areas are covered with grass, as is the Cubulco environ. Along the margins of the highlands where rainfall is greatest, the oak and pine forest merges with the rain forest. Temperature ranges from 30°F to 90°F, and while I have no good figures on rainfall, it is considerably less than, say, Coban.

Now, as to "what the natives said." They referred to a large, hairy creature, which sometimes walked on two legs, and apparently ran on all fours. I considered bear first of all, and queried them regarding size, shape, appearance, etc. The answer was that it looked like a bear, but it wasn't from the description they gave—no conspicuous ears, no "snout"—it was somewhat taller than a man, and considerably broader, covered with darkish hair, and the locals live in mortal dread of disturbing it. Occasionally, one or two of the natives who got drunk or particularly boastful would go half way up the ridge and make a big show of "hunting" it, but no one ever killed one that I learned. Several persons reported they were chased by it down the mountain, although with the fear they have of whatever it is, they probably just caught a glimpse of it and ran all the way down the mountain at top speed. No one seemed very anxious to guide us to the spot, or spots, but one of the braver souls agreed to do so finally. Unfortunately, we never got to it, for which you will curse, no doubt. I have no way of determining from their descriptions whether it was a bear or a Sisemite or something else, but it would seem reasonable that something is back there. You will be somewhat interested in the fact that natives reported to me that this thing "calls" every so often, and they hear it from time to time when they are travelling about the ridges.

One cannot lay any store by "calls," for the tiny Douroucouli, or Night-Monkey of South America (*Aötes*), can almost blast you out of bed when it really gets going, and the Howler Monkey (*Alouatta*), can individually make a series of noises that sound just like a dozen jaguars fighting in a thunderstorm. My point here is that I know Cal Brown and Wendell Skousen and the others very well indeed and have done so for many years. They are the hardest-boiled collection of skeptics I have ever met; they were more than just impressed—they were astonished.

What they have told me, moreover, acquires a certain added interest when one reads in *The Museum Journal* (Vol. VI, No. 3, September, 1915), published quarterly by the University Museum of the University of Pennsylvania in Philadelphia, the following excerpts on what are therein described as Guatemaltecan mythology [sic]:

> There is a monster that lives in the forest. He is taller than the tallest man and in appearance he is between a man and a monkey. His body is so well protected by a mass of matted hair that a bullet cannot harm him. His tracks have been seen on the mountains, but it is impossible to follow his trail because he can reverse his feet and thus baffle the most successful hunter. His great ambition, which he has never been able to achieve, is to make fire. When the hunters have left their camp fires he comes and sits by the embers until they are cold, when he greedily devours the charcoal and ashes. Occasionally the hunters see in the forest little piles of twigs which have been brought together by El Sisemite [also called Sisimici] in an unsuccessful effort to make fire in imitation of men. His strength is so great that he can break down the biggest trees in the forest. If a woman sees a Sisemite, her life is infinitely prolonged, but a man never lives more than a month after he has looked into the eyes of the monster. If a Sisemite captures a man he rends the body and crushes the bones between his teeth in great enjoyment of the flesh and blood. If he captures a woman, she is carried to his cave, where she is kept a prisoner.
>
> Besides his wish to make fire the Sisemite has another ambition. He sometimes steals children in the belief that from these he may acquire the gift of human speech. When a person is captured by a Sisemite the fact becomes known to his near relations and friends, who at the moment are seized with a fit of shivering. Numerous tales are told of people who have been captured by the Sisemite. The following incident is related by a woman who had it from her grandmother:
>
> A young couple, recently married, went to live in a

182

hut in the woods on the edge of their milpa (cornfield) in order that they might harvest the maize. On the road Rosalia stepped on a thorn and next morning her foot was so sore that she was unable to help Felipe with the harvesting, so he went out alone, leaving one of their two dogs with her. He had not been working long when the dreaded feeling, which he recognized as Sisemite shivers, took hold of him and he hastily returned to the hut to find his wife gone and the dog in a great fright. He immediately set out for the village, but met on the road the girl's parents, who exclaimed, "You have let the Sisemite steal our child, our feelings have told us so." He answered, "It is as you say."

The case was taken up by the authorities and investigated. The boy was cross-examined, but always answered, "The Sisemite took her, no more than that I know." He was, in spite of the girl's parents' protests, suspected of having murdered his young wife, and was thrown into jail, where he remained many years.

At last a party of hunters reported having seen on Mount Kacharul a curious being with hairy body and flowing locks that fled at the sight of them. A party was organized which went out with the object of trying to capture this creature at any cost. Some days later this party returned with what seemed to be a wild woman, of whom the leader reported as follows. "On Mount Kacharul we hid in the bushes. For 2 days we saw nothing, but on the third day about noon this creature came to the brook to drink and we captured her, though she struggled violently. As we were crossing the brook with her, a Sisemite appeared on the hillside, waving his arms and yelling. On his back was a child or monkey child which he took in his hands and held aloft as if to show it to the woman, who renewed her struggle to be free. The Sisemite came far down the hill almost to the brook; he dropped the child and tore off great branches from big trees which he threw at us."

The young man was brought from his cell into the presence of this wild creature and asked if he recognized her. He replied, "My wife was young and beautiful; the woman I see is old and ugly." The woman never spoke a word from that time on made no sound. She refused to eat and a few days after her capture she died.

Felipe lived to be an old man, and the grandmother of the woman who told this story remembered him as

the man whose wife had been carried away by the Sisemite.

This account would have been relegated to "Myth, Legend, and Folklore," had not an almost identical story, in the form of a complaint on a police-blotter, turned up in Coban, in the same region in the early 1940's. This was made by one Miguel Huzul and was to the effect that his son-in-law was delinquent in having permitted his daughter to be seized by a creature of the mountains to which he gave a name that was apparently too much for the recording officer and which he therefore put down as "a sort of gorilla or man" as far as it could be deciphered and transliterated. I had a copy of this document once, with a tracing of this passage, made for me by a Puerto Rican American who was baffled by the local Spanish and did not know any Mayan. Unfortunately my original went up under a wartime bomb, but we are searching for the records from which it came. All I can add is from memory, but this is pretty vivid in this case as you can imagine, for it was "in my district" at the time, I then being engaged in collecting in the area. It related, in substance, that the *Sisemite* had entered the young man's house and in the presence of other witnesses gathered up his young wife and carried her off while he, the husband, just sat there shivering. No action was taken because the father was disbelieved, while it was rather nicely pointed out that if all that is said about the *Sisemite* is true, the young man could not be accused of cowardice and/or delinquency. I presume there is no precise law covering the matter!

Even then, I would still relegate both stories to M, L, and/or F were it not for my own personal observations, very close by in British Honduras. While there, my wife and I penetrated some distance into these Maya Mountains, not an easy task in the absence of any paths or people, their almost straight up and down topography, and the virtual nonexistence of people willing to carry things in all surrounding areas. While camped up there, the Senior Forestry Officer of the colony—one, Mr. Neil Stevenson—visited us, and we took a day's exploratory and collecting trip up to the top of the next ridge into the magnificent montane palm forest which is sufficiently "open" to be able to permit a view. On the ridge beyond that, then and still now totally unexplored and never even yet attained, there were rectangular areas of forest of distinctly different color, showing that they had once been cleared for cultivation. Later, we saw smoke rising from those forests, and Mr. Stevenson heard cocks crowing therein in the clear mountain air at dawn. When the Shell Oil Company later made a detailed survey of that whole mountain block by aerial, stereoscopic, photography, they brought to light further evidence that there were people living there. Yet, this mountain block stands up like an island in a sea of lowlands which have been crisscrossed for generations by mahogany workers and chicle collectors. Not one single human being has ever been known to come out of it.

Who are these people? Some Mayas left over since pre-colonial days; *pre*-Mayan people; or whom? Whoever they may be, they must be getting a strange education, for their home lies under one of the main commercial airline routes [from Florida, New Orleans, and Merida, Yucatan, to Guatemala City], while we ourselves once sat up on the lower slopes and watched the *Queen Mary* glide majestically by below, down the Gulf of Honduras on her way to Puerto Barrios, on a cruise! This is only a couple of hours flight from Miami, and yet there are apparently *people* living there who have never contacted other people since the time of Columbus.

Now, I am not suggesting that these tree-clearing, chicken-raising chaps, whoever they may be, are ABSMs; but, what I am suggesting, is that if such people can continue to live in magnificent isolation for 450 years, in a tiny country such as this, not more than 50 miles from a number of settled communities [in all directions, as a crow is alleged to fly], there could perfectly well be all sorts of other types living nearby too. And this is just what the people who live *around* the area affirm.

These people are of two major types—Amerinds, and sundry settlers of mixed Amerindian stock in Punta Gorda on the south, and related kinds of people to the north, plus what are called the *Caribs,* along the coast. These latter are not in any way the Amerindian Caribs who gave their name to the Caribbean, but are a group of West Africans of Sudanese Negro stock, who obtained their freedom on the Lesser Antilles in early days, and then sailed their own ships to the mainland coast. They are very strange people with their own language, customs, and religion; great boating people; fearless, and rather fearful. They don't trust anybody and they don't seem to like anybody, and whatever they say they should not be trusted

—not because they are untrustworthy at all but because they learned long ago never again to trust any white.

Both these peoples—the regular British Hondurans or Belizians, and the Coast Caribs—assert that there dwell in the tall, wet forests of the southern half of their country certain small semi-human creatures which they call *Dwendis,* a form of *Duende,* Spanish for goblin. To the very well-educated Belizians, these are regarded more as we regard fairies than as real entities—*unless* they have lived or worked in the southern forested area. Then they, like the Caribs, take quite another view of the matter. I lived in that country off and on for years while we traveled Central America and the West Indies, and I talked to innumerable people there about them. Dozens told me of having seen them, and these were mostly men of substance who had worked for responsible organizations like the Forestry Department and who had, in several cases, been schooled or trained either in Europe or the United States. One, a junior forestry officer born locally, described in great detail two of these little creatures that he had suddenly noticed quietly watching him on several occasions at the edge of the forestry reserve near the foot of the Maya Mountains when he was "cruising" and marking young mahogany trees. His description of them coincided with that of all the others who were serious.

These little folk were described as being between three foot six and four foot six, well proportioned but with very heavy shoulders and rather long arms; clothed in thick, tight, close, brown hair looking like that of a short-coated dog; having very flat yellowish faces but head-hair no longer than the body hair except down the back of the neck and midback. Everybody said that these *Dwendis* have very pronounced calves but that the most outstanding thing of all about them is that they almost always held either a piece of dried palm leaf or something looking like a Mexican-type hat over their heads. This at first sounds like the silliest thing, but when one has heard it from highly educated men as well as from simple peasants, and of half a dozen nationalities and in three languages, and all over an area as great as that from the Peten to Nicaragua, one begins to wonder. Then, one day, I came across a lone chimpanzee in West Africa in an open patch of forest and on the ground; and, *by jingo,* it was solemnly holding a large section of dead palm frond over its head, just like an umbrella and looking exactly like a large Mexican straw hat!

Dwendis are said to appear suddenly in the forest both by day and night and to watch you from a discreet distance. They are silent but seem to be very curious. I heard of no case of their ever making any threatening move, but I was time and time again told of them chasing, sometimes catching, and carrying off dogs. They are said to leave very deep little footprints, *that have pointed heels.*

One does not really know quite what to make of all this. If you go to Belize—and a more delightful spot there can hardly be on earth for a vacation or just to live—and ask around about these things you will be met with gay smiles and probably a healthy quote from some classic such as *The Water Babies* but if you persist you will quite soon find some man who has timber-cruised, or been in the bush farming, and he will surely come out with some details about these mysterious little imps of the forests.

Perspective is a hard thing to evaluate on ancient carvings since captives bearing gifts to an important potentate may be made very small, compared to the monarch. Nevertheless, there are many Mayan bas-reliefs that show pairs of tiny little men with big hats but no clothes, standing among trees and amid the vast legs of demi-gods, priests, and warriors. They are also much smaller than the peasants bearing gifts to the temples!

As we have gotten on to the Pigmies again we might as well follow them. I have a letter from a well-known animal dealer of Guayaquil, Ecuador—Herr Claus U. Oheim—who knows his zoology, and who has a very long and intimate experience of the forests of his country and those of Colombia on the Pacific slopes of the Andes. In this he says:

> The so-called Shiru, I have heard of from the Indians and a few white hunters on both sides of the Andes, but decidedly more so on the eastern slopes, where vast mountainous areas are still quite unexplored, and rarely if ever visited. All reports describe the Shiru as a small [4–5 feet] creature, decidedly hominid, but fully covered with short, dark brown fur. All agreed that the Shiru was very shy, with the exception of one Indian, who claimed having been charged after having missed with his one and only shot from a muzzle loading shotgun, a weapon still used by the majority of Indians, along with the blowgun. These reports were rather sober and objective, and in no way tinged with the colorful imagination, into which Latin-Americans are prone to lapse.

187

This business of the "eastern slopes" is going to get us into unwarranted difficulties unless we once again resort to a map. I think the best way to contemplate South America is as if it were made up of a number of large islands comprising those blocks of territory today enclosed within the 500-meter contours. This gives us a picture like that shown on Map IX, on which both the 200-meter and 500-meter [1500-foot] contours are shown, and from which it may be seen that the uplands consist of the continuous line of the Andes; the Guiana Massif; and the Brazilian Uplands (composed of those surrounding the Matto Grosso, and the great Caãtinga). The 200-meter contour shows how these would be connected if there was any slight lowering of the land or an uprise of the sea. The Caãtinga would still be joined to the Matto Grosso, and then both by a narrow land-bridge to the Andean chain. The Guiana Massif, which is the most isolated, would in turn be joined to the Colombian Massif by a lowland bridge.

The "spine" of the Andes runs just about down the middle of that colossal range. The important fact to grasp is that this forms a complete break between the forests of the Amazon and the eastern part of the continent on the one side, and the small patch to the west, on the Pacific slopes on the other. This latter small area, has a noticeably different fauna and flora from that of the east and the Amazon. It is terminated to the south on the Pacific coast by the southern deserts. ABSMs in South America are reported from both sides of the Colombian Massif, from the Guiana Massif, and from the Matto Grosso. [The Patagonian affair is, I believe, something quite else.] I have some extremely funny reports from the Pacific side of the Colombian block but, while the strangest things have recently been found there * and monstrous foot-tracks have been reported in the same area, there has not been any suggestion that any of the latter were humanoid. Colombian scientists have taken the matter of what they call "an ape" fairly seriously but all the talk has concentrated on the forests of the eastern slopes. It was once thought that

* I have for some years been interested in the reported existence of giant Earthworms in this area, based upon some correspondence and some extraordinary bas-reliefs on ancient pottery from that country. In 1956 and again in 1957, Mrs. William (Marté) Latham made trips to the Pacific slopes of the Andes and obtained numbers of these—5 feet long when contracted, and over 2 inches in diameter. Preserved materials of them is lodged with the Smithsonian Institute.

Pigmies, or ABSMs of the little *Orang Pendek* type had cropped up again in the Motilone territory in that area but, as Heuvelmans points out, a perfectly good Amerindian tribal grouping named the Marakshitos, averaging only about 5 feet in stature (like the central Mayas, incidentally), have been fully studied by the Marquis de Wavrin, while surrounding peoples admit that these are the "creatures" that they call *Guayazis* and which they regard as bestial. In the Colombian block, a man-sized kind has been rumored. This has been very greatly muddled and muddied by a most preposterous business about a photograph of a Spider-Monkey (*Ateles sp.*) for which the most extravagant claims have been made, and for which a number of serious-minded and otherwise highly critical people seem to have fallen.

As this matter has played such a prominent and, in my opinion, harmful and misleading part in ABSMery, I would like to try and dispose of it once and for all—or, at least, once again; for this has really been done several times already.

First, this picture produced by one Dr. François de Loys is obviously that of a Spider-Monkey which is a very distinct type of South American primate that may be seen in any zoo. It displays all the characteristics of that genus— narrow shoulders and pinched chest; comparative lengths of upper and lower arms and legs; the hands and feet in detail; and the enlarged clitoris of a female. In fact, it is a pretty clear picture of one of these animals—dead. However, of much more importance is the box on which it is perched. Anybody who has ever been outside a tourist hotel in the tropics will have run into the fuel problem. Since the discovery of petroleum oils, they—including gasoline and kerosene—have been shipped all over the world in pairs of 5-gallon cans, or rather light tins, fitted into cheap wooden cases, measuring exactly 20½ inches long, by 10½ inches from front to back, and 15½ inches high. The better grade boxes are bound with metal tape around the two ends. The case shown in de Loys picture is such an object, and stenciled lettering may be seen on it under the monkey's right leg. Such lettering is also standard and is usually stamped over two of the four 4-inch bits of board of which the sides are invariably constructed. Thus the animal, with its head poked up to an unnatural degree by a stick, measures about 27 inches [it measuring 10x:6x as against the box]. This is a fair-sized Spider-Monkey but not even a large one.

189

The original photograph is not just a case of mistaken identity; it is an outright hoax, and an obnoxious one at that, being a deliberate deception. I would have thought that anybody might have suspected this, even without seeing the picture, from the originator's story. According to this, he was threatened by this creature and its mate on the ground when in company of one of his assistants; shot it; photographed it; counted its teeth; and then—despite the fact that he was a man of scientific training, and considered his specimen so odd (though out of his field), as to warrant all this trouble—solemnly gave the head to his cook to boil, and permitted that worthy to employ the cranium as a salt container, which "dried up and was lost bit by bit." But worse than even this is a lot of mumbo-jumbo about having other photographs that were lost in a river during a flood. This is the kind of nonsense that has done more harm to the cause of any serious search for ABSMs, and other creatures as yet unknown, than anything I can name, and it is to be most utterly deplored.

Quite apart from anything, the picture alone, if analyzed, displays the creature shown, to be a maximum of 48 inches from crown to heel. This is indeed large for a female *Ateles* but is really substandard for large females of the northern *A. Beelzebub* group. Then again, gigantism is not uncommon among all the South American *Cebidae*. Finally, I may add, de Loys' photograph shows an animal that I would say had started to decompose and was well on the way to being "blown," a condition common in the tropics in daytime in a few hours, in which not just the body cavities but the whole body becomes puffy and bloated. Even if this should be a very large specimen of an as yet unknown *species* of Spider-Monkey (and even if, by some accident or deformity it happened *not* to have had a tail, which I very much doubt), there is no justification whatsoever for giving it a technical name on the strength of a single photograph, and especially one so grandiose, so misleading, and unscientific as *Ameranthropoides loysi* (Montandon) which means, literally "Mr. Loys' Ape-like American."

The harm done by this obnoxious effort has been widespread. Above all it has put the whole of ABSMery, in this area, into eclipse. No serious-minded person, zoologist or otherwise, seeing this ridiculous picture and having heard the equally ridiculous claims made by some for it, can be expected either to lend any credence to or even listen to the accounts of others who state that they have met unknown creatures of a Hominid form in this country. Yet, there have been some vague accounts thereabouts.

The earliest is that of the Baron Alexander von Humboldt, being a careful record of the local Amerindians' descriptions of a creature they called the *Vasitri* which, they said, constructed primitive huts, was carnivorous, and would eat men but carried off women for breeding purposes. There is nothing outrageous about this, for many ABSMs have now been reported to be carnivorous (at least at times), and their carrying off of women for reproduction is almost standard. [Something, incidentally, that all Africans that I have met who know and live among gorillas and chimps absolutely deny that those apes ever do.] Several other early writers are said to have mentioned the same creatures in this area.

Bernard Heuvelmans discusses an alleged encounter with an ABSM in this area by a Mr. Roger Courteville but shows that we cannot place any reliance upon it. The raconteur's description does include some odd items that are not otherwise to be noted in accounts from South America but which concur with, of all people, Mr. Ostman's description from *British* Columbia. These are: a tuft of thick hair running across the forehead; a powerful neck towering from a V-shaped torso; and long body-hair. However, the rest of the description, and particularly the "darting" blue-gray eyes, leave one in the gravest doubts. The only other definite information I have ever seen from this whole area is derived fourth hand from the Motilone Indians who are said to state that there is an "apelike" terrestrial creature in the Sierra de Perijaá, the scene of de Loys' exploit, and which is quite common. Thus, apart from the little *Shiru* amd the possibility that von Humboldt left us a record of something real, there is actually *no evidence* whatsoever for any ABSM in this whole area. Apart from one locality—the somewhat mysterious Guiana Massif, there is not, as a matter of fact much if any ABSMery in the whole of South America.

There is, however, the strange matter of "giant footprints" in Patagonia but I do not know of any proper investigation of these, either firsthand in the field or even bibliographic, ever having been made. From what I have been able to unearth it would seem that the imprints mostly refer to those of ground-sloths and in some cases those of the Giant Ground-Sloth (*Megatherium*) itself, which are altogether bizarre, since it walked on the outsides of its enormous feet. There has been a terrific rumpus about ground-sloths in the Argentine that has been going on for decades. A dried skin of one, found hanging over a fence on an estancia in 1898, led certain persons to prosecute a hunt for the animal, believing it still to be alive. This led to a cave in which strange stone corrals were found deeply piled within with the dung of these huge beasts, while other evidence seemed clearly to indicate that they had been penned therein by men. After considerable excitement promoted by the notion that some of the smaller forms at least might still be found alive, and after the discovery of early records by the Spanish colonizers to the effect that the local natives caught huge shaggy animals in pits and killed them by building fires on top of the hapless beasts [because their skins were so thick and filled with little bones that they could not be pierced with their primitive stone-headed weapons], the whole thing died down.

However, mixed up in all this uproar there were reports of giant footprints of a very humanoid form being seen all over Patagonia. There was a period during which there was much speculation upon the possibility of a giant race of Amerinds living in that region but this later became a somewhat debilitated notion—to wit, that some large indigenous Patagonians had large feet. It is true that some now almost extinct southern Amerinds were among the tallest races of men ever on record, and they seem to have been large all over.

Today, most of Patagonia is sheep country. It was cleared of its indigenous human population over wide areas by the simple and ingenious procedure of poisoning all the available wells and other available water supplies. It is now a vacation land for the more rugged "sportsmen" and it must be admitted that the best trout fishing in the world is there available. However, there still are some enormous areas of a kind of desiccated tangle of large bushes that somehow manage to grow in endless blankets upon utterly dry ground for mile after mile. In these it is quite possible that some smaller types of ground-sloth, such as that called by the aborigines the *Ellengassen,* might still exist; but of ABSMs there is no trace—reports of giant humanoid footprints notwithstanding.

Almost the same may be said of the Caātinga. Herr Sick, the author of the book mentioned above, makes some casual remarks about unknown animals possibly still remaining to be found in that desolation; but he also makes some very dubious remarks, such as that "desiccated *Hy-*

aena droppings may be found" there. Not even the ebullient Argentine Professor Ameghino suggested the presence of *that* group of animals in South America; so one must take all these statements with more than just the average grain of salt. But, when we come to the Matto Grosso, matters are rather different.

Here we hit something much more persistent and much more concrete. Not only are there endless accounts of giant human-type footprints and tracks, usually given as being some 20 inches in length, but there is the matter of the mass slaughter of cattle for months on end from time to time, by the extraordinary device of ripping their tongues out. These inexplicable excesses are reported to be accompanied by roarings so terrible that even the locals —who are profoundly Amerindian, be it noted—become very nearly hysterical. The perpetrators of these dastardly acts are, the locals assert, to be called *Mapinguarys,* and to them the locals attribute all manner of appalling qualities. In fact, we have here for the first time on our trip to contend with some real imaginative and traditional frills and furbelows. There is obviously a gross clash here between the perfectly prosaic Brazilian *estancieros,* with their modern herdbooks and statistics, on the one hand, and a local population of truly "superstitious natives" on the other. This clash has not been resolved to anybody's satisfaction, least of all the herd owners who are periodically rendered clean out of pocket by some hundreds of head of good cattle. The "natives" seem, every time that this has happened, to have adopted a sort of "We told you so" attitude. This is not very helpful, but the Brazilian Government apparently has had no better ideas.

The only known animal that can kill cattle in that part of South America is the jaguar, but these large cats don't, and cannot, go around tearing the tongues out of steers. They jump on their backs and break their necks by pulling their noses around with a forepaw—when they attack cattle at all. Try pulling the tongue out of, say, a dead rabbit sometime. You will find that despite one's enormous size compared to the rabbit, plus inborn finger dexterity, you will have one heck of a hard time. Pulling tongues out of oxen calls for both extraordinary hand dexterity and positively phenomenal strength. What on earth may have such strength? The locals say *"Mapinguary,"* and point to giant humanoid foot-tracks on sandbars. Cattle owners just fume and say "rubbish." This is obviously not getting the latter anywhere since this sort of thing seems to crop up every few years.

Nobody seems ever to have seen this ox-tongue-puller* but there is one story that Bernard Heuvelmans has dredged up from what can only be described as unimpeachable sources. With his permission I reproduce this in its entirety from his book, *On the Track of Unknown Animals*. This account was given to Dr. Heuvelmans by a correspondent, Senhora Anna Isabel de Sal Leitao Texeira, who obtained it from Dom Paulo Saldanha Sobrino, a much respected Brazilian writer with a very wide knowledge of his country. His informant was in turn the principal in the account; one known simply as Inocêncio. Heuvelmans writes:

In 1930 he went on an expedition of 10 men led by one Santanna. They went up the Uatumã towards the sources of the Urubú. When their boat came to an impassable waterfall they cut out across the jungle to reach the Urubú watershed. After 2 days they reached a stream which the leader decided to follow. Inocêncio was in the party going upstream, but after 2 hours' march he was led astray by a troop of black monkeys which he followed in the hopes of shooting one. When he realized that it would take him some time to reach the stream again, it was already too late. He shouted and fired his gun, but there was no reply except the chatter of monkeys and squawks of angry birds. So he began to walk almost blindly, feeling he must do something in such a critical situation until night fell, when he climbed into a large tree and settled himself in a fork between the branches. As it grew dark the night was filled with jungle noises, and Inocêncio rested happily enough until suddenly there was a cry which at first he thought was a man calling, but he realized at once that no one would look for him in the middle of the night. Then he heard the cry nearer at hand and more clearly. It was a wild and dismal sound. Inocêncio, very frightened, settled himself more firmly into the tree and loaded his gun. Then the cry rang out a third time and now that it was so close it sounded horrible, deafening and inhuman.

Some 40 yards away was a small clearing where a

* Just such sub-hominids were described by Col. P. H. Fawcett in 1914. See forth-coming sequel to this book. *Editor*.

samaumeira had fallen and its branches had brought down other smaller trees. This was where the last cry had come from. Immediately afterwards there was a loud noise of footsteps, as if a large animal was coming towards me at top speed. When it reached the fallen tree it gave a grunt and stopped. . . . Finally a silhouette the size of a man of middle height appeared in the clearing.

The night was clear. There was no moon, but the starry sky gave a pale light which somehow filtered through the tangled vegetation. In this half-light Inocêncio saw a thick-set black figure "which stood upright like a man."

It remained where it stood, looking perhaps suspiciously at the place where I was. Then it roared again as before. I could wait no longer and fired without even troubling to take proper aim. There was a savage roar and then a noise of crashing bushes. I was alarmed to see the animal rush growling towards me and I fired a second bullet. The terrifying creature was hit and gave an incredibly swift leap and hid near the old samaumeria. From behind this barricade it gave threatening growls so fiercely that the tree to which I was clinging seemed to shake. I had previously been on jaguar-hunts and taken an active part in them, and I know how savage this cat is when it is run down and at bay. But the roars of the animal that attacked me that night were more terrible and deafening than a jaguar's.

I loaded my gun again and fearing another attack, fired in the direction of the roaring. The black shape roared again more loudly, but retreated and disappeared into the depths of the forest. From time to time I could still hear its growl of pain until at last it ceased. Dawn was just breaking.

Not until the sun was well up did Inocêncio dare to come from his perch. In the clearing he found blood, broken boughs of bushes and smashed shrubs. Everywhere there was a sour penetrating smell. Naturally he did not dare to follow the trail of blood for fear of meeting a creature which would be even more dangerous now that it was wounded. Taking a bearing on the sun, he at last reached a stream and rejoined his companions, who fired shots so that he should know where they were.

I maintain I have seen the mapinguary [Inocêncio said

**to Paulo Saldanha]. It is not armoured as people would
have you believe. They say that to wound it fatally you
must hit the one vulnerable spot: the middle of the belly.
I can't say where it was wounded by my bullet, but I
know it was hit, for there was blood everywhere.**

I have heard many stories like this but, like Bernard
Heuvelmans, I feel there is something sincere about this
one. No; not just sincere; but factual. I have lived through
some much lesser experiences myself in the tropical rain-
forests that I could never have reported so pragmatically;
and there are junctures in the telling of this one that are so
frightfully "right." If the teller had wanted even to exag-
gerate he could so very easily have done so but he did not.
And yet, of course, it is ridiculous. But is it? There are still
those tongue-twisters to be accounted for, and their little
efforts are on the books. Do we therefore have a rather
rough race of the otherwise bland and retiring *Sasquatch*
—*Oh-Mah* type ABSM tucked away here in the soggy
wilderness of the Matto Grosso who somehow got cut off,
sometime, by a mass flooding of the continent that they
had strayed into? If puny little Amerindian Man came
over the Bering Straits and got right down to Tierra del
Fuego, millennia ago, there is no conceivable reason why
some more lowly type of Hominid may not also have done
so. Perhaps he got there before "the flood" as it were.

The Matto Grosso uplands seem to have been above
water for quite a long time but, according to their flora
and fauna today, which is not particularly odd, they do not
seem to have been so privileged as another area. This is
the great Guianese Massif. Here, if anywhere, is the place
where really ancient relics should have been able to linger;
and there are some real lulus that have done so there. It is
notable that the representatives of almost all the great
groups of mammals, birds, reptiles, amphibians, and especially of fishes and insects, found in South America turn
up there in strange and sometimes fabulous guises. There
are great numbers of living fossils in this area; creatures
like the Hoatzin or "Stinking Pheasant," a bird that, when
young, has a clawed finger on its wing, like an Archaeop-
teryx. This block of ancient mountains seems, indeed, to
have been a refuge from flooding throughout geological
ages—a sort of last retreat for wave after wave of creatures throughout time, driven out of their previous habitats
by shifts or submergences of the earth's crust. This is where
we would most expect to come across ABSMs if there are

any, or have ever been any, on this continent. And it is indeed from there that the most reports, and the most definite ones, have come.

In the Guianas—Venezuelan, British, Dutch (Surinam), French, and Brazilian—the name for these creatures is everywhere something like *Deedee* or *Didi,* with sundry prefixes and suffixes like *"Dru-di-di"* or *"Didi-aguiri,"* most of which mean something simple, such as "nasty" or "of the water." The whole concept is, however, as far as I was able to find out, very muddled in the native mind. This is probably because most of the current "natives" are not indigenous or in any way *native* to the country. It is only when you go among the now rapidly disappearing Amerinds—Caribs, Arawaks, and such—that you get any clear picture of this creature. Conversation with these folk is almost impossible as their languages are not known and are extremely difficult to apprehend. Also, they are naturally very cagey.

I first stumbled across this business when on my constant quest for animals which entailed endless patience in asking anybody and everybody about *all* the kinds of animals they had ever heard of. It was with the Primates—or monkey kingdom—that I kept getting information about more and ever more kinds that I had not yet seen. This started in British Guiana and went on in Surinam [then Dutch Guiana]. It seemed that there was no end to the kinds available and, to my great surprise, the locals were as good as their tales, for more and still more kinds were brought to us—or we were taken to them. I saw monkeys alive—and in captivity—in that country to which I could not and still cannot give even a familial name. And from quite early on we kept being told about these *Didis.* They lived way back in the hills, and they were pretty smart "Kwasi," which is the generalized name for all Primates in that area. Also, they had no tails, lived on the ground, had thumbs like men, and built crude bush-houses of palm leaves. They usually ran away but if a large party of men should penetrate into those completely uninhabited mountains they would come, a lot together, and throw sticks and mud at your canoe. So went the stories.

I never saw a *Didi* but then we never got really far into the uninhabited territory but I did come across some extremely large human footprints in the mud of a tiny side creek off a main river right up by the first cataract and 40 miles above the last known village. I put them down to visiting Jukas upriver to hunt, or to a band of roving

Amerinds—for there were still some in the district though nobody had seen them for over a decade—but I was mystified. I did not connect them with the *Didis;* but I have since often wondered. It is so easy to find plausible explanations of odd facts. Besides, some other dashed rum things happened at that camp.

The story of the *Didis* goes back to the first days of European exploration of the Guianas. Sir Walter Raleigh's chroniclers mentioned them; the early Spaniards said that the natives spoke of them; and in 1769 Edward Bancroft [*] wrote of them, saying that the Indians said they were about 5 feet tall, erect, and clothed in black hair. Once again also, the redoubtable Bernard Heuvelmans has brought to light some specific statements on these elusive creatures. These he gives us as follows:

> In 1868, a century after Dr. Bancroft, Charles Barrington Brown, who was then Government Surveyor in British Guiana, heard new rumours on the Upper Mazaruni on the Venezuelan frontier that a sort of hairy men lived there. Oddly enough, it was after hearing the "plaintive moan or howl!" which Ciezo de Leon also alleged these ape-men made.
>
> The first night after leaving Peaimah we heard a long, and most melancholy whistle, proceeding from the direction of the depths of the forest, at which some of the men exclaimed, in an awed tone of voice, "The Didi." Two or three times the whistle was repeated, sounding like that made by a human being, beginning in a high key and dying slowly and gradually away in a low one. . . .
>
> The "Didi" is said by the Indians to be a short, thickset, and powerful wild man, whose body is covered with hair, and who lives in the forest. A belief in the existence of this fabulous creature is universal over the whole of British, Venezuelan and Brazilian Guiana. On the Demerara river, some years after this, I met a halfbreed woodcutter, who related an encounter that he had with two Didi—a male and a female—in which he successfully resisted their attacks with his axe. In the fray, he stated, he was a good deal scratched.

* Called himself Jacobus Van Zandt, spied on Benjamin Franklin in Paris, and almost kept France from joining our War of Independence. He was a well-known botanist and naturalist, as well as a doctor!

In 1931 Professor Nello Beccari, an Italian anthropologist, Dr. Renzo Giglioli and Ugo Ignesti, made an expedition to British Guiana, where one of their secondary objects was to attack the problem of Loys' ape. For in this area the fauna, flora, climate and indeed the whole ecological pattern—what is now called the "biotope"—are the same as in the Sierra de Perijaá * and Beccari had read in Elisée Reclus's geographical encyclopedia that according to Indian legend the forests in British Guiana were haunted by fabulous hairy men called di-di, which all the Indians fear, although they have never seen them. But it was not until he was just about to return to Italy that he heard any definite information about where this beast lived.

On his return from several months in the interior, he met the British Resident Magistrate, Mr. Haines, who was then living on the Rupununi. Haines told him that he had come upon a couple of di-di many years before when he was prospecting for gold. In 1910 he was going through the forest along the Konawaruk, a tributary which joins the Essequibo just above its junction with the Potaro, when he suddenly came upon two strange creatures, which stood up on their hind-feet when they saw him. They had human features but were entirely covered with reddish brown fur. Haines was unarmed and did not know what he could do if the encounter took a turn for the worse, but the two creatures retreated slowly and disappeared into the forest without once taking their eyes off him. When he had recovered from his surprise he realized that they were unknown apes and recalled the legend of the di-di which he had been told by the Indians with whom he had lived for many years.

When Miegam, the guide of the Italian expedition, heard this story he remembered that he had had a similar adventure in 1918. He was going up the Berbice with three men, Orella, Gibbs and an American whose

* This statement is not strictly true. There are most marked botanical and zoological differences between these two areas, while their forests are completely separated by a wide belt of orchard-bush and open savannahs which form a barrier just as complete as if a sea. The Guiana Massif, moreover, is the more isolated in technical parlance, and has been so much longer and more often in the past. Sub-hominids and submen would be just about the only animals that could cross the open country but even modern forest peoples prefer not to do so.

199

name he had forgotten. A little beyond Mambaca they saw on a sandy beach on the river-bank two creatures which from a distance they took for men, and hailed them to ask if the fishing was good. The unknown creatures did not reply but merely slunk away into the forest. The four men were puzzled and landed on the beach, where they were staggered to find that the footprints were apes', not men's. Miegam could not say whether the creatures had a tail, but it could hardly have been conspicuous, or he would not have mistaken them for men. He did, however, say that two other settlers called Melville and Klawstky had similar adventures in other places.

Professor Beccari obtained further information about the di-di from an old negro at Mackenzie, famed for his wisdom, learning and experience. Everyone on the banks of the Demerara called him "Oncle Brun"—presumably he had come from French Guiana or the French West Indies—but the few Indians that survived in the neighborhood respected him so much they named him "The Governor." "Oncle Brun" had been told by the Indians that the di-di lived in pairs and that it was extremely dangerous to kill one of them, for the other would inevitably revenge its mate by coming at night and strangling its murderer in his hammock. Beccari did not trust the more fanciful part of this story, but felt that it must have a kernel of truth. Loys, like Haines and Miegam, had also met a pair, and so had Barrington Brown's woodcutter. Most South American monkeys live in largish troops, and this habit alone suggests that this is a very peculiar species.

The most significant single fact about these reports from Guiana is that never once has any local person—nor any person reporting what a local person says—so much as indicated that these creatures are just "monkeys." In all cases they have specified that they are tailless, erect, and have human attributes, even to building huts and *throwing* things. This is an altogether different matter from de Loys' asinine "ape." We are, in fact, once again, confronted with the strange fact that great numbers of people of all manner of tribes, nationalities, and even races, insist that ABSMs are wild men, as opposed to manlike animals. This is the one theme that runs consistently through all ABSMery.

9. Africa—the "Darkest"

SOME RUMOURS AND SOME
FLAT STATEMENTS

In some respects the continent of Africa has much the same structure as that of South America, but in reverse, or rather, mirrored, the Congo Basin being equivalent to the Amazon Basin; the great upland chain of its east side being comparable to the Great Andean chain on South America's west side; and there being a number of isolated mountain blocks dotted about the rest of it. However, if the sea flooded in to the 200-meter contour, Africa though looking a bit smaller would retain its present shape. Much more of it is composed of uplands above 500-meter contour; and upon these are raised many mighty mountain ranges. Yet, the Congo is like the Amazon in one essential respect. It also was once, and until fairly recently, flooded, but it appears to have formed either an enormous lake or a completely landlocked sea. Finally, it broke out to the Atlantic by cutting a deep and narrow gorge through the Crystal Mountains that join the lower Gabun with the Angolan uplands.

The Congo Basin today is the home of several very unique and ancient forms of animals—a strange Water-Civet (*Osbornictis*) found only once, in 1916, which seems since then to have vanished; the forest giraffe or Okapi (*Okapia*); and the famous Congo Peacock (*Afropavo*)—but, like the Amazon, it seems nevertheless to have been repopulated comparatively recently from the slopes of the surrounding mountain blocks, and all the funniest plants and animals in it tend still to be found around its edges rather than in its middle.

Then, there is another very important thing about Africa. This fact is that, actually, very little of it is forested, and especially by true lowland Equatorial Rain Forest (or T-E-F, as it is called). Apart from the Congo, there are really only two such areas; the west Guinea coast, and the Nigeria-Camerun-Gabun coasts. That over on the east coast is not typical T-E-F, and a lot of it is not even closed-canopy forest. Moreover, even on the west coast there are open areas within the main lowland forest blocks, while the center of Nigeria has now been almost entirely cleared, and there are large orchard-bush and savannah areas even in the Congo itself. This clothes the slopes of the mountains to comparatively great heights up the sides of all those blocks in the equatorial belt, which face those lowlands clothed in rain-forest. This is so of the south face of the Guinea block; both sides of the Gabun-Camerun block; the south face of the Ubangi-Shari; and a swath running south from the Bar-el-Ghazal to Kasai. It is in these forests that the more ancient and retiring creatures make their abode. They, also, are the least known parts of the continent (see Map X).

ABSMs have been reported from three areas in Africa —the southern face of the Guinea Massif; the east side of the Congo Basin; and the eastern escarpment of Tanganyika. This makes very clear sense both from a geographical and zoological point of view because each has an adjacent mountainous area as a retreat in case of general land subsidence or of flooding by the general sea level rising. The Gabun-Camerun west face might be expected to be included in ABSM distribution but it is not, so far as I know. Before coming to the details of the ABSMery hereabouts, I must point out a new factor in our history that now appears for the first time and which will be with us through the Orient, and until we go to Eurasia.

It is that we now have interjected into the scheme of things the *Apes*. There is a point here that puzzles everybody and which must be cleared up if possible. This is a hang-over from the initial pronouncement of Darwin's theory of our origin and that of Men generally. While it is pretty universally recognized that Darwin never did say that we were *descended* from apes, but that both we and the apes had a common ancestor, there is still an almost universally held belief that, nonetheless, "monkeys" came first, then "apes," and finally "men." This is partially correct in that the monkeys do seem to be of "older" stock and they are certainly more primitive or lower down the scale; but when it comes to apes and men, ever more evidence is piling up to indicate that we both started off at the same time; but out of step. Following this line of reasoning, the two lots of us were at one time very alike but, as time went on, and both our branches proliferated into various kinds, we drifted even farther apart. Just because some "men" (or, better, Hominids) retained a hairy coat and small brains, does not actually mean that they remained apelike. Conversely, just because the living apes still have a complete furry coat and small brains does not mean that they have *evolved* any less far from their origins than we have. They just have changed in other directions. And, along our lines, there were just such (probably) hairy chaps with very small brains—*vide: Zinjanthropus* from East Africa, and the other Australopithecines from South Africa.

Nonetheless, as of now—and if we preclude the possibility of ABSMs—the Hominids have changed a great deal, but lost all but one of their branches; while the apes have sort of got stuck, but still exist in about twenty distinct forms.* There is no reason, however, why there should not still be other kinds of *apes* still living today that we have not yet found. The Pigmy Chimp (*Pan paniscus*) was a long time being accepted; there is supposed to be a pigmy species of Gorilla of which we think we have skins and skulls, but which has never been seen by scientific collectors in the wild; and there is the extremely odd Lesser Siamang of South Pagi Island, of the Mentawi Group, off the west coast of Sumatra (*Brachytanites klossi*), that was not recognized till 1903. Then, in 1955, a professional American animal-collector brought back parts of a preserved specimen of a small kind of ape from the Gabun that is now lodged in the museum in Zurich, Switzerland. He also had photographs of the animal when alive, and it was certainly the oddest-looking creature; like a tiny orang-utan, with a high-domed forehead and quite unchimplike face, clothed in black hair, but having *no thumbs!* The collector insisted that the local natives know these animals well; that they are not chimps; and unlike chimps, they are completely arboreal, travel in parties of about 40, and never come to the ground. This specimen has been tentatively put down as an extremely abnormal baby chimp but it has a complete set of adult teeth!

There may indeed still be not one but several Apes (i.e. Pongids) to be discovered, and more than one in Africa.

* The popular belief is that there are but four living apes—the Gorilla, Chimpanzee, Mias (Orang), and Gibbon. This is not so. See *The Monkey Kingdom* by the author.

This tends to muddle the issue and more especially because many Africans regard the gorillas—though never the chimp, it seems—as a form of degenerate race of *men*. Thus, when they speak of any equivalent of an ABSM, they often do not make any distinction between man and apes in describing it. This, however, is particularly the case only with man-sized or larger alleged creatures. One and all are insistent that the pigmy types are little men, *not* animals. Therefore, we must be on guard from now on against interpreting all reports as those of potential ABSMs, and we must bear in mind that other apes—perhaps even bipedal, terrestrial forms—could exist on this continent and, though not so likely, in the Orient as well. Some certainly seem to exist in Africa.

Reports of what appear to be pigmy types of ABSMs turn up on the west and east sides of the continent—that is on the southern edge of the Guinea Massif and on the eastern side of the main upland area about Tanzania and Mozambique. Those from the former consist of a single series of statements made to Bernard Heuvelmans by a scientific correspondent who investigated some reports in what used to be the Ivory Coast. As these are original and unique, I have sought permission to reproduce them here in their entirety. Apart from them, I have only vague folk tales from the Nigeria area of the former existence of pigmies in that country.

In the Ivory Coast, almost at the opposite end of Africa, there is a legend of reddish hairy dwarfs identical in every respect with that in Tanganyika, as I learn from private information kindly supplied by Professor A. Ledoux of the Faculty of Science of Toulouse University. In 1947 he was the head of the Zoological Department of the Institute of Education and Research at Adiopodoumé, which was then being formed 12 miles from Abidjar.

One evening a young African who worked in his laboratory came and saw him after dinner and went rather furtively about asking him the simple question whether there were pygmies in Africa. The professor told him that they were found in Central and Equatorial Africa and lent him a book on the subject. All the same he was puzzled at this conspiratorial manner and asked him why he wanted to know. Because, the African replied, one of his colleagues in another scientific department of the Institute had seen one not far away on the previous day.

The professor raised his eyebrows.

"A pygmy, here?"

"Yes, about 500 yards from here."

The professor nearly fell out of his chair in surprise. The Institute was surrounded by forest, but though it was thick in places it was very well known and natives were constantly passing through it. The story seemed most suspect.

"Why didn't your friend come and tell me at once?" he asked suspiciously.

The young man explained that since the whites disbelieved the rumours about pygmies in the neighbourhood his friends had been loath to be laughed at or thought to be mad. But he knew the man well enough to know that he had not made it up, so he decided to make inquires for himself.

Professor Ledoux was more and more intrigued and insisted that the eye-witness should come and see him. He promised that he would not make fun of him and would not tell anyone his story.

The next day [the Professor tells me] I had a visit from the boy responsible for the observation. He was well-educated and had a certificate for primary studies. I asked him about the circumstances in which he saw the "pygmy."

It happened near the Meteorological set when they were taking their daily readings at 8 o'clock in the morning. Among the roots of a silk-cotton tree (Bombax) there suddenly appeared a little man with long reddish fur and long hair on his head—"same like white man" —but also reddish. [The long hair on the head, like a European's, was reported by all the Africans Professor Ledoux questioned. This feature could obviously not apply to true pygmies.]

At once the little red man and the large black one took to their heels in opposite directions. For, according to the legends, the little forestmen brought bad luck. You only saw them once in a lifetime and you had to be alone.

I went to the place with my two informants. It lay in the shadow of thick forest, but was not too overgrown since the silk-cotton tree grew near a path. It was very

205

likely that if there had been anything there it would have been easy to see.

I asked to be informed at once if a similar meeting occurred again, but this never happened.

Professor Ledoux admits that he was then very incredulous. It seemed unthinkable that within 12 miles of a big town like Abidjan, and 500 yards from huts inhabited by 6 Europeans and some 300 Africans, there could be unknown creatures in forest which though thick was far from virgin. Moreover the African who claimed to have seen the mysterious pygmy did not come from the Lower Ivory Coast but from the Middle Coast, which is wooded savannah country. Perhaps the great forest, which is most impressive, had over-excited his imagination. And in his solitary walks in the forest the professor had often put up bushbuck. If the African had seen the russet back of one of these antelopes among the bushes it was not impossible that his imagination should have led him to think that it was one of the "little hairy men" of the legends. At all events when the professor showed him a book containing pictures of Central African pygmies he insisted that his creature was not like them.

Despite his scepticism Professor Ledoux decided to make discreet inquiries about the native legends and what they were based on. He questioned several Africans who trusted him, and he pretended that he fully believed their stories, thus putting them at their ease and getting much more detailed information. In this way he came to visit most of the neighbouring villages.

As a matter of fact I did not obtain any important information, for while there were plenty of men who "had seen" (?) them, they were reticent on the subject, always concluding that they were probably mistaken for all the encounters had taken place at nightfall. This is likely enough.

There was one relatively exact fact. In March 1946 a team of workmen under one Djaco—who later became my lab-boy and my informant and who died of poisoning in 1949—together with a European of whom I can find no trace, were supposed to have seen one of these little red men, at about 8 in the morning, in a tall tree in a very wooded little valley about half a mile from the future site of the station. The European asked what it was and the Negroes explained what a rare thing it was to see such a creature and the evil effects of doing so.

I was at once deluged with stories of dwarfs with their feet back to front, people who lived half in the lagoon and half on land (I think that manatees must be responsible for this legend). These tales were of no interest to me, but I mention them so that the record should be complete.

He then questioned the Europeans who had travelled in the Ivory Coast.

One of them told me the following:

During one of his expeditions in the course of 1947 the great elephant-hunter Dunckel killed a peculiar primate unknown to him; it was small with reddish-brown hair and was shot in the great forest between Guiglo and Toulépeu, that is, between the Sassandra and Cavally rivers. Its remains disappeared while it was being carried home, no doubt having been disposed of by superstitious porters. Dunckel even offered to take my informant to the place and he in turn invited me to go with them.

In 1951 the professor's new boy, in reply to his usual barrage of questions, told him that when he was young, probably around 1941, he had himself seen a hunter at Seguéla bring back a little man with red hair in a cage. The local official had put clothes on it for decency's sake and sent it to Abijan by way of Bouaké. The boy did not know what happened to the little prisoner afterwards.

This tale seems to me to have been embroidered somewhat. If the creature was really human it would not have been put in a cage, and if it was an ape the official would not have worried whether it was decently dressed. Either it was a creature half way between man and an ape, or more likely, it was an unknown primate which had been dressed up as a joke, as tame monkeys so often are.

Professor Ledoux remarks that these tales of an unknown reddish-brown primate in the Ivory Coast are overlaid with the very firmly held belief that there are pygmies in the forest between the Sassandra and Cavally rivers.

According to an African technician of mine from Toulépleu called Méhaud Taou, an intelligent boy keenly interested in these questions, there was recently a system of barter between the negroes and these forest creatures; various manufactured goods were left in the forest in exchange for various fruits. This was supposed to have gone on until 1935. The little men who practised this barter were hardly known even to the negroes themselves. The Guérés called them Séhité.

It is possible that these Séhités may be true pygmies like those in Central Africa.

The professor's inquiries among the Europeans brought out a significant fact. Those who had never spent any length of time between the Sassandra and the Cavally denied out of hand that there could be any little men in the forest, whether they were true pygmies or unknown primates. On the other hand those who had lived in this area were seriously prepared to consider that pygmies might have lived there in the past and also that there might be a real basis for the legend of the red dwarfs. His own impression was that the legends and rumours in the Ivory Coast were based on the fairly recent presence of pygmies and the present existence of reddish-haired primates whose exact nature was still problematical.

The reports from the east side of the continent are more numerous and varied, and come from more separate sources. Central to these is a statement, that has been repeatedly republished, by one Capt. William Hichens in *Discovery* for December, 1937, included in an article entitled "African Mystery Beast." This goes as follows:

Some years ago I was sent on an official lion-hunt to this area [Ussure and Simbiti forests on the western side of the Wembare plains] and, while waiting in a forest glade for a man-eater, I saw two small, brown, furry creatures come from dense forest on one side of the glade and disappear into the thickets on the other. They were like little men, about 4 feet high, walking upright, but clad in russet hair. The native hunter with me gazed in mingled fear and amazement. They were, he said, agogwe, the little furry men whom one does not see once in a lifetime. I made desperate efforts to find them, but without avail in that wellnigh impenetrable forest. They may have been monkeys, but, if so, they were no ordinary monkeys, nor baboons, nor colobus, nor Sykes, nor any other kind found in Tanganyika. What were they?

Subsequent to the publication of this observation, a gentleman by the name of Mr. Cuthbert Burgoyne wrote to the publication *Discovery,* seconding Captain Hichens' story with the following:

> In 1927 I was with my wife coasting Portuguese East Africa in a Japanese cargo boat. We were sufficiently near to land to see objects clearly with a glass of 12 magnifications. There was a sloping beach with light bush above upon which several dozen baboons were hunting for and picking up shell fish or crabs, to judge by their movements. Two pure white baboons were amongst them. These are very rare but I had heard of them previously. As we watched, two little brown men walked together out of the bush and down among the baboons. They were certainly not any known monkey and they must have been akin or they would have disturbed the baboons. They were too far away to see in detail, but these small human-like animals were probably between 4 and 5 feet tall, quite upright and graceful in figure. At the time I was thrilled as they were quite evidently no beast of which I had heard or read. Later a friend and big game hunter told me he was in Portuguese East Africa with his wife and three hunters, and saw a mother, father, and child, of apparently a similar animal species, walk across the further side of a bush clearing. The natives loudly forbade him to shoot.

Once again Bernard Heuvelmans has brought to light two further reports, albeit brief. The first appeared in *The Journal of the East Africa and Uganda Natural History Society* in 1924, from the pen of one Mr. S. V. Cook. This states that:

> Fifteen miles east of Embu Station there rises from the Emberre plains the lofty hills of Dwa Ngombe, nearly 6,000 feet high. They are inhabited, the Embu natives say, by buffalo and a race of little red men who are very jealous of their mountain rights. Old Salim, the intrepreter at Embu, tells me with great dramatic effect how he and some natives once climbed to near the top when suddenly an icy cold wind blew and they were pelted with showers of small stones by some unseen adversaries. Happening to look up in a pause in their hasty retreat, he assures me that he saw scores of little red men hurling pebbles and waving defiance from

the craggy heights. To this day even the most intrepid honey hunters will not venture into the hills.

The final scrap of confirmation comes secondhand from Roger Courtenay who tells in his *The Greenhorn in Africa* a story related to him by his guide named—as is almost invariable, all down the east side of Africa—*Ali*. Using Courtenay's own words, this goes:

"But have you heard of the little people who live in the Mau—small men, who are less men than monkeys? Less than shenzi (i.e. loathsome foreigners), these little men, and almost monkeys in their lives and ways." And he went on to tell how his own father, who was driving his sheep to pasture on the slopes of Mount Longenot, fell into the hands of these gnomes when he went into a cave, following the trail of blood left by one of his cattle that had been stolen. He was stunned from behind, and when he came around he found he was surrounded by strange little creatures. "The Mau men were lower even," he told his son, "than those little people of the forest [the pygmies] for, though they had no tails that I could see, they were as the monkeys that swing in the forest trees. Their skins were white, with the whiteness of the belly of a lizard, and their faces and bodies were covered with long, black hair." To his great surprise the shepherd noticed that his spear was still lying at his side. "The Mau men who are so nearly monkeys did not know what was the spear. It is possible they did not know I could have fought with it and killed many of them."

The first reaction to reading these reports is, perhaps naturally, to suggest that all the reporters, both local and foreign, had stumbled upon a group of true Pigmies, the race of little men who are so well-known in the Uele District of the Congo, and at some other points about central Africa. It is true that the skins of these people are not by any means lacking in a fine, yellowish, downy hair, and that they also make a practice of painting themselves white or red for certain ceremonial purposes. Also, they are tiny and primitive enough to fit the bill. Further, there is no doubt that they were once very much more widely distributed almost all over Ethiopian Africa. Then also, we must remember that there was once—and there are some still living in the Kalahari area—also another completely different race of men that were spread all over the continent, and perhaps even into what is now Europe in the middle Stone Age. These are the yellowish-red-skinned Bushmen. Some of them are, and were, very small but have no body hair.

The Negroid peoples are apparently the most modern or newest development among human beings, and have very specialized characteristics. It seems that they did not even appear on the scene until just about the beginning of historical times, and their point of origin appears to have been about the headwaters of the Nile. Thence they spread outward in all directions possible but in two main streams, one to the west across the three Sudans; the other to the east and then south around the great lakes and down the eastern uplands. As a matter of fact, the Negro peoples only reached South Africa just about the same time as the white men did from Europe by the sea in the 16th century. These eastern tribes, by interbreeding with early Caucasoid types, produced first the Bantu peoples, and later the Hamitic. The former wheeled west and crossed the Congo, reaching the Cameroons. The tribes that went directly west through the Central and into the Western Sudan, encountered a different state of affairs. North of the Congo Basin, and all the way to the bulge of Africa to the west, there were no Caucasoids to intermingle with but there were apparently lots of peoples of the Bushman variety, living in the forests at a very low stage of culture. These, the Negroes did not absorb to any substantial degree. Instead, they either exterminated or completely enslaved them. This is a most important fact that is not customarily known about forest West Africa.

I was once greatly surprised when, upon inviting a whole large village of the Akunakuna tribe on the Cross River in Nigeria to gather for an evening of music and other festivities, to see the community drawn up in four very clearly separated groups; two in the foreground with the Paramount Chief and assorted Chiefs and Sub-Chiefs in front, and two other groups on either side, far behind. It was still daylight when they assembled and to our greatest surprise we suddenly saw that we were looking at two quite different peoples composed of: tall, dark-brown skinned Negro men, and sturdy tall women of the same cast of feature and skin color, *and* of very short, almost pigmy men, with pale reddish-brown skins, flat faces, broad noses, hugely everted lips and little bandy legs on

211

the one side, and a mass of tiny but very fat women of the same type and color on the other, all of whom had tremendous bottoms. Demanding to know from the local Headman "What be those?" and why everybody was not mixing it up in the truly democratic way, I was solemnly informed that, as I was not a government official, I would be pleased to know that those others were "slave-man." Slavery being absolutely taboo in that [then British] Protectorate, I sought further information and learned that there are whole enslaved peoples living within the body of many tribes in the general area, who are hewers of wood and drawers of water and with whom it is, and always has been, absolutely verboten to interbreed. These people were as good "Bushmen" types as I have ever seen.

We must therefore bear in mind that really extremely primitive peoples do still exist all over Ethiopian Africa, and that these have manifestly been either enslaved, or actually hunted by the tall, proud Negro peoples for centuries but still survive. Those not enslaved must be pretty wary and adept at concealment. Nonetheless, both the Sudanese in the west and the Bantus in the east seem to insist that such as the *Sehités* and *Agogwes,* though *men* all right, are even more lowly and ancient than those Bushmen-like primitives. I do not think that we have to go so far as to dredge up the Australopithecines to explain them [though that, of course, is by no means impossible] because there must have been innumerable races and subraces of men, submen, and apelike-looking men (or Apemen, if you will) in the intermediate 500,000 years. Relics of goodness knows how many races could still be lingering on in the montane forests of Africa. Let us not forget that it was not till 1910 that the second largest land animal in the world was found in Africa (Cotton's Ceratothere, or *Ceratotherium cottoni*)—a kind of Rhino —and the fabulous Okapi (*Okapia johnsoni*) turned up. The Congo Peacock had to wait till 1936! To say that there is no place where creatures, even of the size of pigmies, could still lurk unknown on this continent is outright stupidity, as evidence the arrival upon the zoological horizon this past year of the large *Ufiti*. This ought to be an object lesson to all skeptics.

This story broke in February, 1960, with a news report that sounded as wacky as any we have so far encountered. It read, in one version (*The Sunday Mail,* Zomba, Nyasaland, February 14, 1960):

Nyasaland game rangers, investigating reports of a "black, shaggy monster" seen in the forest region of Nkata Bay, Lake Nyasa, have discovered more than 30 mysterious tree-top structures in the area. In an official report, the Chief Ranger, Mr. Oliver Cary, says they are believed to be lairs [sic] built by these strange creatures. Known locally as "Ufiti"—the ghost of the supernatural—various reports have described the animal as black with long hair, a colorless posterior, no tail, broad-chested, and about 5 ft. tall. One was photographed recently by a Public Works Department employee, Mr. D. McLagen, in the vicinity of Limpasa Bridge which crosses a stream near Nkata Bay on Lake Nyasa in the Northern Province of the territory.

This is a very good example of the sort of report with which we have to deal as a normal course of events in ABSMery. It is nonetheless shot full of blather; so let us just look at it critically before we come to the windup of this story.

First, as usual, anything not previously and definitely known of the animal kind is invariably and immediately called a "monster." This is totally irresponsible and especially in a case like this when, as it turned out, the object involved was something that every foreigner should have seen many times in any zoo. Next, the designation of certain objects as "mysterious tree-top structures" is deliberately misleading. Why didn't the reporter state what sort of structures they were, and why they were mysterious? Birdhouses made of plywood, or Amerindian-type wigwams in Nyasaland *would* be mysterious, but these crude nestlike platforms of twisted branches and twigs were not—they were typical. Then, if the creatures were known locally by a perfectly good name, there was nothing really mysterious about the platforms. To call their makers' "ghosts" is going a bit far. Since when have ghosts been reported making treetop nests? But, when we contemplate the phrase *"the ghost of the supernatural"* one—at least one whose native tongue is the English language—stands aghast. Aren't ghosts supernatural anyway? Or am I mistaken? And what the heck is *the* ghost of the supernatural? What is more, the writer immediately goes on to call the thing an "animal" with a "colorless posterior"! What is "colorless"? Was the damned thing's fundament black, white, or yellow, like peoples' or was it just a great "nothing." "Words," as a famous British parliamentarian once said, "should convey meaning." Why this obvious axiom should not apply also to official reports and news-stories I cannot for the life of me see. Finally, we are informed that one was photographed; but no reproduction is attached to the story. Was the picture "classified"; was it so bad you couldn't see what it was; or was it so bloody obvious that nobody dared show it for fear of being called an ass. Or, alternatively, was it so clear but "out of context" that nobody wanted to admit it?

The whole story, as it was subsequently unfolded, is a classic; and it may well serve as an example of the functioning of the modern world in face of anything unexpected and frankly unwanted. It had the usual red herrings; some ridiculous, others most extremely interesting. The first were bandied about infinitely; the latter have been totally ignored. Then everybody, at first, said that it was a "native myth"; next, they got it as an animal; then they affirmed that it had run away from a circus [what circus in a patch of forest not previously penetrated in "darkest" Africa?]; and then the real "wipe" began. The "experts," having been confounded by the production of photos and the insistence of "authority" that the thing existed—they having said that it couldn't—could not "explain it away." This time, however, photographs seem to show clearly that the creature seen was a representative of a race of chimpanzees indigenous to this large patch of closed-canopy forest isolated from the nearest of their race, or any such forest by no less than 700 miles. [This conclusion has, nonetheless, been nicely covered by a firm order that, in no circumstances, is one of these creatures to be caught or killed for proper examination.]

This is all very well but it has a number of singularly unpleasant aspects. First, the natives thereabouts seem to have known the thing quite well and to have had a name for it; yet, the nearest whites and even the game people treated the thing as a "story." True, this creature, like ABSMs in many places, was only brought to light when the first road was pushed into this forest—shades of Jerry Crew—but then everybody indulged the most ridiculous folderol about "ghosts of the supernatural." * Then, the alleged photos had not been published. They arrived in

---

* I am wondering if by this expression the writer meant that a ghost of something invisible and probably nonexistent might, by inference, be presumed to be something visible and substantial. I cannot quite conceive of a ghost of a ghost.

Salisbury, capital of the Federation, on February 6 and were said next day to have "puzzled anthropologists and zoologists." We then get "A spokesman for the Victoria Memorial Museum in Salisbury" saying that the pictures were not sufficiently clear for positive identification. He pointed out, however, that "the picture [singular, this time] and description tallied with a Bushman painting found in the Ruwa region that had been thought to be a 'bear.'" [This is a near classic in that no bears now live in nor have any fossils of any one of them ever been found anywhere in Africa south of Morocco and Algeria.] Be that as it may, we then read on—and I quote from *The Rhodesia Herald*, of February 7, 1960:

An eminent Rhodesian zoologist, Mr. R. H. N. Smithers, of the National Museum, was able, even from the poor pictures available, to point out several unusual features. He said:

"From the statements I have heard from Nyasaland, and from the pictures, the animal would at first appear to be a chimpanzee. There are, however, two facts that do not support this contention. The animal has a distinctly muzzle-like face, while the chimpanzee has a flat 'pushed in' type of face. Secondly, the animal is, as far as I can recollect, more than a thousand miles from where it should be if it was a chimpanzee. The beast is obviously not a baboon, even though it has a baboon-like face, as baboons have tails and are not black in colour. In addition, a baboon does not have this animal's posture and bearing. Then there is the enormous size of the animal, which does not agree with either the chimpanzee or the baboon." Mr. Smithers said it was most unlikely that the animal was of a new species, and added that, if better photographs could be obtained as well as plaster casts of the feet, it would probably be possible to identify it.

Just what the worthy zoologist meant by "a new species" I cannot determine.

This is all very splendid but then history began to change. I have a set of press releases on the subject, issued with the compliments of the Nyasaland Information Department, P.O. Box 22, Zomba, Nyasaland, and numbered 28/60, 38/60, 51/60, 69/60, 73/60, 81/60, 93/60, and 106/60. These constitute ten legal-sized mimeod sheets of most fascinating reading. I wish only that I could reproduce them for you in full as they constitute a most exemplary public relations procedure and a most typical example of what a press officer has to contend with when dealing with "experts." Here is the whole story, told officially, starting with a report from two pragmatic Public Works Department officials on December 16, 1959, of "an unknown animal seen on a road" to a final pronouncement by two "game experts" from the Rhodes-Livingstone Museum on the following March 17, 1960. This last I herewith reproduce.

PRESS RELEASE NO. 106/60.
(Issued Wire & Telephone services)
UFITI STILL ELUSIVE

Zomba, Thursday.

Nyasaland's rain-forest monster, Ufiti, has been identified as a new sub-species of chimpanzee by two game experts from the Rhodes-Livingstone Museum.

Mr. B. L. Mitchell and Mr. C. Holliday, who are keeping the creature under almost daily observation, have not yet been able to obtain any photographs.* Ufiti remains as elusive as ever, vanishing as soon as she is approached, and thick bush and poor light add to the difficulties of getting clear pictures.

Ufiti, who is believed to be in season, has returned to her favourite observation point at the Limpasa Bridge after an absence of about a fortnight. The Chief Conservator of Forests, Mr. R. G. M. Willan, who is touring the area, was among several people who saw the creature when it reappeared near the road on Tuesday.

The two game experts, who are collecting photographs* and other forms of visible evidence, hope to arrange a bigger expedition to explore the whole rain-forest area.

It is unlikely, however, that any scientific expedition will be allowed to capture Ufiti for closer examination until it can be established that more of the creatures exist in the rain-forest.

Issued by the Press Section,
Nyasaland Information Department,
P.O. Box 22,
Zomba, Nyasaland   March 17, 1960

* Please note! (*Author*)

This would at first sight all appear to be more than satisfactory. For once, it would seem, the mystery has been explained, the "monster" identified, and zoological knowledge enhanced. But unfortunately and quite apart from the fact that nothing further has been done about anything, a number of most pertinent questions have either been left hanging or neatly buried. Let me dredge up some of these from the official releases first. For instance, in Release No. 93/60, we read the curious statement that "Although reports indicate that *Ufiti* is likely to prove a giant subspecies of Chimpanzee, her *pug* [sic] marks are said to be more human than animal. *She* is unusually large for a chimpanzee and her mouth is much smaller." Then, in Release No. 81/60 we find "*He* appears to be almost 6 feet tall with short legs and powerful arms, and most observers estimate his weight in the region of 150 lbs." In the same issue it goes on to say "Plaster casts of *its* hind footprints reveal *three* [italics mine] toes and a large thumb." I had better cut in here to point out a few items.

Either footprints were obtained or they were not; if they were, they were either more human, or more animal; but no human has only three toes and a large "thumb" on its foot, while gorillas and chimps have four toes and a widely separated and enormous big toe. Then, no chimp ever stood 6 feet tall, or even 5 feet; chimps of those dimensions being unable to stand on their puny hind legs alone. What is more, if this is a chimp, and of that size, it would weigh more in the neighborhood of 300 pounds, by the very construction of the beast. These are official conundrums. Others come from nonofficial sources. The first is in the form of a letter to the *Rhodesian Herald, of* February 24, 1960, from a Mrs. Ida P. Wood. This reads:

> **Sir,—Further to your article on the unknown animal photographed by "Lofty" McLaren, perhaps the following would be of use to you and to the authorities, who seemed doubtful of the identity of the beast. During an explanation to my houseboy on the picture of a tiger on a certain breakfast cereal packet, I told him that this animal did not live in Africa, and the animal he calls tiger was not in fact a tiger at all and that the one on the box was very strong. The word strong seemed to strike a bell because, cutting the story as short as possible, he asked me then, did I know the "Strong Man." After much hand-waving indicating height and breadth, and**

217

after being told that it was like a baboon only much, much bigger, I came to the conclusion he meant a gorilla.

I said, yes, I did know it, but had not seen one out here. He, it seems, had seen them in Nyasaland. He went on to describe them, said there were two kinds, a grey and a black one, the black being slightly smaller than the grey, about his own height to be exact, 5 ft. 8 in.–5 ft. 9 in. The boy comes from Nyasaland and says he saw the first black one in the forests near a village by the name of Nazombea in 1952. The other he saw in P. E. A. in 1953 by the village of Kurriwe.

Both these names are the Chinyanja pronunciation and the animals in Chinyanja are called Fireti. I questioned him closely about the possibility of the black one being a different kind but "no," he said, "they are the same, only one black, one grey, and only ever one at a time."

It makes a bed as a gorilla* does, large and untidy, usually sleeps in it only once, I suppose to eliminate the possibility of discovery.

I should be interested to know what the anthropologists interested in the previous article think of this information if you would be good enough to pass it on. Have the photographs been printed yet?

(signed)   Mrs. Ida P. Wood
Sinoia

This clearly indicates that these creatures *are* known in the area, and I have no doubt that a little ingenious and patient inquiry among the "benighted local natives" would disclose the fact that they have always been very widely known. I should explain that this business of "there is a black one and a white one" is almost universal in Africa and usually denotes marked sexual dimorphism, which is displayed by so many animals. [Incidentally in many parts of Africa only three colors are recognized— black, white, and red. The last is all the earth colors from deep orange, through all the browns to deep red. Everything, including blues and greens are either white or black according to whether they are in strong light or in shade. All shades of color are "so-so" red, black, or white.] This African's insistence that, although there are two kinds,

---

* How did Mrs. Wood (or her houseboy) know of this?— *Author*.

they are the same beast, would indicate that the differences are either sexual or due to age.

The other concurrent oddity was from quite another part of Africa, 1400 miles distant, and in an area from which we had not previously had any reports. This is actually a very astonishing report and one that should be taken most seriously in view of the almost constant surprises that are coming out of Southwest Africa and Angola. This part of Africa is rapidly assuming the guise of truly "The Darkest," for big game never even known to exist there is turning up, and among it are many record specimens, while it is the home of the otherwise nonexistent, Giant Sable Antelope, and so forth. This apparent ABSM was originally reported in the *Evening Standard* of Salisbury for November 18, 1959 but did not become fully recognized until after the *Ufiti* or *Fireti* affair broke. It reads as follows:

> **WINDHOEK, WED.—The authorities in South-West Africa and farmers in the vicinity of Outjo are wondering whether a large shambling ape or monkey which has been seen on farms near Outjo is not a gorilla. People who have seen the animal state emphatically that it is not a large baboon. According to their descriptions, the animal closely resembles a gorilla. Its footprints are also like those of a gorilla. A farmer, Mr. Thuys Maritz, who's Ovambo herdboy reported that the animal had stolen his blankets and food, tried to track the animal down but lost the trail over rocky ground. The spoor clearly showed that the animal walks on two legs. Occasionally, prints resembling knuckle impressions were found next to the spoor. The footprints are about 5½ in. wide and resemble marks made by a human hand. The five fingers or toes are clearly defined. The authorities have appealed to farmers not to shoot the animal but to try to capture it alive. The nearest place where gorillas are known to live is in the Belgian Congo, nearly 1000 miles from South-West Africa.**

Disregarding this report, and reverting to the *Ufiti* for a moment, it should be pointed out that there is something very wrong with the whole thing. I cannot bring myself to believe that game wardens, forest officers, and such other solid citizens could all have been absolutely ignorant of chimpanzees as specific animals. Had none of them ever been to a zoo where one was housed, or seen so much as a picture of one in a book? Even a fleeting sight of such an animal ought to have been enough for them to recognize it—if it *was* a chimpanzee. Zoologists and anthropologists ought, almost to the same degree, to have been able to spot such an animal from any photograph that displayed anything even approaching an outline. That any could be in doubt about the identity of a picture which was clear enough to ascertain that the animal depicted was *not* a baboon, is frankly amazing. There is nothing impossible in a sub-species of chimpanzee turning up in this forest and having been there all along though in several respects it might be considered unlikely, but there is absolutely no doubt about the footprint of an ape. It is utterly different from that of any Hominid. There can be no doubts here. The matter of the *Ufiti* is a most damning indictment of "the experts" for, from the published record on file, they would obviously then be shown not to know the first thing about their claimed specialties. I now have copies of the photographs mentioned together with some other most clear close-ups taken later. All, and even the foggiest, clearly shows a robust, and typical chimpanzee in very fine coat, either peering intently down from a tree in typical Pongid fashion, or standing stolidly on all fours in the preferred Great Ape stance. [No walking about on *her* back legs, mark you.] The photographs of two footprints, part of a track in soft earth, are at first rather startling as they look almost human but have only four toes. However, it is the photo not the prints that is startling for, viewed from other angles the "missing toe," namely the great one that is very widely—and properly for a chimp—separated is quite plain. This is a tale of woe but most important to our search, because it goes far to show just what appalling mistakes can be made, misconceptions built up, and fantasies conceived in a matter such as this.

When we come to the last great area for alleged "unknowns" in Africa we do not, thank goodness, have to deal with experts. However, we have to rely on travelers, big-game hunters, and other nonexperts who are sometimes almost as bad. [Oh, for the good old days of bulldozer-operators, and timber-cruisers!] However, there is one very bright gleam ahead and this—and almost for the first and only time—is a real, honest-to-goodness, fully trained, truly expert, and also successful professional "animal collector"; none other than Charles Cordier, the Swiss, who has persistently brought back to museums and zoos what they really want; properly housed and fed, or properly preserved. Here at last is a man whom we can not only rely on for common sense reporting, but who really knows his animals and his zoology, as well as a great part of the world. You may place more reliance on what he says than upon almost all of the rest of the involuntary and even the voluntary ABSM hunters combined.

This information comes to me once again from Bernard Heuvelmans who had just [at the time of writing] received it from Cordier who (January, 1961) was somewhere in the Congo. Charles Cordier wrote Bernard: "We met three tracks of hind feet—no knuckle marks—in soft mud near water. The tracks were most unusual," he says. Also, they were not those of a gorilla; and, Cordier goes on: "I ought to know, I have a silverback. These 12″ tracks were no gorillas." [The gorilla imprint should be compared with the photograph of one made in plaster see Appendix "A."] This find was made, as far as we know of now, somewhere in the Bakavu area. The track-maker is obviously some new form of large Pongid.

This brings up a whole new string of stories from less reliable sources. These begin with something that has been named the Tano Giant, and was first described by one, Louis Bowler, half a century ago. It has some funny features, and some illogicalities. It states:

Far away in the primeval forests of the Upper Tono, in the Gold Coast Colony, a strange tale is told by the natives of a wild man of the woods, which would appear from the description given to be a white ape of extraordinary stature and human instinct. The natives who live in the village near to the haunts of this freak of nature are terrified out of their wits. They barricade their doors at night, and place broiled plantains and cassava on the jungle paths leading into the village to propitiate him and appease his hunger. They declare he comes to the village at night, and only runs when fire is thrown at him. The women especially are almost scared to death, and go in a body to their plantain farms. It appears that two women while gathering plantains were confronted by this creature. One he seized and flung over his shoulder carrying her off; the other ran screaming with fright back to the village. No trace of the other woman has been found. Several children have been taken by this creature, their mutilated bodies being found with the whole of their bowels devoured.

221

The hunter and women who have seen this animal describe him as "past all man" in size; his arms they describe as thick as a man's body; his skin "all the same as a white man," with black hairs growing thereon. The hands have four fingers but no thumb, the head is flat, and, as they describe it, "left small for big monkey head," meaning that it was very near or like a large monkey's head. They say the mouth "was all the same as monkey with big teeth sticking out, and he carries a skin of bush cow," which the natives say "he carries for cloth when small cold, catch him," meaning he wraps himself up in it when feeling cold. A hunter tried to shoot him, but he smashed the gun and broke both the hunter's arms. Many other incidents are related of this terror of the Upper Plains.

The most outstanding aspect of this report is, to me, that once again it is of something definitely Hominid and that came out of a montane forest onto orchard-bush, as in the Southwestern case from Windhoek. This is indeed unusual. The other outstanding fact is the mention of the absence of a thumb. I understand that it is believed that the thumb of *Plesianthropus* was exceptionally small for the size of its hand, and was placed very high up on that hand. Is it possible that it might have been carried pressed against the side of the palm and so not be apparent? The fact that this creature was alleged to have a light skin covered with black hairs is also novel. The whole account is actually more than just aggravating in several respects because it stands absolutely alone as far as I have been able to find out. Naturally, one presumes that it is but a traveler's tale picked from native imagination to give it a tone of authenticity; yet, among such tales—and I have hundreds—it is one of the few that seems in some way to have validity.

Perhaps this is because I got to know the West Africans rather well myself once; and, while I fully appreciate their great storytelling abilities, I did find them essentially most down-to-earth people when it comes to the question of their native fauna. West Africans told us some of the wildest-sounding things about their local animals but, in almost every case, they made good on their words by producing the darned things. They are not the sort to think up "thumblessness," a white skin, or a head "left small for big monkey head." If they said that—and these purport to be firsthand accounts, not traditional tales—they meant it, and precisely. The disemboweling of the children also seems to smack of the real thing. I know just what the teller meant to imply: namely, "Don't try and tell me this was a leopard because I know, even if you don't, that that is not the way they start to eat you."

The only other African ABSM that has been mentioned, and this several times, and by several different travelers, is the *Muhalu*. This is a muddled issue as may be seen from the following extract from the book *Hunting We Will Go* by Mrs. Attilio Gatti. This reads as follows:

> Then there are rumors about strange anthropoids. One is a large ape which is said to live in the Rainy Forest, the pygmy tribes call it the Muhalu. Commander Attilio Gatti, the well-known African explorer, has repeatedly declared that he, for one, believes in the existence of the Muhalu and willingly accepts the descriptions of the pygmies who say that it is exceptionally large, walks erect habitually, and is covered with very dark, possibly black, fur, except for the face, where the hairs are white.
>
> Another again, and the worst of all, is a big animal with a coat of long hair, black on the back, white on the other parts of the body. And it is enough to be seen by this monster, for one to die in the most atrocious agony.
>
> We found awaiting us a man from Soli's to say that the pygmies had been on the trail of a Bongo mother and young one, and that if the Bwana would come they were sure they would capture the little one.
>
> So Tille decided to have one more fling. He also decided to take a group of our own boys with him to act as porters. Before they could start, however, an event occurred which reduced all Kalume's men to panic.
>
> Ever since we had been in the Ituri we had heard repeated tales and rumors of a great animal called by the Bondande, "muhalu." Of all things that could arouse terror, this muhalu was the King Bee. Tille had been extremely interested in the matter and believed that the creature really did exist and was a hitherto unknown fifth anthropoid or subhuman.
>
> At this time, however, he had done no more than talk about it now and then. Now, on this morning, one of our men rushed into the clearing, his face gray with fright, babbling about the dread muhalu. His stories were conflicting. First he said it had knocked him down, and this seemed odd because the natives firmly believed

that a muhalu had only to look at a man and that man would instantly die. Then the boy said he had seen the muhalu first and ran away. No matter what had actually happened, the news that a muhalu was in the vicinity nearly paralyzed our men.

Tille insisted on going to investigate at the point where the boy claimed to have seen the beast. I don't know how he succeeded in dragging that boy, half-dead with fright, or in flicking the pride of Lamese and two of the other men until they agreed to accompany him.

He did find enormous footprints, and several stiff black hairs in the hollow of a tree where the evidence showed the brute had been sitting. Neither hairs no print corresponded to any other known ape.

But the panic of our natives had grown so fast that Tille could not stem it. Even Kalume begged us, with all his heart, to leave Tambehe and come down to his village. All of our natives, though they had no wish to abandon us, were preparing to leave.

In this area, namely the southern face of the Ubangi-Shari Massif, it would seem that we have to deal with two quite separate entities—one an unknown Pongid, and another a Hominid, or ABSM. Despite the rather obvious exaggerations of the descriptions given by locals—and notably by the Pigmies, with whom it is extremely difficult, if really at all possible, to communicate—neither appear really to be too outrageous. Perhaps one is the terrestrial ape that leaves the odd prints now recorded by Cordier, while the other is something akin to the Tano Giant. There are a set of tracks recorded from Bakumu which the locals say were made by what they call the *Apamandi*, which they there describe as a very heavily built small man, clothed in black hair, but having a light skin. These prints are approximately eight inches long, very short and broad, and have the strange distinction of having the second toe longer than either the first or third, and being somewhat separated from the first or big toe. The significance of this toe proportion will become apparent when we come to investigate the *Meh-Teh*, or Snowman of the Himalayas.

The accounts of these two [or is it but a single] creatures are very vague, fragmentary, and rare. Yet, if you visit the northwestern edge of the Ituri Forest you will find that it (or they) are taken quite for granted as being rare, but by no means excessively rare, units of the local fauna; living in the upper montane forests to the north, and from time to time coming down on to the lowlands. I have talked to many people who have been into this, previously unadministered, area but only those who were specifically interested in its fauna, or who spent time investigating the ideas and knowledge of the locals, had ever heard of it. Those who did so, however, all seem to be of the opinion that there is a race of gorilla in the area, or that there is at least some large terrestrial ape there. When I asked if, in their opinion, it could be a primitive Hominid rather than an advanced ape, the opinions have been violently divided. Most returned my query with a perfectly blank stare; but some said "Yes" and invariably went on to talk about the possibility of some larger form of Australopithecine having survived thereabouts—and they usually pick on *Plesianthropus,* probably because that form has been so well publicized, along with reconstructions of it.

Africa is undoubtedly the land of Pigmies and of some Great Apes, but it does not seem to sport any giant Hominids. At least the Africans don't imply this, even if they do refer to the Tano character and the *Muhalu* (or one of them) as being very big. Our real *Oh-Mah* types would be the perfect target for African bogeyman stories, but they just don't appear here, and we shall not meet them again until we reach just the place where they ought to be.

10. The East—the "Mysterious"

REPORTS FROM SUMATRA AND THE MALAY PENINSULA

We are now going to make a major hop across an ocean, from East Africa to what is commonly called the Orient, and specifically to southeast Asia. This may look like, and in point of fact is, a long hop spatially, and it may seem doubly exaggerated because we are going also to skip over all that lies between the two points specified, such as Arabia, India, and Ceylon, though they manifestly form sort of steppingstones along this route. This is nevertheless justified on more than one count.

First, there is no current ABSMery to be discussed in those intermediate areas, though there is quite a lot of myth, legend, and folklore, especially in Ceylon. Second, geologists tell us that there was once a great land-connection between the two extremes (Africa and southeast Asia), which they have named Gondwanaland, and it is obvious that lots of primitive animals still living today are represented by different but either comparable or obviously related kinds on the two sides of the Indian Ocean. Whether individual examples of these emigrated from one side to the other, or vice versa, is no concern of ours, but it is certain that there was from very early times such a connection between the two sides of this ocean. A good example is the Lorisoid Lemurs of Africa, and of the Orient *; another is the flightless birds called Ratites, including the Ostriches (*Struthio*), on the one hand, the Emu (*Dromiceius*) and the Cassowaries (*Casuarius*) on the other. Then again, the Great Apes are found on both sides, as are different forms of the very specialized Leaf-eating Monkeys or Coloboids—the Guerezas in Africa;

---

* The Pottos (*Periodicticus*) and Bushbabies (*Galago*) of Africa and the Lorises (*Loris*) of the Orient.

the Langurs in the Orient. These each represent different ages at which this land connection existed.

Primitive men and the Hominids generally, seem also to straddle this ocean. Whether the land-connection still remained above sea level when the most primitive of the latter were evolved—such as the Australopithecines of South Africa, and the Pithecanthropines of Indonesia—is not yet known, but it is almost certain that it did not do so when the first races of True Man were spread all over both sides (or, alternatively, passed from one to the other). These most primitive peoples are today the Pigmies of which there are representatives in forest Africa, on some Indian Ocean islands, in the Massif on the Malay Peninsula, and in the Philippines. [It should be noted that the pigmy people of the west end of New Guinea are now thought to be merely "pigmy" breeds of the otherwise tall Papuans of that island.] These little people have much in common on both sides of the Indian Ocean, and they are now thought to constitute a real sub-species of the human race.

These Pigmies are indeed primitive, but even they say that they were not the first people in the countries they now inhabit, and the Semang of Malaya state that there remain some living representatives of these still earlier people in their country. Malays call these "Devil Sakai," * (Hantu Sakai) and say that they live in and move about through the trees; an astonishing statement since the Senoi also readily take to the trees, and are highly agile therein. There is evidence that these proto-Pigmies [which simply means, Those-who-were-before-the-Pigmies] once were spread very widely in East Africa, southern Arabia, India, Ceylon especially, and throughout Malaya and Indonesia. We will find allusions to them cropping up all the way through our story for some time from now on and we must watch out for them because in this area (i.e. eastern Orientalia; namely, the whole of that subcontinent apart from India and Ceylon) there is really no clear line of demarcation between fossil sub-hominids that *are* known, really primitive Men, and what we are calling in this book ABSMs.

This is a point that I would like to stress forthwith. On account of that awful expression "the abominable snowman" and all the fuss that has been made over "it" in

* The term *Sakai* means degenerate and is not the real name of a people and is also applied to the Vedda-like *Senoi* of Malaya.

the Himalayas, not only the popular concept of such creatures, but our whole thinking from a purely scientific point of view also is colored by a picture of some mythical exaggeration pounding about on a snowfield, ripping apart yaks or hapless Sherpas. Actually, if one comes to examine the matter more closely, and in its entirety, as we are trying to do in this book, it should be apparent that what we are dealing with is really the whole history, past and present, of the Hominids, and the origins of Man per se. Frankly, our term "ABSM" really means *hominid, other than known kinds of modern man;* no more and no less; and it is my firm belief that in due course, the whole business will be lifted clean out of the "mystery class" and simply become a part of physical anthropology. Even if no example of any of the (as it now seems) dozen or so ABSMs is ever caught, I further think it will be found that all which has been reported upon them throughout the world may legitimately be taken into consideration in trying to reconstruct the past history of man, and fill in some of the vast gap in that history that at present lies between little *Oreopithecus* of the Miocene coal strata of Italy and, say, the Bushmen or the Pigmies. Moreover, it is in this Oriental Region that we are going to come closest to the chain of stages that linked, and that still links, those two extremes.

Our first port of call in this new region is perhaps one of the oddest, oldest, and from a zoologist's point of view, the most exciting in the world. This is the southwest portion of the great island of Sumatra and a string of islands off its west coast called the Mentawis. The whole of Sumatra is odd in several respects and not entirely due to its enormous size, dense forests, comparatively small human population, and virtual neglect throughout history. It, with the foot of the Malay Peninsula, Java, Borneo, and some associated smaller islands [and possibly Palawan, which is usually grouped with the Philippines] forms a zoogeographical sub-area with most special aspects (see Map XIII). Not only does this sub-area contain elephants, rhinoceroses, tigers, and other mainland Asiatic animals, it has some even odder and more ancient animals—the Malayan Tapir, the Orang-utan (or *Mia*), the Siamangs, the Tarsiers, and the little, most primitive of all living Primates, the Pen- or Feather-tails (*Ptilocercus*). Actually, the list even of mammals is extraordinary, and there are here unique birds, reptiles, amphibians, fishes, and invertebrates of all kinds. It is a sort of leftover land to which all manner of creatures have at times of climatic change, crustal shift, or oceanic flooding, retreated. But, within this limited area, there is an even more peculiar sub-sub-area. This is the Mentawi Island chain and the immediately opposite Barisan Mountains of southern Sumatra (see Map XIV).

Here there are absolutely unique and really very strange animals. To exemplify, I need mention only what is called the Mentawi Islands Langur, and the South Pagi Island Pigmy Siamang. The first is not really a langur monkey at all but a short-tailed Snub-nosed Monkey (named *Simias concolor*) that constitutes a genus all by itself and which is completely unlike anything known anywhere else. The Pigmy Siamang (*Brachytanites klossi*) is a diminutive ape, classed with the Gibbons and standing somewhere between them and the much bigger and more "advanced" Siamang (*Symphalangus*) of mainland Sumatra and Malaya. It seems in fact that this bottom bit of Sumatra is a retreat within a retreat, and the animals which retreated thereto are usually relics. You will notice from the map that the Barisan Mountains, though continuous with the Boekits and the rest of those of west Sumatra right up into Achin, are coastal. Also, they culminate in the northwest in Mount Marapi, north of Padang, beyond which there is a distinct break. The flora and fauna of the Barisans has more in common with the Mentawis than with the mountains of northern Sumatra. [Eng-gano Island is even more odd.] This sort of fossil attic is the headquarters of a group of Oriental ABSMs and notably one that is called locally the *Sedapa* or, in kitchen-Malay, the *Orang Pendek* (Little Man) or *Orang Letjo* (the Gibbering Man).

Here, we come to a pretty problem. There is spread all over what is called by zoologists the Malaysian Subregion—i.e. that described above as encompassing the foot of the Malay Peninsula, Sumatra, Borneo, and Java—a wealth of folklore concerning not just this *Sedapa,* but also a man-sized ABSM, and, in Sumatra, a giant type called very simply and logically the *Orang Gadang,* or Great Man. This folklore is very specific. In Java, it is buried, and deeply so, in pre-Hindu mythology; that island having been so highly civilized and so thickly populated for so many millennia that, although there still remain in it some really wild areas and even relic animals such as a special rhinoceros, any primitive hominid that may have lingered there since the time of *Pithecanthropus* and *Meganthropus* was long since exterminated. Borneo, on the other hand, has remained very wild and forms a special case. It too has its zoological oddities (like the Proboscis Monkey) but not apparently even any folk memories of ABSMs[1] —though a very strange story of one such having arrived there not too long ago on a boat as a captive of pirates was published! Sumatra and Malaya proper, on the other hand, are rife with not just hints but most definite reports of at least three kinds of primitive hominids or ABSMs.

The Philippines constitute another zoological sub-area; and the Celebes and their associated islands, still another. Both have unique animals, and the latter, though lying on the Australian side of Wallace's Line, the great divide between that continent and Asia, has a mixture of marsupial mammals and other typically Austral fauna and forms with obvious Asiatic affiliations. Among these are the small black baboon, known as the Black Ape (*Cynopithecus*), and two species of a Macaque Monkey (*Maurus*). Of ABSMs there are none reported from either of these sub-areas, but there are genuine Negrito Pigmies in the Philippines, and there are constant references to "men with tails" from there and especially from the Island of Palawan. The whole question of tailed hominids is a sorry subject and has been going on throughout the ages. Many peoples have attributed tails to their neighbors or more distant foreigners with the sole implication that they were a lowly lot of rascals. Others mistook crude accounts and pictures of monkeys for lowly forms of humans in other lands. Finally, people are sometimes born with fairly decent tails. [There was a very nice fellow at school with me who had a 3-inch job clothed in reddish-brown, fine hair about an inch long.] This is said to be an "atavism." This is hardly the right word for it, as it would then be a throwback to the time before either apes or men got started.

Let us, then, return to Sumatra and investigate the matter of the *Sedapa*. The existence of wild men in this island has been rumored since ancient times. It was mentioned by Marco Polo [though he also has tails on the brutes, and naked ones at that]. Its existence was first definitely reported by an Englishman named William Marsden who was resident at Benkoelen on the west coast of Sumatra in 1818, but it was not till this century that definite reports were made by Westerners. As everywhere else, both the veracity of the reporters and the possibility of the existence of any such creatures was heatedly denied

---

[1] A flood of reports, however, emanated from Borneo in 1967.

by just about everybody who did not reside in Sumatra, and particularly by those who had not ever been there. This attitude to the matter was taken to great extremes by the Dutch curator of the museum at Buitenzorg in Java, Dr. K. W. Dammerman. Most, but not all scientists followed his example until World War II. Then, when Indonesia gained her independence, there was at first a very noticeable change in opinion, especially as displayed in the Indonesian press. However, the general attitude has reverted to type more recently, so that the present professor of anthropology at the university at Djakarta wrote to my friend Prof. Corrado Gini of the Institut International de Sociologie in Italy, stating flatly that the *"Orang Pendek* is only a variety of the Orang Kubu, a primitive people, quite human in character, of whom the Indonesian Government takes special care."

While I am glad to hear of the Indonesian Government's special concern for the Kubu, something that must be somewhat difficult to exercise in the political circumstances, I would point out that while Sumatra is Indonesian territory, the Indonesian Government is actually Javanese and really knows extremely little about Sumatra—rather less, in fact, than the Hollanders once did. Also, I am not interested in the Kubu people who have been well known for centuries but rather in the Orang Gugu. The Kubu are not hairy; the Gugu *are* said to be, whether they exist or not. As Marsden first clearly pointed out, the Kubu are hairless humans at a primitive stage of culture but great hunters, and live in the Barisans. The Gugu are not human, were even then very much rarer, and lived in the depths of the montane forest, and had no language. The Malayan peoples of Sumatra called them by various native names such as *Atu, Sedabo,* or *Sedapa.* They often appended their word *pendek* or *pendak* to these to indicate that they were refering to a small one, of two—the other being *gadang,* which simply means large.

On the validity of the *Sedapa* I cannot offer anything but the accounts as published. That such a creature could exist is not only quite possible but, I think, almost probable —and especially if the local native and indigenous peoples say that it does—and the Barisan Mountains area is just the place where the ancient forms of Hominids might most likely have been able to survive. As we shall see, there is no dearth of candidates for the *Sedapa* along the Hominid branch of the family tree; and then, we have the near presence of the Pithecanthropines of Java. Also, the existence of the Malayan Tapir (*Tapirus indicus*), whose sole remaining relatives live in tropical America, shows just how safe a retreat this corner of the world really is. When it comes to "available space" for any such creatures to live more or less unseen, words almost fail me. I spent many happy months wandering about Sumatra in my youth accompanied by an Achinese (with the very sensible name of Achi, as it happened) and all I can say is that its forests put most others in the world to shame, and they seem just to go on and on forever. The known population is comparatively minute, and the amount of the country that is opened up is quite minor. Apart from the rivers, the great swamplands are not penetrated at all; the lowland forests are tall and dense, and the montane growth is intolerable.

The history of the *Sedapa,* as far as the Western world is concerned, is due mostly to the researches of Drs. W. C. Osman Hill of the Zoological Society of London, and, once again, Dr. Bernard Heuvelmans of Paris. There were certain Hollanders who somewhat earlier devoted themselves to the pursuit of this matter in Sumatra. Notable among these was a Dr. Edward Jacobson, who first brought the subject up in *De Tropische Natuur* [once published in Weltevreden, Java] in an issue of 1917. However, Dr. Jacobson's investigations went back to 1910 and it was under his aegis that some facts collected by Mr. L. C. Westenek, once Governor of Sumatra, came to light. The earliest of these is the report of an overseer of an estate, who was staking out a newly acquired and large tract of virgin land in the Barisans near a place called Loobuk Salasik. This man left a carefully worded written statement. This was that, at a distance of only 15 yards, he saw "a large creature, low on its feet, which ran like a man, and was about to cross my path; it was very hairy and it was not an orang-utan; but its face was not like an ordinary man's. It silently and gravely gave the men a disagreeable stare and then ran calmly away. The workers ran faster in the other direction." The overseer remained where he stood, quite dumfounded.

The significance of this statement centers around the definite statement that the creature was *not* an orang-utan, that it stood on its hind legs and ran on the ground, and that it was "low on its feet." This latter seems to indicate that it had short legs, which is really another way of saying that it had overly long arms in proportion to its torso and legs; and all this, in turn, emphasizes that it was not an orang-utan; an animal that, except when young, cannot even walk on its hind legs alone. Dr. Jacobson became greatly interested in this matter when camping on the slopes of Mount Kaba in the Boekits in early July, 1916. Two hunters came to him there one day and said that they had seen a *Sedapa* breaking open a fallen tree at a distance of only some 20 yards from them. It was apparently looking for beetle larvae—a delicacy relished by many peoples the world over—but when it realized that it was being observed, it ran off on its hind legs. Otherwise, this description agreed in every other respect with the traditional one of the *Sedapa*. It was clothed all over in short, black hair.

I should point out here, and rather strongly, that the larger Siamang, a really big and sturdy ape, intermediate in many respects between the Gibbons and the Great Apes, though highly adapted for life in the treetops, quite often comes to the ground upon which it runs along on its hind legs, swinging its arms instead of holding them aloft as the gibbons do when *running* as opposed to just walking. Also, I have myself come across Siamangs going meticulously over fallen rotten logs collecting the insects that often crowd into their cracks. I owned a Wow-wow Gibbon (*Hylobates moloch*) during the whole year that I was in Indonesia. It had been raised in a human family and it traveled all over the Indies with me. I happened to be collecting insects on that trip, and the majority that I obtained were actually found, caught, and then handed carefully to me by this small anthropoid companion. It used to run ahead on its hind legs in the forest, holding its long chain off the ground with one hand, and upon locating a rotten log climb aboard and start probing into all the cracks with its long forefinger [he was left-handed] and producing all manner of rare specimens that I simply never could find by myself. It was uncanny, as was the manner in which he used to offer me the first and all subsequent ones of the same kind until I indicated that I had enough specimens: then he ate the rest. Gibbons may be Pongids but they certainly are "almost human" in many respects. The related Siamang is almost more so; and, in fact, the Malays often treat them as such.

Later, Dr. Jacobson was shown tracks of the alleged *Sedapa* on Mt. Kerintji. These were definitely not those of a gibbon, siamang, or any other ape, all of which have a widely opposed and very large great toe; it was exactly human but tiny, very broad and short. Quite a number of alleged *Sedapa* footprints have been recorded. These vary rather bewilderingly. In 1958 some plaster casts of some prints were obtained about halfway between the Siak and Kampar Rivers by Harry Gilmore. These, however, are almost undoubtedly those of the small, Malayan Sun-Bear (*Helarctos*). This animal stands erect and even walks along, though it never runs, on its hind legs more frequently than any of the other bears. It is about 4 to 5 feet tall, is covered in short black hair, and has surprisingly broad shoulders. It may even swing its arms when walking. Also, it has a pale face which, when seen head-on in the poor light of the high forest floor, may give it a startlingly human look—I know, I was nearly scared out of my wits by these animals, standing silently watching me, on more than one occasion. The hind footprints left by this animal are nonetheless fairly distinctive and are not like the drawings, tracings, and cast taken of alleged *Sedapa;* like all bears, their toes increase, albeit in this case only slightly, in length from both sides to the middle toe; they are packed together, not splayed; and claw marks are almost invariably present. The Siak River, moreover, is somewhat out of the range of the *Sedapa* proper, though there is plenty of tradition about it in those parts.

In 1917, according to Westenek, a Mr. Oostingh, while in the Boekits and near the same mountain where Dr. Jacobson had been when the hunters said they saw a *Sedapa,* became "bushed." He wandered around in circles for several hours, as one invariably does if one gets lost in high forest. Suddenly, as his account goes, he came upon what he thought was a local man sitting on a log with his back toward him. Overjoyed to see any human being, as one also invariably is when so exhausted, he went forward but then got a profound shock. I let him tell about it in his own words, as taken from Westenek's account in *De Tropische Natuur,* and translated by Richard Garnett. This reads:

I saw that he had short hair, cut short, I thought; and I suddenly realised that his neck was oddly leathery and extremely filthy. "That chap's got a very dirty and wrinkled neck!" I said to myself.

His body was as large as a medium-sized native's and he had thick square shoulders, not sloping at all. The colour was not brown, but looked like black earth, a sort of dusty black, more grey than black.

He clearly noticed my presence. He did not so much

as turn his head, but stood up on his feet; he seemed to be quite as tall as I (about 5 feet 9 inches).

Then I saw that it was not a man, and I started back, for I was not armed. The creature calmly took several paces, without the least haste, and then, with his ludicrously long arm, grasped a sapling, which threatened to break under its weight, and quietly sprang into a tree, swinging in great leaps alternately to right and to left.

My chief impression was and still is: "What an enormously large beast!" It was not an orang-utan; I had seen one of these large apes a short time before at Artis [the Amsterdam Zoo].

It was more like a monstrously large siamang, but a siamang has long hair, and there was no doubt that it had short hair. I did not see its face, for, indeed, it never once looked at me.

Here again, the most obvious suggestion is, just as Mr. Oostingh himself says, that the creature was an enormous Siamang, perhaps a lone old one somewhat short on hair. That it was more likely an ape than a Hominid is also perhaps further impressed upon us by the remark that it had "ludicrously long arm[s]." I do not know what to make of this report but I certainly wish that the creature had left some footprints.

Meantime, there was a Mr. Van Heerwarden timber-cruising from the other side (the northeast) of the Barisans in Palembang province, but down in the swamp forests by the coast near the Banjoe-Asin River. In 1918 he spotted two series of tracks on the banks of a small creek in the Musi River district; one larger than the other, as if of a mother and child, as he remarks. These were perfectly human but exceedingly small. Later he discovered that a Mr. Breikers had also found such tracks in the same area. He then started making serious inquiries among—and this is of considerable significance in view of the Indonesian Government's statement given above—the Kubus; and he found three who had all, but unknown to the others, seen *Gugus* (i.e. *Sedapas,* or *Orang Pendeks*) in that region. Their descriptions agreed perfectly in that they were about 5 feet tall, walked erect, were clothed in black hair that formed a mane, and had prominent teeth. Van Heerwarden later heard that a hunter had found a dead one and tried to carry it back to his village but its body was much decomposed and the hunter himself died shortly afterward. Another, he learned, was said to have been spotted in a river and surrounded by locals in canoes but it dived adroitly and escaped.

By this time Mr. van Heerwarden was convinced that there really was some small hairy Hominid in these forests and he devoted much time to inquiries among the local hunters as to where they were most frequently seen. In time he was directed to a particular spot and decided to do exactly the right thing—namely, go there, sit down, shut up, and wait. And, he appears to have been well rewarded for, unless he is not only a complete but most adept liar, he got an extremely good look at one of the elusive creatures. He tells us that he was wild-pig hunting in an area of forest surrounded by rivers named Pulu-Rimau, in October, 1923, and, having failed to come up with the sounder (herd) decided to do this quiet sitting, and so went into hiding. For an hour or so nothing happened and then something in a tree caught his attention. He says:

> Then I happened by chance to look round to the left and spotted a slight movement in a small tree that stood alone. By now it was time for me to be going home, for it was not advisable to journey through such country after sundown. But all the same I was tempted out of curiosity to go and see what had caused the movement I had noticed. What sort of animal could be in that tree? My first quick look revealed nothing. But after walking round the tree again, I discovered a dark and hairy creature on a branch, the front of its body pressed tightly against the tree. It looked as if it were trying to make itself inconspicuous and felt that it was about to be discovered.
>
> It must be a sedapa. Hunters will understand the excitement that possessed me. At first I merely watched and examined the beast which still clung motionless to the tree. While I kept my gun ready to fire, I tried to attract the sedapa's attention, by calling to it, but it would not budge. What was I to do? I could not get help to capture the beast. And as time was running short I was obliged to tackle it myself. I tried kicking the trunk of the tree, without the least result. I laid my gun on the ground and tried to get nearer the animal. I had hardly climbed 3 or 4 feet into the tree when the body above me began to move. The creature lifted itself a little from the branch and leant over the side so that

I could then see its hair, its forehead and a pair of eyes which stared at me. Its movements had at first been slow and cautious, but as soon as the sedapa saw me the whole situation changed. It became nervous and trembled all over its body. In order to see it better I slid down on to the ground again.

The sedapa was also hairy on the front of its body; the colour there was a little lighter than on the back. The very dark hair on its head fell to just below the shoulder-blades or even almost to the waist. It was fairly thick and very shaggy. The lower part of its face seemed to end in more of a point than a man's; this brown face was almost hairless, whilst its forehead seemed to be high rather than low. Its eybrows were the same colour as its hair and were very bushy. The eyes were frankly moving; they were of the darkest colour, very lively, and like human eyes. The nose was broad with fairly large nostrils, but in no way clumsy; it reminded me a little of a Kaffir's. Its lips were quite ordinary, but the width of its mouth was strikingly wide when open. Its canines showed clearly from time to time as its mouth twitched nervously. They seemed fairly large to me, at all events they were more developed than a man's. The incisors were regular. The colour of the teeth was yellowish white. Its chin was somewhat receding. For a moment, during a quick movement, I was able to see its right ear which was exactly like a little human ear. Its hands were slightly hairy on the back. Had it been standing, its arms would have reached to a little above its knees; they were therefore long, but its legs seemed to me rather short. I did not see its feet, but I did see some toes which were shaped in a very normal manner. This specimen was of the female sex and about 5 feet high.

There was nothing repulsive or ugly about its face, nor was it at all ape-like, although the quick nervous movements of its eyes and mouth were very like those of a monkey in distress. I began to walk in a calm and friendly way to the sedapa, as if I were soothing a frightened dog or horse; but it did not make much difference. When I raised my gun to the little female I heard a plaintive "hu-hu," which was at once answered by similar echoes in the forest nearby.

I laid down my gun and climbed into the tree again. I had almost reached the foot of the bough when the

237

sedapa ran very fast out along the branch, which bent heavily, hung on to the end and then dropped a good 10 feet to the ground. I slid hastily back to the ground, but before I could reach my gun again, the beast was almost 30 yards away. It went on running and gave a sort of whistle. Many people may think me childish if I say that when I saw its flying hair in the sights I did not pull the trigger. I suddenly felt that I was going to commit murder. I lifted my gun to my shoulder again, but once more my courage failed me. As far as I could see, its feet were broad and short, but that the sepada runs with its heels foremost is quite untrue.

This has always seemed to me to be a most straightforward report so it is interesting to note the reception it received when poor Mr. van Heerwarden finally told of it. Even the equable Heuvelmans cannot restrain himself from quoting certain of these expressions by people who were neither there nor, in some cases had then ever been anywhere near Sumatra, and most notably those of the same Dr. K. W. Dammerman of Buitenzorg. This is so delightful that I herewith re-reproduce it for your edification and guidance as a glorious example of the sort of rubbish spouted by experts and for which you have to be constantly on the lookout. This savant, after saying that no white man except Mr. Van Heerwarden had ever so much as said that he had seen a *Sedapa*, goes on to say: "But this writer is almost too exact in his description of the animal, so it does not seem impossible that the incident was either based on his imagination [i.e. that he was a liar—*Author*], or, that he has written it strongly impressed by the stories about the *Orang Pendek*. But, even while admitting the general truth of the story [i.e. not daring to say that he *was* a liar—*Author*], would it not be more likely that the animal in question was an Orang utan?" No it would *not*. I am wondering if Dr. Dammerman knew *any* zoology; I can hardly credit it.

This is by far the most complete account of the *Sedapa* but it was by no means the last. The matter has been going on ever since, and plenty of people, both native and foreign, have said they have seen the creatures. There were also other events. In 1927 one was said to have been caught in a tiger trap, and once again the irrepressible Dr. Dammerman gets into the act: this time as serological (blood) and trichological (hair) expert but without any better results. In fact, he becomes quite blathering, for, of some blood and hair found in this trap, he stated that "it was impossible to obtain any results with regard to the hair [this is indeed plausible, as identification of hairs is not easy—*Author*], but the blood pointed *faintly to human origin* [italics, mine]. However, we may not accept for a fact that the blood found came from the escaped animal: it is quite possible that it came from some native who had injured himself while handling the trap." I may just point out here that if you have a large enough specimen for any analysis there is no question as to whether it is human or not, so that it cannot "point faintly" to anything. Secondly, the "natives" of that area are Malays, of the mongoloid branch of humanity, who have no body hair but most distinctive head-hair. Thirdly, who said that an "animal" had been caught in the trap? At this point words do fail me.

Our principal trouble with the *Sedapa* is that, not only has there been a great deal of double-talk of this nature on the one hand, but that, on the other, there have been not a few obvious and deliberate hoaxes. The worst occurred in 1932 when local newsmen in Sumatra attributed the shooting of a mother *Sedapa* and the taking of its infant to the much respected local dignitary, the Rajah of Rokan. The world press went a bit mad about this, but only a little local inquiry elucidated the fact that the Rajah had had nothing to do with the incident—though he had for some time been interested in the matter, and had offered certain inducements to anybody who could produce definite evidence of the existence of these beings—but that two hunters had produced a "*baby Sedapa.*" Dammerman said it was a mutilated young Socrili (*Semnopithecus*), although he gave the name of the *Javanese* species! More reliable sources indicate it to have been a Lutong (*Trachypithecus* sp.). This was said to be dead; about 17 inches long; with a skin the color of an *Orang blunda* (or White Man); and, naked, but for a thick topknot. Said "baby" was obtained by purchase and sent to the same Dr. Dammerman who was able actually to demonstrate, for once, its complete lack of authenticity. It turned out to be a young monkey of the genus known as *Presbytis* (or the Leaf-Monkeys) that had been shaved; had its long tail cut off; and its skull crushed and face remodeled with bits of wood inserted under the skin of the nose to make it look more human.

This making of "incubi" is an age-old practice in Sumatra, having been mentioned by Marco Polo, and being one of the principal sources of those horrible little homunculi that were exhibited at museums and displays of curios in Europe from the 17th to the 19th centuries. These were monkeys' dried bodies to which were sewn all manner of unpleasant heads and appendicularia, and which were sold to sailors. It is possible therefore, that the very strange affair of the "Sindai" of 1957 may have had a similar origin.

This began with an international wire-service story that some form of subhuman had been "captured" in southern Sumatra. This was said to be a young female (about 17 years old) "Sindai," which, it was implied, was a rare "something" well-known to the natives and which was considered very important by them. It was hinted, or rather queried, that this might be the first real example of a "missing-link" yet caught. This report came out of Palembang just when a local revolution was in full swing in that area. News from those parts, thereafter, tended to be somewhat unreliable and garbled.

I have definite statements about this "Sindai" teen-ager, stating that it was clothed in short, fine, pure white hair, and had no tail, walked on its (her) hind legs, and in every other way behaved like a tiny human being, but apparently had no speech and ate only raw foods. It was then stated that it had been shipped to Java for "examination by leading scientists." And that, frankly, is the last that was ever heard of it. It was also said to have been taken to Palembang, en route. The only thing I can add to this bizarre news-story is that there is a form of Coloboid Monkey named the *Simpai,* or Banded Leaf-Monkey (*Presbytis* to zoologists).* As far as I am concerned, therefore, and in the meantime, I preserve not a little restraint in trying to assess the matter. I feel that there are sufficient reports that look genuine enough to warrant a lively interest in the affair; but, there is the presence of the little, sometimes bipedal, Malayan Sun-Bear, and of the Siamangs. Both certainly muddle the issue. Yet, the thing has been going on too long, and I only wish that I had had the opportunity to talk at length to the local people—as I have had the privilege of doing in so many

* It should be carefully noted that modern nomenclature has now adopted the name *Trachypithecus* for the Lutongs, *Semnopithecus* for the true Langurs, *Kasi* for the Purple-faced Monkeys, and *Pyagathrix* for the Doucs. One of the *Presbytis* does sometimes display an almost pure white form. Philologists tell me that a conversion of *simpai* to *sindai* is almost natural!

other countries—even in a debased form of kitchen-Malay, so that I could have assessed for myself the depth of their sincerity; the position that they assign to it in the general scheme of "things"; and could have learned some more details about their notion of it from a biologist's point of view. [Biologists can ask the damnedest questions!]

Traveling on to the mainland of Malaya we encounter quite a different and, in many ways, exactly contrary state of affairs. Here, the actual reports are extremely limited; the local native knowledge is very extensive; and the creatures concerned could not possibly be mistaken for any of the local fauna. This is what has so stimulated even the natural skeptics—and has been the cause of the British Army being called out on two occasions to try and do something about it. Here, however, we are going to run head-on into the problem of men versus sub-men that we mentioned above as becoming troublesome in this area.

There is a most remarkable book entitled *The Pagan Races of the Malay Peninsula* by Messrs. W. W. Skeat and C. D. Blagden, published in London in 1906, that is a real eye-opener. This is a solemn, ponderous, and somewhat pompous, scientific account of the peoples inhabiting this somewhat limited area, done in the painstaking and slightly Germanic style prevalent at the turn of the century. There is nothing excitable about it. It is simply a sort of official statement of the facts, as then known, about the peoples of the area. It makes most astonishing reading.

In this book, not only are the Malayan peoples now settled in the country fully discussed, but the Sakai (i.e. the *Senoi*), those strange retiring mountain peoples are fully examined, and then the Semang, a really primitive Negrito group. The way of life of the last, as herein described, is really hardly human. It should be read in the original. Then, the *Santu Sakai* (or Devil Sakai) are brought up, and are stated [though admittedly second hand from the Sakai; the Semang being almost uncommunicable-with] to be hairy, and definitely not human. The authors then go into the "myths, legends, and folklore" of the various people, including the little Senoi; and they dredge up from these, tailed men, with razor-bones on the outer back sides of their forearms, *and* a larger type that stinks. These are said to be "men" all right, but to be wilder than any of the rest of the line-up. There is a curious tradition about this last type that needs airing.

It is reported that they live (and only) in the upper

montane mist forests of the higher mountain ranges, both in the boot of the Malay Peninsula and in the next bit north —*vide:* Tenasserim (see Map XIV): and that they customarily stay up there. However, it is likewise reported that they do sometimes come down on to the lowlands and that, at that time, they are highly carnivorous, rapacious, and what is commonly, but perhaps inaccurately, called "cannibalistic"; meaning that they catch, kill, and eat humans. Also, and note this, it is absolutely affirmed that these descents occur only after unusually prolonged periods of cloudy weather or a succession of very rainy and overcast seasons; and that, then, said creatures attack *only thin people*. This may at first sound absolutely absurd but I would urge a note of caution.

In Norway, perfectly good "werewolves" are on medical record. They are teen-agers—and usually males—mentally deficient; with a grotesque growth of head and body hair often growing right up to the tops of their cheekbones and down to meet their eyebrows; prognathous jaws; and sometimes even short bowed legs and enlarged irregular teeth. They are nothing more than kids who grew up in the almost perpetually sunless and rainy climate of the upper mountain valleys of the western side of Norway and, before the discovery of the existence of vitamins, had gone into a physical decline due to a lack of what are called the "sunshine vitamins" (E, and its concomitant, D). These poor wretches, cast out of the community, or having run away due to their abnormalities, sometimes managed to maintain life by hand-hunting and gathering, and one and all seem to have an insatiable desire for raw meat. At the same time, they show a very pronounced intolerance to fats of any kind. What they wanted and apparently needed was lean meat and entrails.

We may now reconsider the status, condition, and the sometime plight of a race of Hominids; driven way back up into the upper montane forests in an equatorial region. Deprived of many of the foods to which they had formerly been accustomed and to which they had been evolved, they did the best they could; but, when the climate continued in such a manner that some of the few essentials that they needed did not flower or seed, their whole metabolism went haywire. To counterbalance this, their bodies demanded that they do something; so, overcoming their natural racial fear, they descended upon their old homelands looking for what they needed—i.e., what we call "red meat." And, to take this to its end, let us say that, fats nauseating them, they picked the lean—and what easier than thin people?

This is one of the most abtruse niches in all ABSMery but it has intrigued me for years. Anybody can make up any kind of story but why anything which sounds to us so utterly bizarre? There ought to be a reason. There may be others, and many of them, but, in the meantime, this one *could* make sense.

Yet, these ultra-primitive humans or sub-humans, or other even more lowly forms of Hominids, do not seem to be the only conundrums in this small but extremely esoteric area. Maybe they are the "Stinking Ones": maybe they are something else. Nevertheless, the former turned up in a very definite manner in 1953, and so concretely so, and so many times in rapid succession, that not only the benighted natives, but the European overseers, the local militia, the museum authorities, and even the "Government" itself became apprised of the matter and lent a hand. This is really a rather unusual turnout in ABSMery. It now transpires that just the same sort of thing had been going on throughout peninsular Malaya a few miles back from the few main roads since way back. These incidents had been either not reported, reported but not listened to, disbelieved, ridiculed, or actually suppressed, and, perhaps, latterly because of Communist guerrilla activities. However, this one got out—and, as the colloquialism goes, "but good." Looking over what published accounts of this incident there are, a really extraordinary number of quite baffling things come to light. I would say that this too is a classic example of what happens when a good case of ABSMery—or any other matter that is not at present accepted—occurs. But, first let me give the facts, as reported, chronologically.

It appears that on Christmas Day, 1953, a young Chinese girl by the name of Wong Yee Moi was engaged tapping rubber trees on an estate run by a Scot named Mr. G. M. Browne, in the Reserve that is called variously the Trolak, Trollak, or Trolek, in south Perak State, northern Malaya. According to her account, she felt a hand placed lightly on her shoulder and, turning around, was confronted by a most revolting female. This poor character wore, according to Moi, only an abbreviated loincloth of bark, was covered with hair, had a white (i.e. Caucasoid-type) skin, long black head-hair and a mustache; and she stank as if "of an animal." Half hysterical, Moi fled for the compound, but not before spotting two somewhat similar types which she said were males [no loincloths?] standing in the shade of some trees by a nearby river. These, she said, had mustaches hanging down to their waists. Up till this point, the account is fairly rational, even including Moi's addendum to the effect that the female grinned and showed long nasty fangs in what she (Moi) seems to have considered, despite her panic, to have been a friendly gesture. After this report, everybody became slightly insane.

Analyzing all the published reports that I can lay my hands on, it seems that this Mr. Browne immediately called up Security Forces' local headquarters—there being a continuing Communist emergency in the whole area— and, in response, a posse of the Malayan Security Guard was dispatched immediately under the leadership of one Corporal Talib, who seems to have been an extremely intelligent and also sensible man. He immediately deployed his forces and made search of the estate, in due course coming to the river mentioned by Moi and spotting three just such hairy types on its banks. However, upon bringing his platoon's arms to the ready, said creatures dived into the river, swam under water, emerged on the far bank, and forthwith vanished into the jungle. Subsequent to this, the only concrete facts in the case are that a Hindu Indian worker, named Appaisamy, on the same estate, the next day, also while squatting to shave the bark to bring on a flow of rubber latex, was suddenly encircled by a pair of hairy arms. He became completely panic-stricken; broke loose; headed for the compound, but fell down in a dead faint on the way. As he revived, the same trio were nearby and laughing at his discomfiture. He admitted this. That same day, a patrol of Corporal Talib's Guard again spotted the trio on the same riverbank.

This is all we have, apart from a few further anatomical details of the creatures given in retrospect by the various witnesses. Then, however, the experts, and other nonpresent commentators got into the act. And they provided the international wire services with some pretty interesting material. All kinds of previously unheard-of official departments came to light such as that of "The Aborigines" at Kuala Lumpur; the "Federation's Department of Museums and Aboriginal Research" and even "Radio Malaya" in the person of its Assistant Director, one Mr. Tony Beamish. These people made various suggestions. They ridiculed an idea put forward some years before, when an almost exactly similar incident had occurred, that the creatures seen were AWOL Japanese soldiers tired of the war, and who had managed to survive life in the jungle; though they did dredge up the old one about having "white skins because they had lived in the dim light of the jungles so long." [This is, of course, rubbish; though it is true that a *White* man will get a lot whiter in such an environment.] But, some people came up with some really startling ideas.

Most prevalent were hints that these things could be, or might have been "primitive humans trying to get away from British aerial bombing, or flooding of their jungle abodes"; or again, "that they might be descendants of a race of hairy aborigines who, according to old legends, once roamed the forests of northern Malaya." What I would like to ask is, what had the Department of Aboriginal Affairs been up to prior to this astonishing suggestion, and why had they not turned up some evidence [other than that of Messrs. Skeat and Blagden] of the necessity for protecting them? Also, as that excellent radio person—Tony Beamish—is alleged to have said, this could be "one of the most valuable anthropological discoveries for years." (Actually, it would have been *the* greatest of *all* times.) It is really rather remarkable that nothing was finally done about it. Experts of the same "Department of Museums, etc." did state that they were trying to organize an expedition and they made a statement. Statements are always good; and they are often good for a laugh. This one was a near classic. It stated:

1. The creatures apparently had seen rifles because they fled when a security force corporal raised his rifle. Some of the "things" jumped in the river and swam away. Another ran into the jungle.

2. Their light skin probably indicates they have lived for years in the dark, overgrown Malayan jungles where sunlight rarely penetrates.

3. They recognized a crop of tapioca on one estate as food, pulling up roots and munching.

4. They spoke a language that was clearly not Chinese or Malayan, but more of a series of guttural grunts.

And this, mind you, from persons who were not only scientists and experts but officials. We stand amazed; but we make certain notes and reservations.

The number of ABSMs that jumped into the river has now changed from "all" to some; they are now alleged to have pulled tapioca roots and eaten them; they had a language. I cannot find any of these facts in the original report of the Christmas, 1953 case but they do indeed appear in earlier cases, and in other parts of Malaya. In fact, it appears quite obvious from these latter that there had been quite a lot more information on this unpleasant subject in the files of the Department of Museums, etc., long before this time.

The most outstanding aspect of this case is perhaps the alleged "stink" of the creatures, as recorded by all witnesses who were near enough to them, and included in similar statements that emerged later about others, reported to have raided crops in different parts of Malaya. This single fact is exactly in accord with the age-old statements of the locals about such creatures. It is also in accord with some of the statements of the Amerinds about their large ABSMs in Canada and the northwestern United States. It accords too, with remarks passed about them, almost casually, by Kurds, Sinkiangese, Mongolians, and others. Apart from this, the fangs, hairiness of body, but ultra-long-hairedness of face and head, the suggestion of primitive clothing, and the general "comehitherness" of these creatures speaks a great deal.

It is interesting to note, anent this matter of a powerful stench exuded by ABSMs, that when the last of the Mau-Mau leaders—Dedan Kimathi—was finally tracked down and captured along with some of his men, in Kenya, not only the white men present but the local natives—the same people as Kimathi—agreed that to smell the band was so sickening as almost to prevent handling of the captives. This is the more odd because any real "bush men" (as opposed to *Bushman*) never washes, though of course he may bathe, when in the forest simply because by so doing, and especially with soap, he removes all the natural oils from his skin and these oils are among the most powerful insect repellents and anti-fungus spore deterrents known. [And this goes for white men who really know the forest and have to work therein for periods.] It is the sweat itself that causes the smell, and this by going putrid in clothing, so that a real bushwhacker changes his clothes at least three times during the twenty-four hours. Kimathi's gang wore untanned animal skins. So did the mustachioed manlike ABSMs that invaded the Malayan rubber estates.

Another fascinating fact appeared from the prolonged Kimathi hunt. This was that Kimathi himself developed a sensitivity, not only of his five major and some twenty (now recognized) other senses, but some other unknown attribute so incredibly acute that he became almost unapproachable. It is said that he would awake from sleep on the (unauthorized) cracking of so much as a single twig at great distances and immediately vanish. Sometimes even his own men just found him gone. If men—and many of Kimathi's, and even he himself, had not previously been true bush men—can develop such acute senses in so short a time, how much more may not ABSMs that have for hundreds of millennia been as much of the wild as non-domesticated animals. This is one of my strongest arguments against trying to hunt them: I personally think the idea worthless on this account. It is also one of the reasons why I think that the employment of dogs is the worst idea of all. Dogs are purely "artificial" animals, as well as being domesticated, and they have an odor which is instantly spotted by any truly wild creature. Then again, there is still another point.

It has been observed that animals, such as antelopes, which are born to and used to being hunted, do not even bother to move aside when for instance a cheetah rushes a group. Only one animal takes off and the cheetah goes straight for it. [It is often old or sick.] Also lions may be seen lying almost back to back with their natural food-animals in the daytime. But animals that are *not* used to being food for other animals are excessively wary. So are the predators themselves. Just try hunting a marten or any other weasel for that matter. ABSMs are neither born to, used to, or prepared to be hunted, any more than men are; *and,* they have both some intelligence *and* the senses of the wild predator to boot. In order to "collect" one therefore, methods quite other than hunting must be employed. Personally, I suggest an appeal to their inquisitiveness—it almost never fails.

By the accounts, these are no hairy, gibbering monsters, or even pigmies, but man-sized and, at least partly, man-thinking entities who seemed above all to want to "make friends." Could it really be that Communist-hunting, bombing, and general modern military maneuvering since the Japanese invasion, had caused some otherwise amiable primitives to move, and come looking for handouts?

11. The Great Mix-Up

THINGS IN THE INDOCHINESE PENINSULA

We now turn northward and start climbing, and we are going to need maps as we never needed them before. The area of the world which we are now approaching is perhaps the most puzzling and, to us, seemingly the most mixed-up in the world. The political situation is bad enough (see Map XI) but the topography is frankly awful, so that even a physical map is utterly confusing. This confusion, moreover, is worse confounded by our use of "feet" for measuring altitude. In this area they just aren't big enough, and maps showing the usual contour changes of color at 600, 1500, 3000, 12,000, and 18,000 foot levels end up as one glorious mishmash in which the main and basic features of the land are obscured. If, however, we do our measuring (and coloring) in meters, matters become much clearer. I have therefore constructed the map showing this province (Map XIII) on the 500 and 5000 meter contours, with a special shading for one particular area (Tibet) for reasons that will be explained later (see Maps XII and XV). This device brings out at a glance more or less all that we want to know, and makes it possible to attempt a more detailed explanation of the more difficult parts. We are now approaching the summit of our interests and we will have to take our cue from the mountaineers and initiate what they succinctly refer to as an "attack" upon the problem. In order to do this we have first to try and sweep away a whole handful of misconceptions.

The first and most basic of these is to attempt to get rid of the notion that the Orient [or *Orientalia* as it is better called] is just a part of Asia. To the contrary, just as what we call Europe—the boundaries of which have been in dispute throughout history, and still are—is *not* a separate continent but merely one large peninsular of a much larger land-mass called Eurasia, so, conversely is Orientalia not a part of that land-mass but a quite separate continent. Its climate, past history, geology, and, above all, its vegetation are quite different from that of Eurasia. Also, it is almost absolutely separated from Eurasia by a continuous physical feature that is every bit as divisive as an ocean. This is a tremendous mountain barrier that runs from Baluchistan in the west to the plains of Kian-Su in north China in the east. However, here comes the second and most important point of all.

The mightiest mountain range in the world, the Himalayas, lies well *south* of this line and is in Orientalia and *not* in Eurasia. Further, the massif which mounts to the highest peak on land in the world, Mt. Everest, straddles this division. Using the 5000-meter contour, we see that between the southern barrier of Tibet proper and what is now called the "Lesser Himalayan Range" there is really a great gutter at comparatively much lower level. It is in this gutter that the small state of Nepal lies. Thus, when we come to the Himalaya province, we must bear in mind that we will still be in Orientalia, and that we shall continue to be as we approach Mt. Everest from the south side until we top this Tibetan barrier. This is frightfully important because the flora and fauna of the Himalayas —and there is a great deal of vegetative growth forming massed forests that run up almost to the snow line all over them—is quite unlike that of Tibet but has relationships with that of the Indo-Chinese Massif. And this brings us to our third problem.

It will be seen from Maps XII and XIII that this Indo-Chinese block terminates abruptly to the north against a monumental barrier of towering mountain ranges that are confluent with Tibet. These actually form a small "peninsula" of Eurasia that sticks down into this part of Orientalia as shown. On an ordinary physical map it will be seen that the Indo-Chinese block is formed of endless sub-parallel mountain ranges and strings of ranges, with very narrow deep valleys between them, running roughly from north to south. These form fingers going south into the Annams, down central Thailand, and down the Tenasserim peninsula. There also depends from them the parallel sub-massif composed of the Naga Hills and the Arakan. In the northwest, this block is very clearly and widely marked off from the east end of the Himalayas by a horn of true lowland equatorial forests. This, contrary to expectation, instead of separating the two upland masses actually cements them firmly together, from the plant and animal point of view, for the same forests cover both facing slopes to form a perfect bridge for both the migrants, emigrants, and immigrants from one side to the other. To the northeast, affairs are quite different.

Here, there is first, to the north, a small enclave of comparatively modest uplands running down from the Tibet plateau to the Red Basin of Szechwan (see Map XV). These have a Chinese flora and fauna. Then, south of these, the Indo-Chinese Massif abuts on to the more modest upland mass of Southern China, from the south of which a long thin chain of mountains—in Si-Kiang—runs east. This funny little promontory is rather important because a lot of myth, legend, and folklore pertaining to ABSMs extends that way. The south China uplands are of course densely populated and have been for a very long time so that their vegetative cover is now quite different from that of the Indo-Chinese Massif. If the two were ever alike is questionable, for the south China uplands really form quite a separate biotope, or florofaunal area. The Indo-Chinese province is therefore really rather isolated and distinct. It is also quite unique in many other ways. Armed with these facts we may now enter this Indo-Chinese country from the south, and immediately run into difficulties. This is the country in which the second largest form of the bovine or ox-cow tribe turned up in 1938—the Kouprey (*Bos sauveli*)—to the great consternation of established zoological thinking. It looks like a large edition of the now extinct Aurochs (*Bos primigenius*) of Europe, with widespreading horns, but the bulls have large tassels, the strands of which go upward, just short of the tips of their horns. This was an astonishing discovery in a land inhabited, and thickly, since most ancient times. Of more interest to us, however, are the Primates of the area.

These include a lot of strange types. First, it is the headquarters of the little apes called gibbons, one species of which, the Hoolock (*Hylobates hooloch*) reaches north and into the Himalayas. Then, there are also there the Doucs (*Pygathrix nemaeus* and *nigripes*) which is one of the most brightly and variegatedly colored of all mammals; and, the Snub-nosed Monkeys. There are two distinct genera of these, one found in Tonkin (*Presbytiscus avunculus*); the other being the large and very extraordinary *Rhinopithecus*. Of the latter there are three species: Biet's Monkey (*R. bieti*) from Yunnan which forms a part of the Indo-Chinese Massif; Brelich's Monkey (*R. brelichi*) a really enormous form with a large white cap over its shoulders which lives in the Van Gin Shan mountains in west central China; and the Golden Monkey (*R. roxellanae*) of the upper end of the Indo-Chinese block and extending up that small enclave facing the Red Basin mentioned before. This animal is a glowing metallic gold all over but has a sky-blue face. These monkeys really are gigantic and look even bigger since they are clothed in long thick fur that forms a cape.

This is not to say that there are not other monkeys in this province; to the contrary, there are dozens of species of Leaf-Monkeys and Langurs, while there are also lesser Primates. It is, in fact a sort of hotbed of Primates, in and around which most of the living apes reside, a large proportion of known fossil Hominids have been found; and quite a "coterie" of different ABSMs are rumored. Here, what is more, we have a state of affairs comparable to that which we encountered in Africa, but compounded, for, in addition to having apes (or Pongids) to contend with as well as fossil Hominids and alleged ABSMs, we have also lots of large terrestrial or semi-terrestrial monkeys as well—i.e. the Macaques (which include the Rhesus) and these Snub-nosed jobs. Nor is that all, for the local folklore is full of allusions to "men with tails," on the one hand; and to giant, bipedal monkeys, on the other. This is all very muddling to the layman but seems also to have thrown the specialists—and even those few in the field of ABSMery—into confusion. Then lately, the Chinese have still further muddled the picture by coming up with an exceedingly ABSM-like race of *people* in Yunnan; while anthropologists and ethnologists generally have unearthed all kinds of primitive and most unexpected nations, tribes, and groups in this province.

One of the most extraordinary of these is a group of tribes in the central mountainous region of this territory, who have very pale brownish skins, Caucasoid features, and wavy hair. They keep strictly to themselves and have one curious custom that may be of great significance to those investigating Malayan folklore where there is said once to have lived a race of tailed men who had a cutting edge of bone along the outer (hind) edges of their forearms. These tribesmen possess practically nothing that is traded from outside but they always carry a large sharp knife of a certain shape; and they always carry this pointing backward up the arm and with the blade turned outward. With this they make their way through thick undergrowth at great speed by a curious down-slashing movement of the arm, so avoiding endless entanglements with vines, by swiping at them.

Straight ABSMery in this province is not extensive until we get to the extreme northern end of it. In fact it amounts really to some legend and rumors, except in Yunnan and in northern Burma. Of the first, a Russian writing in *Tekhnika Molodyzhi* (Vols. 4 and 5, 1959) a science magazine for the Youth Movement states:

> In 1954, the Province of Yunnan in China was visited by a representative of the USSR Society for Cultural Relations with Foreign Countries by the name of Chekanov. Speaking to Ma-Yao, the assistant chief of the National Minorities Department of the Kunming City Committee of the Communist Party of China, he learned that at the beginning of that same year, 1954, some people had been found in the mountains of Western Yunnan who in Ma-Yao's opinion were only at the pre-historic stage of their development. They led an animal existence, wore no clothes and had no articulate speech. It seems that Ma-Yao had also mentioned that their bodies had been covered with hair, and that one of them had been captured and brought to Kunming.
>
> Chao Kuo-hoi, head teacher of the Yunnan National Minorities Institute also told Chekanov that the mountains where the people of the Khani nationality lived in the Hung Ho District were also inhabited by some strange people who belonged to no nationality whatever, that they wore no clothes and hid from ordinary people. One of them was captured and brought to Kunming. When he was dressed in human clothes he seemed quite satisfied and smiled.
>
> According to what he had heard, Chekanov recalled that this captive wild man was finally sent to Pekin to be studied by the scientists. All this evidence, however, stems from people who had only heard about the wild inhabitants of the mountains from others.

Of the central area there is not much to be said and actual reports are neither numerous nor extensive. What there are, concern a very large form of ABSM called locally the *Kung-Lu* or "Mouth-Man." This was first, as far as I can discover, mentioned by Hassoldt Davis, the well-known American traveler and author, in his book entitled *Land of the Eye,* which is the account of the Denis-Roosevelt Asiatic Expedition to Burma, China, India, and the "lost kingdom" of Nepal. In this the author says:

> **Jack (John Kenny) was the only one of us who could be called a hunter. He had shot bear and moose in Maine, and here it was his heart's desire to try his skill with tiger or Binturong or the Bear Cat (Artictis) or the great rhinoceros which is now found only in this wild corner of Burma near the Siamese Border. And more exciting even than these was the report of a creature, the Kung-tu, (or Mouth-Man), which had terrified the people for centuries. The Kung-tu, according to Thunderface,* was a monster that resembled a gorilla, a miniature King Kong, about 20 feet tall. It lived on the highest mountains, where its trail of broken trees was often seen, and descended into the villages only when it wanted meat, human meat. We were told also that no one in Kensi † had been eaten by the Kung-Lu for more years than the eldest could remember.**

It is perhaps permissible to speculate on the fact—could it be coincidence—that Chief Thunderface described a rather typical *Sasquatch-Oh-Mah* creature? This was my first reaction; and it was a pretty strong one; but, then, the same thing crops up much more extensively but with less exaggeration farther north where there are not, as far as we know, any Amerinds.

There, there is either a similar creature or a closely related one named the *Tok,* which I am told also means "mouth." My account of this originally came in the form of a personal communication from a gentleman who had heard me discussing ABSMs on the air. He gave me the name and address of a young American, then in the service of his country, who had been born in the Shan States and brought up there, his parents having been mis-

---

* This 'Thunderface' turned out to be a North American "Indian" by the name of Chief Michael Joseph Thunderface, a graduate of the California Mission College, of 1921! He had gone to the Orient as part owner of a small circus that had disbanded, and he had settled down in this Burmese village and in time been elected chief.

† The village of Kensi is now called Kawmyo and is near the Thai border. It is noted for its Naga (the King Cobra snake) worship attended only by priestesses.

sionaries. In turn, I got in touch with this young man, whose name I was asked not to publish, and he told me of two personal encounters—in fact actual physical contacts —with *Toks,* while he gave me several other reports, and passed me on to others who also in turn wrote me their stories. All were Americans with much experience of the country. In the end, it seemed to me that this ABSM may be the same as the Kung-Lu reported from so much farther south, about which there is, once again, that most curious detail of all in ABSM reports; namely, that it, also, attacks *only thin people* and ignores fat ones.

My young American correspondent states that he actually had a *Tok* in his arms twice and when it broke loose it left handfuls of long, coarse, shiny black hairs in his hands. The occasions were when it broke into his family home which was deep in the hill jungles and some distance from the nearest small, permanent settlement. On both occasions it chose a bright moonlight night and both times it crashed about apparently looking for food. Both times the young man tackled it thinking it was a native thief or marauder and, being a powerfully built man and an athlete, and since his parents refused to possess any firearms, he did so with his bare hands. On each occasion it did not attempt to attack him in return, but only to flee, and being immensely strong and well over 6 feet tall it easily broke away, once running straight through a screen door. As it crossed to the forest in the moonlight, my informant had a very good look at it. He tells me that it had very wide shoulders, small head, was covered with jet-black hair, but had straight legs like a man and very pale soles to its feet. From this correspondent, and some of those others he put me on to, emerged various local names for this creature all of which must be translated as "mouth man" or "the man with the incredibly big mouth."

Hassoldt Davis' *Kung-Lu* is from the southern end of the Indo-Chinese mountain area, the *Tok* from the northern, where it would seem to merge with the *Dzu-Teh* of Eastern Tibet (the area that was once called Sikang) on the one hand, and the *Gin-Sung* or Bear-Men of central China on the other. These areas are all adjacent to the places where the teeth and bones of *Gigantopithecus* have been unearthed, and if they are all the same creature, it would bear out Bernard Heuvelmans' theory that they are indeed *Gigantopithecus.* But we will come to the *Dzu-Teh* and *Gin-Sung* later. We must now turn aside for a moment to try and clear up something that is really very puzzling.

In doing this, I am going first to have to jump backward a little and then leap forward right into the middle of the Himalayas and also into the middle of the chronological sequence of events there. This I have to do as we will never make any sense out of the situation in this area unless we get this sort of "appendage" out of the way.

It begins way down in the plateau of Kontum, in what used to be northern Indo-China. There, the locals say they have a kind of enormous *monkey* that walks on its hind legs and which is actually vicious and is quite willing to attack people. They call it the *Kra-Dhan*. In the neighboring territory of the Jölong it is called the *Bêc̆-Bôc* (Bekk-Bok). The mountain people of the south also insist that it is a *monkey*, and not a man or an ape. This is odd, for there are virtually tailless monkeys thereabouts, the Stump-tailed Macaques (*Lyssodes*). At the same time, the locals are equally insistent that these creatures are not ghosts, departed spirits, demigods, or anything nonmaterial; all of which, though they often speak of them, they most clearly distinguish from real physical beings.

There is a report that one of these creatures either committed a murder, or was responsible for a murder near Kontum in 1943. Unfortunately the matter was tried by the local native court, of which no records were sent to the central French authority, while the French Resident of that area at the time is no longer alive, and the native Commune has been dispersed since the retirement of the French. This is not by any means the only report of these *Kra-Dhan* to be made to foreigners, and we have heard of similar entities in areas far to the west of Kontum. There would be nothing unexpected in reports of an unknown *ape* in this area, and I personally would not be a bit surprised if someone told me of an alleged ABSM thereabouts; and for all the same old reasons—ample, unexplored montane forests; small and isolated human communities; and appropriate geographical position. But, the insistence on the "monkey" theme is novel.

Now, as we have said, there have been countless stories throughout the ages about tailed men. However, I know of only one case of a possible ABSM ever having been stated to have one. This is one of the most peculiar of all reports, and is unique in many respects. It happened right smack in the middle of what has now become virtually traditional ABSM territory—namely, on the main route to Katmandu, Nepal from the north. It is alleged to have taken place in June, 1953. Those involved were two Americans,

Dr. George Moore (M.D.) and Dr. George K. Brooks, an entomologist. The former was Chief of the Public Health Division of the U.S. Operations Mission, under the Foreign Operations Administration, and was public health adviser to the Nepalese Government. Dr. Brooks was on his staff. Dr. Moore had been in the country 2 years. They were descending the Gosainkund Pass (of some 17,000 feet) on their way back to Katmandu, the capital, from a trip to the north, and had entered the upper montane forests, there mostly coniferous, leaving their pack-carrying porters far behind. There was a thick mist. But it is better that Dr. Moore tell the incident that then occurred in his own words. It goes:

The forest was deathly still. Fog banks, raw and cold, drifted through the tall pines and left their boughs dripping and slimy.

Rounding a sharp turn in the trail, Brooks stopped abruptly. He leaned against a large rock to extract a leech which was on the point of disappearing over the edge of his boot. I stood there watching Brooks and fumbling for my pipe when an almost imperceptible movement in a clump of tall rhododendron caught my eye. Something had moved, I was sure. There it was again! This time, a few leaves rustled, more than mere chance could move. Brooks, sensing something was wrong, quickly forgot about his leech. Almost simultaneously we both slipped our revolvers out of their holsters. On our right the slope was dangerously steep. Behind us the slope climbed upward. There was a large boulder by the side of the trail and we eased over to it, glad for the protection from the rear it afforded. We waited, tense and expectant. The stillness was awesome. The fog and mist seemed to form weird shapes writhing and twisting through the dense foliage.

Suddenly, from in front of us a raucous scream pierced the air. Another followed from the right. The ghostly quality of the mist and the unreality of the situation had a nightmarish tinge.

"God!" Brooks whispered, "what was that?"

My spine was tingling in high gear now. I gripped my .38 S&W more firmly. About 20 feet away, somewhat in front of our rock, was the clump of rhododendron where the first scream had come from. We fastened our gaze on the leaves, trying to peer through them. Another scream broke the stillness. This time it seemed as though it was behind us.

"Brooks," I managed to whisper, "let's get on this rock in a hurry!"

Brooks did not need a second invitation. In an instant, we had scrambled on top of the massive boulder. From our new perch, we carefully searched in all directions for the next move. Our movements must have been closely watched, for a loud chattering immediately assailed us from the bushes in front. The angry chatter filled the raw air as new cries joined in the chorus from all sides. We were definitely surrounded.

Brooks muttered, "Oh, my God, how many of them are there? And what are they?"

We got some idea of what was there when a hideous face thrust apart the wildly thrashing leaves and gaped at us. It was a face that I shall not long forget. Grayish skin, beetling black eyebrows, a mouth that seemed to extend from ear to ear and long, yellowish teeth were shattering enough. But those eyes . . . beady, yellow eyes that stared at us with obvious demoniacal cunning and anger. That face! Weird ideas were beginning to force their way into mind. Perhaps . . . but no . . . damn it . . . it has to be! This is the Abominable Snowman!

A chill sent gooseflesh along my back. The thought of these creatures had often been in my mind when we had trekked over the snows and high places. No European or American had ever proved the existence of the snowmen, although the natives certainly believed in them. Our boys had entertained us many an evening around the camp fire with horror tales of the snow beast, or "yeti" as they called them. They told how solitary travelers had been found torn to bits in the vast reaches of the mountains; how huge footprints had been found leading away from the murders. A few Sherpas had even met the monsters face to face and lived to tell the tale. We considered these accounts unlikely "hill stories," although I admit now they had left us somewhat uneasy.

No, I insisted to myself, there is no such creature as an Abominable Snowman. This face has to be an ape . . . or a man . . . or a demon . . . or the SNOWMAN!

A hand pushed through the leaves. Then, a quick movement and a shoulder. There, before us, appeared the semblance of a body. Sweat was visible on Brooks' face now as we crouched lower, hugging the rock for what it was worth. My hands looked white in the semi-darkness.

As the creature emerged through the dark leaves, we strained to make out his form. I felt blind panic start through me. Then I stopped. "Balls of fire," I thought, "I've got to get a grip on myself."

The creature was about 5 feet tall, half-crouching on two thin hairy legs, leering at us in undisguised fury. Claws—or hands—seemed dark, perhaps black, while his bedraggled, hairy body was gray and thin. It shuffled along with a stoop the way a neolithic cave man might have walked. Well-built and sinewy, it could prove to be the most formidable opponent. Teeth bared, it snarled like an animal. Two long fangs protruded from its upper lip . . . Suddenly, a sharp flicking movement behind it caught our eyes.

"George! A tail! Look there," Brooks cried.

A thousand thoughts raced through my mind at once.

"Well, Brooks," I replied, "this thing could be the Abominable Snowman but it also could be an ape . . . a langur ape, perhaps."

Truthfully, I was more concerned with survival than identification. The band of animals was certainly aggressive, giving every indication that they meant to destroy us. But I couldn't help thinking about the creatures themselves. They didn't look like the common langur monkeys I'd seen in India. At the same time they had apelike characteristics. Scientific possibilities crowded their way into my mind even as I checked my revolver for the attack. Higher altitudes, less minerals in the water could produce less hair. Lack of heavy timber in the high regions, which would make climbing ability relatively valueless, could produce an erect species. Mutations—the methods by which new species are created—have occurred, and are constantly observable in laboratories. Variations within a single species over a period of time can produce animals greatly different from the parent strain. I had no time to share these thoughts with Brooks. The best I could mumble was an unsteady, "Get ready."

Other figures were approaching now from several directions. We could make out 6 or 7 of them through the mist. One appeared to be carrying a baby around its neck. They seemed to mean business as they growled at each other. The one that had pushed through the foliage first was the leader. There was little question as to his authority as he led the attack.

"Brooks," I said hurriedly, "let's try firing over their heads to see if we can scare them. Don't hit them, for heaven's sake, or we may have them in a frenzy. A wounded animal—if they are animals—won't stop. And if they are demons, the Sherpas will never forgive us if we kill them. The Sherpas, superstitious as they are, would rather be killed than offend their gods, especially here."

"Okay, George, you say when," he replied softly.

We sighted carefully through the fog and waited until the repulsive creatures were about 10 feet away. We squeezed the triggers almost together. The blast swirled the fog in front of us. Splinters of wood and torn leaves fell through the foliage. The creatures stopped abruptly.

The original account, which appeared in the magazine *Sports Afield*, May, 1957, concludes with quite a long passage relating the purely human reactions on the part of the author, his companion, and their Sherpa porters. It is indicated that the latter seem to have assumed that they had met some *Yetis*—the general Nepalese term now used by the Press—and they were greatly relieved that their employers had not been harmed. However, they did not resort to any exaggerated expressions and, it seems to me at least, they were singularly lacking in observations of any kind. In fact, I have an impression that they were somewhat mystified, and perhaps even unbelieving, but too polite to so comment. The account and the locale do not jibe with anything said by any natives of ABSMs on either count.

This is one of the most factual reports we have of any thing [be it of ABSMs or not] to come out of Nepal as we shall most abundantly see in the next chapter. Moreover, it was made by a highly trained medical man, a person of all classes of educated men least likely to panic in face of bodily abnormality, and who must also have had some training in comparative anatomy if nothing else. Also, it occurred at less than 11,000 feet so that there cannot be any accusation of mental fatigue producing illusions that *can* be brought on by very high altitude and rarefied air if one is not acclimatized to them. In addition, the teller had a witness of equally high mental caliber and

259

training. Moreover, if they had wanted to turn the creatures they saw into the traditional "abominable snowman," [of the giant or *Dzu-Teh,* the bestial or *Meh-Teh,* or even of the little forest *Teh-lma,* variety] they could quite well have done so, simply by neglecting to mention the tails. Tails just don't fit onto ABSMs.

There are also some extremely pertinent remarks in this account that have not, as far as I know, been commented upon nor even perhaps noticed. The first, is the very definite statement that their eyes were bright *yellow.* Not much is known or recorded about the color of wild animals' eyes, and quite a number of the stuffed specimens in our great museums have completely the wrong colored irises. One of my duties when I was a collector was to record the colors of the eyes of the animals. No ape has a yellow eye: they all have dark brown eyes; though I have seen an abnormal chimp with pale gray eyes. Many monkeys, on the other hand, do have bright yellow eyes—in fact, this color is rather common among them and it seems to go with lighter coat color. Some of the Langurs have yellow eyes, as do also at least two of their African relatives among the Mangabeys (*Cercocebus*).

Pertinent to this story also, is that I was once "attacked" by a large band of Red-topped Mangabeys (*C. torquatus*), in a mist, on the ground, in an upper montane forest, in West Africa. I say "attacked" advisedly because they ran at me threateningly—and particularly the big males, one of which I was forced to kill and which proved to be the all-time record in length for that species [its skin and skull are in the British Museum]. As I could not run away [which I admit is my natural instinct and invariable practice in face of any such danger], due to the density of the lower-level forest growth under which I had to wriggle along on my stomach, it was manifest that this action was not concerted or carried through. The one I shot did come most alarmingly close and was screaming and grimacing at me, and showing its very long yellow fang-like canine teeth. When it stood up on its hind legs, it seemed almost to be looking at me eye for eye, and I thought it was actually going to jump me. When I shot it, the others just renewed their howling, and they kept this up for about 10 minutes while rushing at me in simulated onslaught. Eventually I just went away, backward on my stomach, and left them.

Another point that Dr. Moore makes is the thinness of the animals' legs. This is a monkey feature, as is also the slimness of their bodies when they stand up. But most significant of all is that he says that "One appeared to be carrying a baby around its neck." This is an odd one. Young baboons and macaques at first hang under their mother's bodies—they being quadrupedal—but they later ride astride their mothers' hind backs, holding on to her back fur. Almost all other monkeys carry their young in their crooked forearms or in one arm, but some of the Lutongs (*Trachypithecus*)—very near relatives of the Langurs or Semnopithecines—wrap them around their necks like feather boas or mink scarfs, *and especially* when they descend to the ground.

The whole attitude of the creatures in this story seems, indeed, to savor much more of a kind of monkey than of an ape or sub-hominid. As of now, I class them as such, but with reservations. Yet, monkey or not, I feel that the report is the truth and that we have therefore to be keenly on the lookout for the interjection of "evidence" presented for the existence of some ABSMs in this area being the result of the existence of giant monkeys. It is clearly manifest that these creatures, and such as the *Kra-Dhan*, actually have nothing to do with ABSMs. They, like the local bears, are just another side issue, and a complication. And this brings up the next of our problems in this mixed-up area. This is the *known* fauna. The trouble here is that none of the people who have been to the Himalayas seem ever to have known anything of what *is* known of the mammalian fauna of the region, while most of those who really do know that fauna are few and far between; either in museums or zoos in Europe or America, and almost none have ever been near the Himalayas. There is thus a most appalling muddle as to just what mammals do live there and which don't.[1]

The worst confusion is over the bears. There are representatives of three genera of bears actually known to live in the Himalayas—the Himalayan or Moon Bear (*Selenarctos*), black with a white V-collar; the Sloth-Bear (*Melursus*), a strange aberrant type with a long nose, which eats mostly insects and honey; and the Brown or Dish-faced Bears (*Ursus*). Of the last, three species, subspecies, or races distinguished by color, have been recorded. These have been called the Red Bear, the Blue Bear, and the Isabelline Bear. There is an appalling muddle over the scientific names of these, apart from the Red Bear,

[1] See appendix B.

which everybody agrees is not red and is simply a local variety of *Ursus arctos,* the Brown Bear of the rest of Eurasia. There is a name, *Ursus isabellinus,* which was once bestowed upon an almost white specimen of Brown Bear from the Karakoram, but which was jauntily and popularly called the "Snow Bear." Later, bluish-gray pelted specimens appeared from other localities and were either so called, or named *Ursus pruinosus* or *Ursus arctos pruinosus.* Some were creamy, others almost white, but most were gray. Nobody today is prepared or can say just how many races of Brown Bears there are in the Himalayan ranges of mountains, nor what their exact ranges are; whether they are full species, sub-species, or merely races; nor even whether they breed true. In other words, this "Isabelline Bear" is a lovely bogey to be waved at people who are not only not specialists in zoology, but particularly not specialists in mammals—and Oriental mammals at that! In my opinion the thing is a myth, just like our North American so-called "Grizzly Bear" which is and can be any Dish-faced Bear [as opposed to one of our Black Bears] that happens to have a grizzled pelage. One almost white specimen of a bear was killed in Tibet, and immediately called an Isabelline Bear but turned out to be an albino Himalayan Black (*Selenarctos*) not a Brown Bear (*Ursus*) at all.

But this is not all. While most bears can stand up on their hind legs for brief periods and can wobble along for a short distance on two legs, they happen to have a certain most peculiar feature. This has already been most ably demonstrated by Dr. Bernard Heuvelmans, and is that all bears are pigeon-toed and thus leave tracks that look as if they were bipedal, but walked with their feet put on backward. The toes point a little inward, the heels outward; in men, it is the other way, except for the Amerinds and some others who often walk absolutely straight ahead. Apart from this, nobody, and least of all a "native," could ever mistake a bear's track, or print, for that of a man, and even more especially that of an "abominable snowman." In bears, the middle toe is the longest, the *outer* one the largest; they leave claw marks in any material into which they sink lower than the hairline on their feet.[2] Finally, they cannot go on their hind legs on anything but level, unencumbered ground, and even then, only for short distances. Bear tracks have been mistaken for ABSM

[2] See Appendix A, page 327.

tracks *but* ABSM tracks have never been mistaken for bear tracks. Bears as an explanation of ABSM tracks, have also been brought up in North, Central, and South America, and in Malaya and Sumatra where species of bears do exist. However, they have not, of course, been able to be used in Ethiopian Africa where this group of animals has never been found or reported. When it comes to animals that could possibly be the origin of Himalayan ABSM reports, the bears are not alone. However, all other kinds of animals so far suggested as being the true origin of ABSMs are absolutely ridiculous. Several have been suggested, such as Langur Monkeys of the species *Semnopithecus entellus,* which happens to be a purely Indian form, the Giant Panda, wolves, the snow-leopard, and even large birds! But when it comes to candidates for scalps and hairs, the list is very much greater.

In leaving the Indo-Chinese province we omitted to stress one point; this was, simply, that its northern part is a meeting place of three outstanding ABSM areas. Each of these appear to have different indigenous kinds. These are of the usual four main forms—namely, a giant, a *Meh-Teh,* a human type, and a pigmy. There is evidence of a very manlike, man-sized one in the south, as we have seen (*vide* in Malaya); to the north in the eastern end of Tibet and the eastern Eurasian area generally there is a very large one, the *Dzu-Teh, Tok, Kung-Lu,* or bearlike *Gin-Sung,* Mountain Man of the Chinese; in the west, that is to say in the Himalayas themselves, there are two kinds; first there is the little 4-foot tall *Teh-lma* of the lower montane forests; and secondly, the heavy-set *Meh-Teh* (the original Abominable Snowman) with a conical head, and very large and widely separated first *and* second toes, which often treks over snow-covered passes from one valley to another. The giant, with almost human-type feet is *not* found in the Himalayas nor along the Tibetan barrier but is confined to the mountains between Tibet, China, and Burma.

12. Anyone for Everest?

ABSMS IN THE HIMALAYAS AND THE GREAT GUTTER

Having now reached the summit, I wish to ask your indulgence. Personally, I am so sick and tired of "Abominable Snowmen" per se, and of foot-tracks in the snow of "Tibet" [sic], and, most of all, of poor, old, long-suffering Mt. Everest, that I simply cannot bring myself to go over the whole dreary business again in detail. Yet, for all that has been published on the subject, which includes really quite a number of books as well as a veritable cascade of news-stories, one thing is most notably lacking to date. This is any real semblance of order upon which the whole picture may be assessed. On this occasion therefore, I ask to be excused for compressing my purely reportorial duties to the limit—in fact, into a chronological list, as you will find a few pages farther on—and thus reserving my energy and what mileage is left for some background information and, I hope, some legitimate comment. Before we tackle the issue, however, a few points should be stressed.

The first is a reiteration, and one that cannot be too often repeated or too strongly stressed. This is that what are most commonly called simply the Himalayas—which is to say these now "lesser Himalayas"—are *not* a part of Tibet, or even in the same continent. Further, the racial, national, political, cultural, and all other aspects of humanity pertaining in this area are extremely complex, most muddling, and very little understood. For once, national boundaries hereabouts serve some really useful purposes (see Map XI): also, some of them even have some actual physical validity and coincide with natural boundaries.

Perhaps the single most interesting fact to emerge from this is that the block of extreme mountains that is peaked by Mt. Everest really lies in Tibet, and is thus more than half in Eurasia. From all the hoopla as well as the very real and legitimate interest that has been engendered by the "attack" on and "conquest" of Everest, a general impression has been gained that either this mountain is more or less synonymous with all the Himalayas, or that it is at least the only important one therein. It is only one of a very great number of monsters on both sides of the Great [Brahmaputra] Gutter, and dominates several others by only a rather modest height. Further, a mountain was seen, and fixed for altitude, by more than one American military plane flying The Hump during the war, that was stated to be very much taller than Everest. So vast is the triangle of uplands between the Pamirs in the west, the Nan-Shans in the northeast, and the mountains of inner Yunnan in the southeast that, despite a healthy expedition led and financed by Mr. Reynolds [of ball-point pen fame] this monstrous thing has never been found again. This mountain has, however, recently been downgraded considerably.

Turning now for a moment to the human element in this chapter of our story, it should be noted that the inhabitants of Tibet are quite distinct from most of the peoples who inhabit the Himalayas, though the famous Sherpas, Ghurkhas, and Lepchas, of Nepal, were originally Tibetans, and are of that group of peoples. However, the true Tibetans inhabit quite a different land, having more intimate connections to the east with the Sikang region [now incorporated into the Chinese Province of Szechwan]. They therefore take quite a different view of things, and this is most noticeable when they come to talk about and describe ABSMs. Another point that is worth bearing in mind is that many of the inhabitants of both areas are most highly educated people, especially the monks of the Lamaist Buddist faith, and the religious mystics and ascetics of the Hindu. An impression has been disseminated that, though the most excellent chaps for mountaineering, fighting, and other forms of endurance, the Nepalese are a poor bunch of uneducated hillsmen, and that all the Tibetans do, apart from spinning prayer wheels, is tend yaks. Some scholars in the monasteries of these countries speak, read, and write a dozen languages, both dead and living ones at that, and they possess vast treasure troves of documents and whole libraries of records. Books published by them five centuries ago on such subjects as history, medicine, and zoology, are as precise and objective as any of our own, as we shall see later when we visit the northern side of their country. Do not, therefore, sell the locals short on either common sense or outright knowledge. They can also be sharper than we are.

Finally, still another note of warning. Sportsmen, in the form of mountaineers, big-game hunters, and so forth, are not the only outsiders who have penetrated and wandered about the Himalayas and the southern rim of the Tibetan Plateau. Sometimes they almost appear to be, because of the Everest business, and the enormous volume of their published works. In these, however, you don't learn much about the country as a whole, whereas you do get a tremendous amount about the mountains (per se; and usually above the snow line) and about mountaineering. As I remarked in the first chapter, if you really want to get at what facts *are* known about the area, the best place to go is to the reports of the various British Government Surveys—political, topographic, and biological—which continued for years with the utmost precision and most painstaking persistance and care. Since the conclusion of those surveys, it is notable that the only people who seem to speak boldly and rationally on quite a number of matters pertaining to these countries have been anthropologists, ethnologists, and botanists, who have really traveled the country at lower levels, and taken the trouble to talk to the local people, learn their customs, and understand their languages and outlook. Some of their expressions have been quite delicious.

Now I shall tackle the facts so that we may try to gain some kind of mutual understanding as to what everybody has been talking about. In my brief introductory history of ABSMery I had of necessity to mention not a few of the items that appear in the following chronology because until now the whole history of this subject has been mostly in and of the "Himalayan" area, and the general popular conception is that it is exclusive to it. By now, however, it should be plain that this is so far from actuality that the Himalayas have really been reduced, if not to a secondary status, at least to only one of three in the major class—the other two being the northwestern North American region, and the central eastern Eurasian. Nonetheless, these facts are important and must be re-emphasized, for I am constantly having to remind myself that hardly anything has been published on all the other areas, while intelligent people still say to me almost daily: "Do you really think there is *an* abominable snowman?" with the same old implication that there is just one individual hairy giant, who has been pounding about the upper Himalayan snow-fields for centuries. This impression has, of course, been deliberately fostered in the mind of the general public by press and science alike, since nothing is better than a good debunking and a great number of people don't want anything of this nature found.

It comes as quite a shock, therefore, when one presents a proper list of those who have said not only that they have found foot-tracks of Himalayan ABSMs, or bits of their fur, or their excrement, but who have stated, and in most categoric and detailed terms, that they have seen them, have hunted or been hunted by them, or who know of people killed by them. Actually, the numbers of persons in all these classes runs into the tens of thousands, and has been going on for millennia. In fact, European and American travelers are the only group who *don't* seem to see ABSMs regularly when going through this area, and even some of *them* do. Perhaps the following inventory may make this a bit clearer. I take the famous year 1920 as my real starting point.

S = **Seen by Foreigners**
NS = **Seen by Local Persons**

1887. Major Lawrence A. Waddell, LL.D., C.B., C.I.E., F.L.S., F.A.I., comes across large tracks in Sikkim.

S. 1906. Mr. H. J. Elwes, well-known botanist and explorer, sees an ABSM run over a ridge.

NS. 1915. J. R. O. Gent, British Forestry Officer in the Darjeeling Division reports tracks in the Phalut area, India, and ABSMs seen by local inhabitants.

S. 1920. Stanley Snaith states in his book *At Grips with Everest* that one Hugh Knight, a British explorer, came face to face with an ABSM carrying a crude bow in this year.*

* The search for this Hugh Knight continues. It (or He) is proving every bit as elusive as any ABSMs. The latest comes from Prof. W. C. Osman Hill, since this was written, and states: "I find a book listed in the Royal Geographical Society [of London] library catalogue by a Captain Knight (no initials given) entitled:—Diary of a Pedestrian in Cashmere and Thibet and dated 1863. It may well be the one we are after and if so antedates Waddell."

S. 1921 Lt. Col. C. K. Howard-Bury, on approaching Everest, watched a group of ABSMs on a snow-field at 20,000 feet, through binoculars. Later found their tracks on the spot.

1922. Tracks found on the Birech Ganga Glacier by Englishman who signed his report "Foreign Sportsman."

S. 1923. Members of an Everest Expedition saw "great hairy, naked, man running across a snowfield below," at 17,000 feet.

1924. ————

S. 1925. A. N. Tombazi, Member of the Royal Geographical Society and leader of a photographic expedition to Sikkim, saw an ABSM grubbing for roots with a stick near the Zemu Gap at foot of Mt. Kabu. Later found humanoid footprints at spot.

1926–30. ————

1931. Wing-Commander E. Bentley Beauman, RAF, found tracks at headwaters of the Ganges.

1932–35. ————

1936. (1) Ronald Kaulbach, botanist and geographer, found tracks at 16,000 feet, on pass between the Chu and Salween Rivers near Bumthang Gompa, Nepal.

(2) Eric E. Shipton, famous mountaineer, found tracks on way back to Katmandu from Everest.

1937. (1) A British traveler who signed himself "Balu" found tracks on the Biafua Glacier in the Karakorams.

(2) F. S. Smythe, reported tracks from the Bhyundar Valley, in Garwhal, India. [These were said to have been made by a bear, but there was some reasonable doubt.]

(3) Sir John Hunt found a set of tracks of something apparently wearing boots on the Zemu Gap, also steps cut in the ice, though nobody had passed that gap at that time.

1938. (1) Cairn on top of sacred mountain, taboo to locals, above Rongbuk Monastery, and placed there by climbers, found to have been destroyed and stones moved.

(2) H. W. Tilman, famous mountaineer, finds apparently booted tracks crossing the Zemu Gap, near Menlung, on Darjeeling side.

(3) First American Karakoram Expedition, reports calls, falling rocks, etc.

N.S. 1939. [Reported by Prince Peter of Greece.] Locals got ABSM drunk by leaving liquor at well-head; captured and bound; but creature revived and burst bonds.

1940–41. ———

S. 1942. One Slavomir Rawicz and four companions on flight from Siberian prison camp to India, reported meeting two ABSMs.

1943. ———

S. 1944. A Mr. W. W. Wood, in company with a Major Kirkland and Capt. John B. Maggs, at Liddarwat, near Srinagar, Kashmir, saw a creature bounding down a hillside with zigzag motion. (See below for possible explanation.)

1945–46. ———

NS. 1947. A Yak breeder named Dakhu, a resident of Pangboche, saw one at 50 yards distance. It walked away.

S. 1948. A very strange story of an encounter and fight with a pair of ABSMs near the Zemu Gap, by two Norwegian uranium prospectors, named Aage Thorberg and Jan Frostis. [Suspected fabrication.]

NS. 1949. (1) A villager of Pangboche named Mingma, heard yells, saw ABSM, took refuge in stone hut and observed.

NS. (2) In November an ABSM came out of the forest and played about near the monastery of Thyangboche until driven away by the monks beating gongs and blowing trumpets.

NS. 1950. (1) Sherpa Sen Tensing in company with others saw ABSM at 25 paces near Thyangboche.

NS. (2) One Lakpa Tensing saw a small one sitting on a rock.

NS. (3) Tibetan Lama Tsangi reports having seen one.

1951. Eric Shipton comes across tracks on the Menlung Tsu Glacier, in the Gauri Sanka Range on the way to Everest. Photographs.

1952. (1) Sherpa Pasang Nyima in company with others went to look for an ABSM seen near Namche Bazar, and observed it at 200 yards.

(2) Sir Edmund Hillary with George Lowe find hair on high pass.

(3) Swiss Expedition. Dr. Edouard Wyss-Dunant, with Tensing Norgay, find tracks.

NS. (4) Villager Anseering and wife of Thamnu, see one by forest.

NS. 1953. (1) A Tibetan Lama named Tsultung Zangbu, traveling in Assam, meets one carrying two large rocks. It passed by.

(2) Edmund Hillary finds tracks in Barun Khola range.

1954. (1) The *Daily Mail* Expedition. Sets of tracks found in four widely separated locations. [See Ralph Izzard's account.]

(2) Two Britishers of Hillary's outfit find tracks in the Choyang Valley.

(3) Swiss Expedition; Dr. Norman G. Dyhrenfurth photographs tracks in company with others.

1955. (1) French Expedition on Makalu, find tracks, photographed by the Abbe Bordet, geologist.

(2) Argentinian Mountaineering Expedition, led by famed climber Huerta, reported that one of their porters was killed by an ABSM. No further details available.

(3) RAF Mountaineerng Club Expedition, found tracks.

S. 1956. John Keel, author of "Jadoo," claims to have followed ABSM for 2 days and finally seen it in a swamp.

NS. 1957. (1) First Slick Expedition. Three sets of tracks, excrement, and hairs found at three widely separated locations.

(2) Two Sherpas told Tom Slick they had seen ABSM early that year.

S. (3) Peter and Bryan Byrne, of the Slick Expedition saw ABSM in the Arun Valley.

NS. 1958. (1) Second Slick Expedition. Two Sherpas

with Gerald Russell at low altitude meet *Teh-lma* (Pigmy-type ABSM) by river; numerous tracks seen by Russell.

S.   (2) One Godwin Spani meets an ABSM.

1959. (1) Third Slick Expedition. Numerous tracks found, and ABSMs followed.

(2) Japanese Expedition under Prof. T. Ogawa, finds tracks.

(3) Fukuoka Daigaku Japanese Expedition finds tracks.

1960. Seven separate parties [but not the Hillary expedition, which saw nothing but tried to debunk scalps] of foreigners and numerous locals reported finding tracks, and caves inhabited by ABSMs.

In addition to this somewhat impressive list I have detailed records of many other sightings by both foreigners and natives, but for which no definite date is given or for which I have been unable to obtain a definite date. Then, I have also some delightful expressions by the ethnologists. These scientists seem not to be in the least interested in the grumblings and mutterings of their confreres in other sciences—notably zoology—and seem to have gone merrily on their way and with their work, adopting a slightly amused attitude, at the discomfiture of others. As a fine example of this calm common sense, one cannot do better than quote Prof. C. von Fürer-Haimendorf of the School of Oriental and African Studies, who wrote: "By coining the picturesque name 'The Abominable Snowman' Westerners have surrounded the *yeti* with an air of mystery; but to the Sherpas there is nothing very mysterious about *yeti;* and they speak of them in much the same way as Indian aboriginals speak of tigers. Most Sherpas have seen *yeti* at some time or other, and wall-paintings in monasteries and temples depict two types of them—one resembling a bear and one resembling a large monkey. It is generally known that there are two such types, and in hard winters they come into the valleys and prey on the Sherpas' potato stores, or even on cattle. The idea that it is unlucky to see a *yeti* may be due to an association between the hardships caused by an abnormally heavy snowfall and the appearance of *yeti* near human habitations on such occasions. No particular virtue is ascribed to the headdress of *yeti*-hide in Pangboche; it is freely handled and treated

271

neither with reverence nor with any superstitious fear."[1]

This is one of, if not the most, refreshing statements that I have come across in over a quarter of a century of investigation of the matter of ABSMs. It also stands out as a statement by any scientist on any subject, and on its own merits, quite apart from ABSMery. Would that a zoologist might just once have so pronounced; but then, none who have made pronouncements have ever been to the Himalayas or considered the matter from the local point of view. Almost equally pragmatic is a passage written by Prof. René von Nebesky-Wojkowitz, after a 3-year sojourn in Tibet and Sikkim devoted to ethnographic studies. This reads:

> It is a remarkable fact that the statements of Tibetans, Sherpas, and Lepchas concerning the Snowman's appearance largely coincide. According to their description a warrant for the arrest of this most "wanted" of all the inhabitants of the Himalayas would read as follows: 7 feet to 7 feet 6 inches tall when erect on his hind legs. Powerful body covered with dark brown hair. Long arms. Oval head running to a point at the top with ape-like face. Face and head are only sparsely covered with hair. He fears the light of a fire, and in spite of his great strength is regarded by the less superstitious inhabitants of the Himalayas as a harmless creature that would attack a man only if wounded.
>
> From what native hunters say, the term "snowman" is a misnomer, since firstly it is not human and secondly it does not live in the zone of snow. Its habitat is rather the impenetrable thickets of the highest tracts of Himalayan forests. During the day it sleeps in its lair, which it does not leave until nightfall. Then its approach may be recognized by the cracking of branches and its peculiar whistling call. In the forest the migo moves on all fours or by swinging from tree to tree. But in the open country it generally walks upright with an unsteady, rolling gait. Why does the creature undertake what must certainly be extremely wearisome expeditions into the inhospitable regions of snow? The natives have what sounds a very credible explanation: they say the Snowman likes a saline moss which it finds on the rocks of

[1] Tom Slick, seconded by Peter Byrne, now tells me that the inhabitants of Pangboche never claimed that this was the scalp of an ABSM, but that it was made *in imitation of one* held in a monastery elsewhere, and made from a goat skin.

the moraine fields. While searching for this moss it leaves its characteristic tracks on the snowfields. When it has satisfied its hunger for salt it returns to the forest.

This is not only founded on good common sense and some proper investigation, it is also truly scientific in that it is "imaginative" in its mention of the search by the creatures for "a saline moss." Actually, there are certain lichens (not mosses) in this area, not saline, but veritable vitamin factories, notably of Vitamin E. It is strange that this report had to wait for an ethnologist's mention, since a similar matter has been known to botanists and zoologists for almost half a century, having been the key to Professor Collett's famous and definitive work on the causes of lemming swarmings and emigration. This, that researcher had shown, was the cause of the sudden great increases in virility and resulting swarms of these small rodents due to the continuous excess of these vitamins in their diet, which consist of these lichens for which they dig under winter snow.

Nor are lemmings alone in making a mad dash to get at this vitamin-rich food. The principal reason why birds take the trouble to fly annually for thousands of miles to the edge of the melting polar snows to breed is that the vegetation coming out from under that snow in the spring, and the insects that feed on it, are so rich in vitamins that young birds can be raised healthily on a very limited area. The ABSMs of this very cloudy area periodically need such vitamin and so go up to grub under the rotting snow for it, led by their age-old knowledge, or what is sometimes called instinct—just as some humans have a mad craving to eat certain earths and know exactly which ones and where to dig for them.[2]

But what, you may still want to know, exactly did all these people say they found or saw. I could quote you their actual statements but am not going to do so for two reasons. First, they are almost all already in print and most of them in readily accessible books as listed in the bibliography. As a guide to them, you should read Bernard Heuvelmans' *On the Track of Unknown Animals*, which fully covers the issue. Second, I refrain from so doing because, frankly, even I find them somewhat boring, for they all are so absolutely alike.

[2] Geophagy is widespread and cropped up in New York City a few years ago.

The great majority of the reports are of a roughly man-sized—though of a very large and sturdy man compared to the wiry little Sherpas—ABSM, with a conical head, bull-neck, prognathous jaw, and very wide mouth but no lips, clothed in reddish-brown, thick, short, hairy fur often grizzled in larger specimens and almost black in the smaller, which goes naked but uses sticks on occasion. Its excrement indicates that it is omnivorous, but feeds mostly on small mammals, insects, young birds that it can catch, snails, and various softer vegetable substances. It lives in the upper montane forests but comes out from time to time to grub under the old snow, and in very severe weather it may descend into inhabited valleys and maraud. It has short, very broad feet, with a second toe larger than its big toe while both of these are much wider than the other three and are separated from them. It is shy and retiring unless provoked or imagines itself cornered, when it will put up a terrific display just like a great ape, but seldom carries through its threats.

This is not just the pattern but the identity of the vast body of the reports. However, it is not by any means the only one. There appear to be at least four if not five quite distinct creatures involved in this general area, only two of which are certainly indigenous to the Himalayan ranges themselves and to the "Great Brahmaputra Gutter" within it. These two are the man-sized ABSM described above which is clearly distinguished by the local inhabitants as the *Meh-Teh*, and the little, pigmy type, only from 4 to 5 feet tall, that inhabits the lower and warmer valleys, eats frogs and insects and is generally omnivorous, and which the natives call the *Teh-lma*. This is clothed in very thick red fur with a slight mane, and leaves tiny, 5-inch-long footprints. The third ABSM appears only *to be spoken of* in the area, being an inhabitant of eastern Tibet, Sikang, and the northern Indo-Chinese Massif. This is the *Tok, Kung-Lu, Gin-Sung* creature called by the Sherpas the *Dzu-Teh,* or literally "The Hulking Thing". This by all accounts is immensely taller and bulkier than the *Meh-Teh*, with a black to dark gray, shaggy and long coat, a flat head, beetling brow with a sort of upcurled bang on it, long powerful arms and huge hands, and very human-type feet that leave imprints like those of a giant man but with *two* subdigital pads under the first toe just like the *Sasquatch* and *Oh-Mah*. This is the creature that Bernard Heuvelmans long ago (1951) suggested might be a descendant of, related to, or even actually a *Gigantopithecus,* which at that time was thought to be a pongid rather than a hominid.

The little *Teh-lmas* present a fine problem all their own. They are the least known and the most neglected by everybody. In fact, it was not really until 1957 that even the most ardent ABSM hunters acknowledged their existence, and only one man has done anything about them —W.M. Russell, commonly known to his countless friends all over the world as Gerald. Yet, this is probably the commonest of all ABSMs with an enormous distribution and is certainly "the *Yeti* most likely to succeed," if only somebody would do something about him.

Philologists, such as one Sri Swami Pranavananda and others, in attempting to debunk the whole of ABSMery through their specialized methodology, have created a positive shambles of the Nepalese languages and dialects thereof, and quite apart from calling them all "Tibetan" [sic]. They have tried to show that *teh* has two stems and meanings: one being *treh, t(r)e* or *dred* which they state means a Brown Bear; the other, *te, dey,* or *da,* meaning a ghost. It transpires that they are wrong on both counts and in both cases. [The crypto-esoteric details of all this have been published elsewhere]. Suffice it to be said here that *teh* turns out to mean "manlike *creature.*" The ending *lma* is actually a Buddhistic inversion of *m/ / la,* which might be written for us phonetically as *m'ghoola.* This, in turn is a southern form of a phrase that sounds something like *me-uleēr,* meaning originally an "incarnate vehicle." When used as a qualifying word attached to the name of an animal or other living creature, it implies "a being" or "thing." Thus, the little *Teh-lma,* is actually called—and rather simply, as it turns out in the end—"The Manlike Being." Nothing could be more pragmatic and appropriate.

There is a wealth of information on the form and behavior of this creature to be gleaned from all the native peoples from the western border of Sikang in the east to the feet of the Pamirs on the west, throughout the Himalayas. Practically nothing of this has been recorded simply because nobody realized that there was more than one "abominable snowman" and, even when they did aspire to this obvious intelligence, they simply could not stomach more than two types. As "the other" place was preempted by the mighty *Gin-Sung* or *Dzu-Teh,* the poor little lowland *Teh-lma,* got lost again. It was Gerald Russell who first spotted it as a quite separate species or type, and,

275

due to his long experience in collecting animals, prompted him to concentrate all his efforts on it—and down in the forests. I give the results to you in the words of Peter Byrne, Deputy Leader of the 1957 Slick-Johnson Expedition to search for ABSMs in Nepal. [This is herewith reproduced in full by the kind permission of Peter Byrne and the North American Newspaper Alliance.]

The first sighting was made by a Sherpa villager who said he was hunting edible frogs by the river at night with a torch hung on a bamboo pole. Moving upstream about 300 yards from Gerald's blind the man came upon a wet footprint on a rock. As he swung his torch low to examine it he saw a snowman squatting on a boulder across the stream, 20 yards away. The Sherpa was terrified, for tales of the Yeti in these mountain villages are full of accounts of the creature's strength and habit of killing and multilating men. He shouted in fright. The beast slowly stood on two feet and lumbered unhurriedly upstream into the darkness.

The following night Gerald's Sherpa guide Da Tempa, a veteran Himalayan tracker from Darjeeling, went out with the villager at midnight, the note relates. While Gerald remarked it was "sporting" of the villager to venture out again, he noticed the fellow was trembling with fear and kept behind Da Tempa as they left the camp. After more than an hour of scouting up and down the Choyang River banks, Da Tempa and his companion were making their way back to Russell's camp when Da Tempa saw movement ahead on the trail. He thought it was probably leaves of a bush rustling, but shone his flashlight at the spot.

There, not more than 10 yards away, stood a small ape-like creature, the Snowman! The Snowman advanced deliberately toward the light, and Da Tempa turned and ran. Next morning Gerald said he found four very clear footprints in the gravel trail, which he has photographed. From questioning Da Tempa and the villager these facts emerged about our elusive quarry:

He is about 4 feet 6 inches high, with hunched shoulders and a very pointed head which slopes back sharply from his forehead. He is covered with thick reddish gray hair. His footprints are about 4 inches long. The villager was shown our pictures of bear, orang utan, chimpanzee, gorilla and prehistoric man. He unhesitatingly pointed to the gorilla picture as being most like the creature he saw, but he emphasized the head was more pointed.

As we trekked up the Choyang Valley to meet Gerald, Bryan and I are speculating what this description of the Snowman may mean. Is the beast sighted by Da Tempa the smaller variety of Snowman known as the Meti? Or is it a young of the giant Yeti which has been described as more than 8 feet tall? The footprints are certainly much smaller than the 10-inch tracks left by the animal that twice visited our camp by night in the Barun Valley. The tracks our expedition photographed last year measured 13 inches.

Peter writes again on June 5th (1958) from Gungthang, Nepal:

Frogs are the clue to the Abominable Snowman, and now we are using them as bait for our elusive quarry. Twice our party has seen the Snowman when he came into the dark gorge of the Choyang River at midnight to catch the foot-long yellow frogs for food. Now we have set out live frogs, tied down by fine nylon fishing line, as a lure. We have built a bamboo "machan," or hunter's blind, in a tree commanding a stretch of river baited with frogs and have a second blind of rocks along the bank farther down. From these points of vantage my brother Bryan and I are watching nightly.

We decided on this tactic after a reconnaissance showed where the Snowman had overturned huge river boulders in his search for food. Some were so large it took two of us to move the stones. And we found two footprints in river sand leading to a flat rock on which were the remains of a half-eaten frog. Toe prints were clearly visible in the sand, but the 4-inch prints were smaller than the ones we photographed in the Barun Valley snows some weeks ago. We have been dogged by foul weather, moonless skies and relentless rain.

Heavy rain, light rain, torrential rain and dreary drizzle. This has been the "Chinese water torture" endured by our expedition for more than a month now. The rain begins at 9 a.m., continues all day and night until the dawn sun breaks through the forest with golden streams of light at 5 a.m. It has hampered our plans for tracking the creature.

At midnight, with the rain pouring down in pitch

blackness and waterfall drowning out even the sounds of breaking twigs and falling stones we hunters learn to follow in the dark, our nightly vigil has been a nightmare.

The *Dzu-Teh* is *not* a Himalayan inhabitant. However, there does appear to be still another creature in this province and on the southern rim of Tibet. Now, there seems to be some evidence pointing to this really being a giant *monkey*. [I am for now ignoring the tailed creatures reported by Drs. Moore and Brooks, which would constitute the fifth local unknown, and which I frankly believe to be some huge species of Coloboid Monkey and thus related to the Mangabeys and Guerezas of Africa, and the Langurs, Leaf-Monkeys, Lutongs, Proboscis and Snub-nosed Monkeys of Orientalia.] The Abbé Pierre Bordet has dredged up a tiny gem that is of great significance to this monkey problem. Namely, that the mountain massif that contains Mt. Everest is called by Indians *Mahalangur Himal*, or "The Mountains of the Great Monkeys"—and *not* of great apes, please note. Then, there is also the fact that the Tibetans, as opposed to the Himalayanese peoples, talk freely of a monstrous monkey in their territory that has nothing to do with either the *Dzu-Teh, Meh-Teh,* or *Teh-lma* (which, incidentally, they call in various parts of their country by numerous other names). It is, they say, nothing more than a monkey and has all the habits and characteristics of a monkey, even to a sort of totalitarian bravado and insufferable provocativeness combined with blind cowardice that in extreme cases of defeat may lead to its turning into a completely insensate homicidal maniac. There is but one group of monkeys that so very well fits this billing.

To me it is very strange indeed that neither this whole idea nor the possibility of this particular group of monkeys being involved seems ever to have even been so much as mentioned. The group encountered is the Cynopithecoids or *Cynopithecidae,* the Dog-faced Monkeys, which includes the Gelada and Hamadryad, the Drill and Mandrill, the Baboons, the Black Ape of the Celebes, and the Macaques and Rhesuses. Not only are the largest monkeys members of this group; they are mostly terrestrial; most of them walk on the whole soles of their feet and hands; they have extremely manlike hands; they are certainly of high sagacity and, despite small brains, have a highly developed "social" (or at least communal) system. They are also strongly xenophobic, and, finally, they are in many cases extraordinarily ingenious, facile, and adept at manipulation with their hands. The ancient Egyptians trained some of them (Hamadryads) to weed gardens, stack cordwood, sweep temples, and serve at banquets: a S. African railroader supposedly taught one to throw switches in a signal box and water the engines, and this animal is alleged to have saved a train wreck by pulling the right switches when its master had had a heart attack. That was a baboon. Even more intelligent and amenable to co-ordinated activities, however, are the Giant Rhesus and the strange Stump-tailed Macaques (*Lyssodes*), to which the Japanese "Ape" belongs. The former are customarily trained to collect coconuts on plantations, and the Malayan Forestry Service trained them to collect botanical specimens from the tops of tall trees. As to the mastery of human affairs on the part of the latter I can personally attest from many years' companionship with several individuals. Some of the things they learned to do altogether surpassed anything I have ever seen an ape do, and they work at it with much greater persistence and reliability than do apes. They are, at the same time, incorrigible "slobs," unpredictable to strangers, and terribly dangerous. But, as if this were not enough, there is a positively enormous species that lives in the mountain recesses of that little enclave of Indo-Chinese territory that runs up the eastern face of the Tibet-Sikang Plateau and mountains. This is known as *Lyssodes* (*Macaca*) *thibetanus*.

These huge monkeys inhabit the fastnesses that are also inhabited by the Giant Panda—and which concealed this animal for so long—and these have never been explored. The species of Dawn-Trees (the *Metasequoias*) discovered not so long ago came from there, as also did the very odd Thorold's Deer (*Cervus albirostis*), as well as other rare creatures like the Royal Chinese Sable (*Mustela liu,* a sort of enormous mink) and a small spotted cat just like an Ocelot. These great monkeys have no visible tail, that object being a tiny, flattened, naked twist concealed in the long, rich reddish-brown to orange overcoat that clothes these animals. Sometimes they descend in hordes upon the cultivated valleys of the hill peasantry and completely devastate everything, even attacking and tearing down houses made of mud and wattle, and not, it appears, being in the least frightened of men, even if they use firearms. And there is another interesting point about their behavior. When there is snow on the ground, they sometimes walk on their hind legs, which are very sturdy, albeit with an arm-swinging and staggering gait but which, I was told by an observer, seems to be due more to the deep snow than to any imbalance. Apparently, like apes, they do not like to get their hands cold by putting them on the snow.

These monkeys have rather short faces that are naked and pink, going bright red in heat and bluish in cold. Their other naked parts are dirty gray. The head is very curiously shaped, having practically no forehead but beetling brows, is flattened from side to side and comes to a point above but then has great domes of long hair running from the corner of the eyes back to the neck to join a profuse mane. Normally, these animals walk on all fours with a kind of strutting pace, the four limbs being of about equal length. One I saw in Hong Kong had a head and body [the head is carried straight ahead but the face does not point downward] length of three foot six, measured directly and *not* along the curvature of the body. My Chinese traveling companion, who had collected in outer Szechwan, told me that this was but a moderately small male and that if a really big leader-male stood up on his feet, as they sometimes do, he would look me eye for eye—I am exactly 6 feet. These monkeys go in snow.

My comment here is that, in view of the existence of these huge, tailless monkeys in the province concerned just east of Tibet, and in view also of certain remarks made by the great 19th-century explorer, General Pereira, who was and is still just about the only Westerner really to have crossed this territory and, again, to passing references made by the Abbé Père David [discoverer of the otherwise extinct primitive deer, named after him, in the Manchu royal parks, and in a way of the *Bei-Shung* or Giant Panda], there could well be a giant species of mountain Macaque in eastern Tibet that may occasionally enter the Himalayan Oriental Province and then become extremely "difficult" if met by a lone yak-herder. [I have a record of a fairly large party of unarmed Indian peasantry being attacked by the ordinary little *Bandas,* or Rhesus Monkeys, in the Punjab.] Also, it is just possible that the same or a related type of Cynopithecoid may be found in the Karakoram, and one of them could be the creature that a Mr. W. W. Wood and companions saw in 1944. He specifically states that this jumped "from side to side" or zigzagged. This is a most typical method of progression of many if not all monkeys when in a hurry on the ground, and especially on downgrades, but one which they adopt even on perfectly level, unencumbered areas. Also, please note that the locals with Mr. Wood definitely called the creature *banda* or "monkeys."

At this point I want to interject a very definite statement to my readers, to persons who may review this book, and to those of the scientific fraternities who might have gotten this far without having used the thing to throw at students or had an apoplectic fit. This is that *I do not for one moment suggest that ABSMs are Giant Rhesus monkeys*.

What I *am* trying to say is that, in addition to the two very distinct forms of ABSM in this, the Himalayan South Tibet province—the *Meh-Teh* and the *Teh-lma*—there *could* be, first, a very large form of Coloboid Monkey in the coniferous montane forests, related to the Langurs and *Rhinopithecus;* and, second, a really giant form of *Lyssodes* or Stump-tailed Macaque, which *might* be the origin of *some* of the Tibetan (and *notably* the Tibetan) reports. The really giant *Dzu-Teh, Tok,* or *Gin-Sung,* of the eastern Eurasian Massif and the Indo-Chinese Block, definitely *is* an ABSM, and more than probably a full Hominid, but is known to the Nepalese only by hearsay from their Tibetan relatives. But there are still more complications in the Himalayan region. These are really of quite a different nature, and extend as far from ABSMery in one way as giant Cynopithecoids do in the other. This is the matter of Men.

This great province is not yet fully explored or known. When some soldiers employed by a person entitled the Rajah of Mustang, a sub-autonomous province of northwestern Nepal, killed an animal a few years ago that they did not know but which had been scaring villagers in their territory, it was declared to be a *yeti* (i.e. an ABSM). The beast was most adequately photographed while still freshly killed, lying on a pristine white sheet. Later, it was carefully skinned with its extremities complete and was shipped with its boiled skull to Katmandu. It turned out to be a Sloth-Bear (*Melursus*). However, this is not the point. What is, is the fact that nobody had ever heard of Mustang; thought it was a kind of wild horse in our "West"; and that somebody was kidding. Even the wire-service representatives in Katmandu, capital of Nepal, could not get any clear answer as to whether there really was such a place, or to whom it belonged, even if only nominally. The same goes for most of the inner Himalaya and much more so for the Karakorams. There are some really delightful stories emanating from these parts, not the least extraordinary of which was solemnly put out by two Canadian scientists named Jill Crossley-Batt and Dr. Irvine Baird of Montreal.

These two allegedly conducted ethnological studies there in the year 1921, and they stated that "In an isolated spot in the Himalayas, at 17,000 feet" they had discovered a "lost tribe of Chaldeans" who painted on goatskins with vegetable dyes, and who all lived to be 107 years old. Statements such as this just about floor me; more especially when some innocent is clobbered for remarking casually that he saw a funny fish in a net off Florida, or some such mild thing. Even the wildest moron playing hookey from a high school would be hard put to it to crowd more extremities into a single statement. Why Chaldeans; and, on what grounds? And who can tell that anybody lives to over 100, let alone a whole tribe; and why 107 years, precisely? The whole thing is a bit balmy but there it is, and we just have to try and cope with it.

This is, indeed, an exceptional case, but there has always been a great deal of mumbling about "lost races," "mystics," hermits, pilgrims, and outcasts in this area. True, quite a number of Hindu pilgrims do visit the Brahmaputra Gutter from India, and there are ascetics living all over the place high above the tree-line: also, there never was capital punishment in Tibet—that country being profoundly Buddhistic—and really annoying persons were always just thrown out of the community and told to fend for themselves. This, they have done for long periods, living until their clothes rotted away, while the law-abiding citizenry was absolutely forbidden to contact, aid, or have anything to do with these criminal outcasts. However, being Tibetans and Himalayans, and thus predominantly Mongoloid, these persons all started out with particularly hairless skins, so that they simply cannot be put forward as candidates for ABSMs. [Besides, they grow very long head-hair.] When, however, it comes to the Buddhist ascetics—the so-called Lung-Gompa—we meet quite a different condition.

These men deny normal life and take first to monasteries where they really study the supernatural, and in patterned stages, under persons with a tremendous fund of knowledge. What they learn is quite beyond us and, frankly, neither understandable to nor even believed in by Westerners. However, they do in time seem to acquire some quite remarkable talents that smack of the magical.

Dr. Julian Huxley has spoken seriously of their ability to melt a circle of 8 feet in diameter in 2-foot snow, simply by taking thought upon the matter; and others have described them as being able to teleport themselves; that is, to be transported instantaneously from one place to another; and, most certainly, to be able to send news in advance as quickly as by radio, though no radio exists. Of all of this I know nothing *factual* but of one fact I do have evidence. This is that the initiates to these disciplines do, at one stage of their training, go galloping about the countryside, stark naked, and in the worst of weather, and particularly at sunrise and sundown, for the good of their souls and the exorcism of sundry worldly hang-overs. They may then be a pretty eerie sight, charging through the rhododendron thickets and sometimes even howling a bit. But these chaps are almost as commonplace to the Himalayans as are mailmen to us: and they are not hairy, don't have separated second and first toes, don't eat raw mouse-hares or any other meat, and don't run around gibbering.

There is one rather delightful story about a *Hindu* pilgrim, however, which just goes to show what human beings can do. A certain Colonel Henniker of the British Army was crossing a 17,000-foot pass in Ladakh in 1930, in a blinding snowstorm, when he perceived a rather skinny fellow, clothed only in a loincloth, and using a staff, tramping stolidly Tibetward. Amazed, he hailed the man in English and received the astonishing and cheery reply "Good morning, Sir: and a Happy Christmas." [It was mid-July]. There may, in fact, be all manner of queer types wandering about in these appalling fastnesses; clothed or unclothed; fed or unfed; and everyone minding his own particular business.

It takes a great deal of patience and some ingenuity—as well as exceedingly good manners and taste—to get in with the local people and to be sufficiently accepted by them to hear what they really have to say. We of the West tend to adopt a lordly attitude to everybody else, and often in our own ignorance give away, by gesture alone, if nothing else, that we are mocking anything that we don't understand. The Himalayans are very wise, and perspicacious people.

But for all their wonderful qualities, it is not to the Sherpas and other Nepalese, nor to the people of the Himalaya as a whole that we must turn for some real pragmatic information about ABSMs. Rather, we should go to the Tibetans proper. Their whole attitude is utterly different, for they appear to have the whole thing down "pat," and, they just don't bother to argue the details. To them, there are three kinds of these creatures—called, as I have already said, by many names. They are not much interested in *Teh-lmas*, in that they dwell in the lower regions, of which there are none in their exalted land. *Meh-Teh* they know and treat as just another thing indigenous to the land, but of the hulking *Dzu-Teh* they take a really peeved notion. They say this vast creature is hard to handle and it raids yak herds; that they go in groups; they can get along in appalling climatic conditions; and they have all the ingenuity of humans, plus strength with which one is really almost unable to cope. That is why, they also say, they keep the skins of those which their compatriots slay, or mummify their bodies and put them away, but not so much out of respect but simply as "hereditary awful-warnings" to other men. Real Tibetans have spoken of all this to both Nepalese and to many foreigners in Nepal, and one much respected Lama named Punyabara even offered to bring back one of each of the three kinds alive, if the Government would put up the money. My permissible comment is herewith terminated but perhaps I can afford to extend myself a little and make a few, more general comments at this point.

With all the above, how is it possible for anyone to state flatly that there is nothing in the Himalayan region to be investigated? This, I personally and simply cannot see. There have been those over the years who have endeavored to prove that nothing exists there; and many have tried by disproving or "showing up" one facet of the matter to show that all the rest is either myth, legend, or folklore. But, when you take each of these individual complaints, you find that none of them jibes with all the others, while each of them in turn itself proves not to hold water. The ever-recurrent notion, for instance, that the tracks are made by local people wearing a particular type of loose footgear resembling a mukluk or moccasin—and which was recently again brought forward by one Michel Peissel in *Argosy* Magazine (December, 1960)—is obviously both absurd and impossible if only the advocates would just spend a few moments thinking logically about the matter. If this Mr. Peissel had considered the following facts for a moment, he would not have written as he did.

If these ABSM tracks—which, you will note, have baffled just about every really experienced mountaineer for over a century—were made by a local man wearing footgear such as he suggests, then, first, every one must have worn out the front half of both feet precisely, and in such a manner that neither shoe ever showed a single mark of where it ended or the bare toes protruded. Second, the men wearing these overshoes must all have been of an extremely rare type—if they ever existed—having the second toe larger than the first, and both of them, and *on both feet,* also widely separated from the rest of the toes. That there could be so many such freaks among the limited population of this one area is much too much to ask. Also, it is manifest that Mr. Peissel has never seen an imprint or a cast of the foot that made the medium-sized [or *Meh-Teh*] tracks. They are positively shocking when first seen, being absolutely enormous—and the gaps between the separated toes are enormous too, which could not happen physically if the whole was enlarged by melting and regelation. Almost the same goes for those, like Sir Edmund Hillary, who have attempted to debunk the scalps. Maybe these are made from the shoulder skins of a Serow (*Capricornis*), but were the makers not imitating something else they knew? And these things are, in any case, only playthings, like Christmas hats. Further, even if they are not genuine yeti scalps, what made the fresh foot-tracks?

Let us not forget that the Kraken, the giant squid, was regarded as a fable for centuries until Prof. A. E. Verrill took a small boat and went and got one alive off the coast of Newfoundland. *Everybody,* except the North Atlantic fishermen had said that they did not, and *could not* exist, but reports of them persisted in coming in every year. I think people should pause, read the facts, and also consider a while, before making definitive statements about the ABSMs of the Himalayas, or of anywhere else, for that matter.

13. The Western Approaches

RUSSIAN FINDINGS IN THE CAUCASUS AND THEREABOUTS

We have now reached the summit. Further, I have to admit, albeit with reluctance, that all my reportage up to this exalted point looks, both in retrospect and in view of what now faces us, pretty paltry. In fact, the old saw about straining at gnats intrudes itself on my attention, unwanted but persistent. It were as if I had up till now been squeezing a sponge of its last drop of information when what has already been said is reviewed in the light of what we now have to tackle. Whereas the reports even from such ASBMally rich areas as British Columbia may be counted on your fingers and toes, we now find ourselves confronted with literally thousands of them, spread over a thousand years in time, and throughout a triangular area with sides measuring approximately 5000, 4000, and 3000 miles in length. Moreover, these reports increase in number per annum on what looks suspiciously like geometrical progression so that the greater part of them are bunched up in the immediate past. Also it now transpires, the matter on hand has been pursued, and even scientifically pursued, in this area for over a century, though that pursuit has been plagued by all the same asininities and obstructions as elsewhere.

At this juncture a few words on the gruesome subject of geopolitics are called for. Most political boundaries are ridiculous. At one extreme we have gross misconceptions about "continents," at the other, such absurdities as the delineation of the North American state of Montana. In between these extremes man has further insisted on erecting quite arbitrary fences—such as that between the United States of northern North America and the United States of Mexico—though these are sometimes called iron, bamboo, or "curtains" of other materials. Ridiculous terms like "the Near East" and "the Middle East," both of which lie in what is manifestly and geographically *The West*, add to the confusion; and then, to top it all off, we get purely political expressions such as "East" and "West," bits of both of which are now scattered all over the globe inside each other. Then, some buffoon (like Haushofer or Treitschke) must needs go and coin the phrase "The Heartland" but omit to define it. In some respects, such a concept is a splendid idea, as it implies a central blob which pumps away without cease or surcease, and, if applied to a certain area in central Eurasia, it makes a lot of sense ethnologically. Yet, the area that was finally pinned down for this happens always to have been one of the greatest ethnological blanks—this is the lowlands between the Urals and the great mountain barrier that cuts straight across Eurasia from southwest to northeast—while the "pumping" appears always to have gone on beyond that lofty barrier to the east.

If people insist on splitting themselves into two ethnological camps and calling these "West" and "East," they would be well advised to consider some ineradicable geographical facts. The most pertinent of these is this monstrous mountain barrier lying athwart Eurasia, since it has always formed, and will always form, the true dividing line between west and east. It lies along and constitutes the *eastern* boundary of the U.S.S.R.; and, if you want to be precise about the matter, it also forms by extension the southern boundary of that vast Union. Today also it forms the boundary between the Mongoloid-type peoples and the Caucasoid-type peoples; and I add the suffix "-type" most firmly because a not inconsiderable body of the peoples west of the barrier were originally Mongoloids, and some on the east side originally Caucasoids but today (in the now almost classic expression of a certain comedian imitating a Chinese waiter): "So funny; all American look alike": so also do all Europeans, even the mongoloid Magyars. This great dividing line is of the utmost significance.

ABSMs are not found west or north [1] of this line but they are reported from all along its edge and more or less all over the eastern area exclusive of the subcontinent of India and the eastern fringe of islands, as we have already

---

[1] Incorrect: They have now been reported from northeastern Siberia. [Private communication from Prof. B. F. Porshnev.]

noted. At the same time our information on ABSMs in this area, apart from the Himalayas and the Indo-Chinese Peninsula, comes almost exclusively from or through the Russians who are, of course, wholly in the *Western* area. This last fact may be rather puzzling to the general reader and somewhat aggravating to students of disciplines other than the purely geographic and biologic. Nonetheless, short of a major shift in the earth's crust, nothing—not even an all-out nuclear war—can alter the facts. Nature constructed our bed in the "West," and we might just as well make up our minds that we have got to lie in it together! [I cannot refrain from adding, purely as a student of plant and animal distribution, that we might also just as well give up any thoughts of trying to go and lie in any other peoples' beds; not only because, as in the case of eastern Eurasia, it is a bit crowded, but much more definitely because none of them are *our* environment. If we do so, we'll go Mongoloid or Negroid in time either by absorption or physical mutation, just as the Magyars have become Caucasoids in a few hundred years after landing up in our bailiwick.]

Considerations such as these are often regarded as what is euphemistically called political. They are not; they are purely biological. What is more, if such *facts* rather than a lot of (often mistaken) *ideas* were used to guide our policies and our activities, our species would get along much better. Early, primitive, and ancient man seems to have appreciated these facts if only instinctively, and acted accordingly. ABSMs seem to have had the clue since the first. Driven out of their original lowland forest homes they retreated into the montane forests, and particularly into those areas within those vegetational zones where Modern Man finds it hardest to get along. This is true "survival of the fittest": we might well emulate the forlorn ABSMs. The process happens also to make an otherwise appalling task a lot easier for this reporter. All I have to do is locate said particular regions, and the great mass of facts now to be presented then falls into a very fair semblance of order. The mess can be broken down into manageable parts—geographical units—and presented one at a time in logical sequence. To this I shall now proceed.

Let us assume that we have ended up at the northwestern end of the Lesser Himalayas. This lands us in an area known as Gilgit which now lies in the north of Western Pakistan. [I apologize for this and a coming plethora of "political" definitions but there is nothing that a mere biologist can do about it.] At this point (see Map XV) you will note that we are very close to (on the right side, going west) the end of the even more mighty Karakorams, which in turn constitute an extension of the "Mother of All Mountains," the *Muh-Dzhura rDzhung pBlhüm* of the Tibetans, and which we have called the southern Tibetan Rim. Ahead of us lies a most unpleasant complex of mountains known as the Pamirs or "The Roof of the World." These form a nodal point for all kinds of things in Eurasia—plants, people and other animals, languages, *and* ABSMs.

The Pamirs may be likened to a monstrous starfish with the appropriate five arms. These are vast strings of mountain ranges that go off in all directions—the Himalayas; the Karakorams; the Kunluns leading to the Altyn Tagh and Nan-Shans; the Altai Tagh leading to the Tien-Shans; and finally the Hindu-Kush going off to the west.[2] From this point we have first to follow the Hindu-Kush in order to get rid of a rather irksome business. This is that ABSMs have been reported from all along the extension of those mountains, which is to say along the Ala Dagh and Elburz in Iran to Azerbaijan and the Caucasus. There are those who regard the Caucasus as being in "Europe." As a matter of fact, nobody has ever made up their minds just where Europe does end in the east [*vide: Europe: How Far?* by W. H. Parker in *The Geographical Journal*, Vol. CXXVI, Part 3, pp. 278–297, September 1960]; and rather naturally, since it does not do so anywhere, being only a large peninsula at the western side of Eurasia. If this peninsula needs definition—and it does—it should be considered as lying west of the 30th meridian east which runs roughly from the White Sea to the Bosphorous. The Caucasus area is profoundly in Eurasia proper.

The Hindu-Kush, Ala Dagh, and Elburz, together with the lower Caspian Sea, form the southern boundary of the Turkmen S.S.R. Between the Caspian and the Black Sea there are really two great mountain ranges with a lowland gutter between them. The southern is composed of Armenia and Azerbaijan in the U.S.S.R.; the north is the Caucasus. Both are still very rugged and over their

[2] Place names from now on are going to become as awful as political definitions. I have tried to confine myself to larger generalities that are shown on the map, and identify places that are not on that map by these generalities.

upper reaches uninhabited by humans, and the latter appears to be a retreat of ABSMs. Their presence is fully accepted over both areas not only by mountain folk but also by inhabitants of the lowland villages and towns around their peripheries. As one of the Russian reports puts its, however, the younger generation put on a show of scoffing at the whole thing, probably in order to appear "modern," while the older people are most reluctant to speak about the creatures for deep-seated and most ancient "religious" reasons. This matter was made abundantly clear to me by the Rabbi Yonah ibn Aharon, who points out that there still remains a prehistoric animism throughout this whole swath of Eurasia in the precepts of which the souls of people enter the lower anthropoids, which latter are consequently held in such great reverence that even the mention of their names is most ill-advised. ABSMs, known in this area as *Kaptar* or *Kheeter*, seem to be regarded as the highest of all anthropoids and nearest of all "animals" to man.

There are dozens of reports on these *Kaptar* having been seen in recent years, as distinct from the endless older reports and myths, legends, and folklore. Many of these are very precise and really quite scientific in that they were reported by properly trained persons with the usual Russian mania for precision and suitable confirmation. This makes them the more instructive and convincing. I would that I could quote them in their original form but, alas, we don't read Russian so the best I can attempt is a paraphrasing of translations, using from time to time phraseology that may look quaint to us but which must be retained as expressing more exactly what the raconteur had in mind in his own language. Russian is almost as "mobile" a language as English and, when reporting in it, shades of meaning are most important. [Calling upon another language, to explain what I mean, the Spanish word *noticias* does not mean precisely "notices"; a good translator expresses it better as "advices upon (a subject) to everybody, by persons who are presumed to know what they are talking about" but with a distinct indication that the editor does not take full responsibility for same. This is a rather more precise form of our loose phrase "informed sources state."] One must bear in mind that the average Russian, especially when making a deposition or statement on which he may be called, often places more emphasis on the qualifying words than, perhaps, on the word itself. Thus "The Engineer X told me in Tomsk that when he was in Omsk . . ." has a very special meaning, and aids us in assessing what he finally records.

I could devote a whole book, let alone a full chapter to these reports of ABSMs from the Caucasus but, for obvious reasons can only give some examples. However, I will add the conclusions of the reporters since they are so very sane, orderly, and significant. The only other people who have published such sane statements on this subject that I know of are the Canadians. It is a pleasure to get back to fact without a gross overlay of preconceived ideas, prejudice and doubt.

The main range of the Caucasus runs from the Black Sea coast about Krasnodar southeast to the peninsula on which the famous port of Baku is situated on the Caspian Sea. The range is divided into two blocks of higher mountains, the smaller in the northwest; the greater forming the boundary between the Dagestan A.S.S.R. and Chechen on the north and east side, and Georgia and what is called the Trans-Caucasian republics (Armenia and Russian Azerbaijan) on the south. There is a particularly wild area cutting across this block and known as the Tlyaratin, which embraces practically the whole basin of the River Jurmut and the upper parts of the Avarskoy Koysu which is a tributary of the Sulak, the main river of Dagestan.[3] These mountainous regions are clothed in dense, montane, coniferous forests right up to the snow line and right down to the edges of the few villages that lie on the adjacent lowlands, and are, over wide stretches, really quite impenetrable. At the same time, the upper crags and rocky reaches are equally unapproachable except by well-organized professional mountaineering expeditions. Despite the most ancient civilization of the

[3] As far as possible I have endeavored to choose place names, such as Krasnodar and Baku, that can be readily found in standard atlases, and to use the traditional English spellings for these though these are almost invariably quite different from the official Russian and/or local spellings. Names that are not to be found on readily obtainable atlases or maps are spelt as given by the translators of the publications from which they were taken. In many cases in this and the following chapter I quote names that do not appear on any obtainable maps. These may well be altogether inaccurately spelt, having been rendered phonetically first into Russian and thence into English. The results may be quite horrible to the local citizens. For this I duly apologize, in the unlikely event that they ever read this book.

Caucasian region as a whole, and of the adjacent Armenian block to the south, huge areas remain quite unexplored. In these, large game reserves have been established, and these are populated by a very large and varied fauna including moose, some remaining Wisent or European Bison, Red Deer, mountain Sheep, Brown Bear, wolves, the great northern Lynx, and the Leopard. [The Snow Leopard's range does not extend west of the Hindu-Kush. However, Tiger occur in the Elburz Ranges even west of Teheran.]

Opposite the Georgians, on the northeast side of the main ranges, the hill folk are called Avars, those herders and hunters who have for centuries penetrated farther upward into these fastnesses than any others. Among them there is universal belief in and acceptance of the ABSMs they call the *Kaptar*. Surrounding peoples regard them with increasing skepticism as Folklore, Legend, or Myth in proportion to their distance from these unexplored uplands; which is the invariable rule as we shall see when we come to examine these matters. The description they give of this creature is remarkably clear and quite invariable except for one set of facts. These concern the number of kinds of *Kaptar* that exist. The discussion on this point stems mostly from those who live farthest from the area where they are met with, and it has become enmeshed in a certain amount of straight myth, notably the curious notion that all of one kind are females. According to Russian investigators, however, those who so claim are the least likely to have firsthand knowledge of the matter, while they were quite unable to explain how this race of females reproduces and maintains itself. The notion of self-perpetuating, virgin birth, if I may so express the notion, has been widespread since time immemorial. It sounds absurd but, of course, it is not biologically impossible per se; at the same time, there is one very simple explanation for it. Even modestly civilized people sometimes separate the sexes in everyday living quarters, and my wife and I once spent some time with a tribal group of South Amerinds and had to reside in separate though adjacent villages. Then again, ABSMs seem to show a marked sexual dimorphism everywhere they are reported, this showing not only in size, but in color of fur or hair, while the young are said to look different again. Also, most ABSMs are stated to be solitary, only occasionally seen in pairs or with young in tow. The females, it seems, tend to associate in going to water, in food gathering, and so forth,

292

while the males range widely. They are food gatherers rather than hunters and this we must not forget.

In the Caucasian region, the males seem to be encountered alone in the upper fastnesses whereas the females, which are readily recognizable it is said by the great and sometimes positively enormous development of their breasts (which, unlike any pongids, are pendant or hanging), show up at lower levels. Then, a Dwarf *Kaptar* is also spoken of, particularly on the southern face of the mountains, but as one Prof. V. K. Leontiev, who studied this business locally, with consummate discipline, observes, nothing is stated about these beings that obviates their being the young ones or "teen-agers," who also tend to band together and go off on their own. They are said to be smaller than the average man and to be clothed in reddish brown wool as opposed to the other two types—one of which, be it noted, is said always to be a male, while the other is always female; from which one may draw a rather obvious assumption one would have supposed—which are variously described as being dark gray, black, or silvered hair. This change of coat color, from gingery to gray-brown, to gray-black, and finally to white with age, is just as consistent with what is found among other Primates as is the change from shiny black in youth, as displayed by the sad little Jacko of the Fraser River, to brown and then grizzly. One must note that, with increasing age, those of us whose head-hair turns white will find that our axillary and pubic hairs do the same while those who have profuse chest hair will see that it also follows the head-hair in this respect. Thus a venerable male ABSM might be as white as the old chap who paced the truck in Oregon (at 35 mph. be it noted) and then popped into a lake. If Neanderthalers were hairy, they may well have had a fluffy wool, like that of a baby One-humped Camel as is so repeatedly stated by almost all the Eurasians who say they have met their local small ABSMs, and an "overcoat" of darker hairs like a muskrat and most other mammals of cooler climates, which develops with age, becomes profuse and dominant in the prime of life, and then goes silvery to pure white with age.

I cannot find any suggestion that there is more than one type of ABSM in this area, despite the fact that three quite distinct sets of names are applied to it there. The indigenous name is *Kaptar* and its derivatives and associates, but the Kirghiz "*Gul-i-aban*" group is also used among peoples of similar origin, while I find that the more distantly originating "*Almas*" stem also crops up in the form of "*Almasty*" and "*Albasty*." Some painstaking analysis of the origins of the reports of these names used in connection with the Caucasus area however brings to light the fact that the reports in which they were used were made by "foreigners" or at least by members of groups that are known to have moved in from the east. The Caucasus is an appalling mix-up; a sort of Grand Central Station for nomads, conquerors, emigrants, immigrants, wanderers, lost tribes, lost causes, and perhaps also indigenous evolution—hence the designation "Caucasoid" which actually means nothing. The oldest people in the area, which is to say those of whom we have no record of immigration, such as the Georgians and Avars, one and all adhere to the *Kaptar* designation for their local ABSMs —which, incidentally, have been perhaps facetiously called "Wind Men" by more frivolous outsiders!

That these manifestly original Caucasians—if not Caucasoids—are of one variety comes as rather a relief, especially at this juncture and before plunging into inner Asia, because there we are going to be beset by affirmations from all sides that there are not just two or three kinds in any one area, but that these are all quite different from others in other areas. I am not quite sure if we will be able to keep our heads through all that, and I am sure that I have not yet myself got it all straight, but in the meantime we may take what the Hollanders call a pause (but pronounce *powzer*) and try to come to grips with the *Kaptar*.

The clearest account of this creature is a firsthand one reported by none other than the Prof. V. K. Leontiev mentioned before and who is graced in one publication [No. 120, of the Third Publication of the Special Commission to Study the Snowman of the U.S.S.R. Academy of Sciences, under the Direction of Prof. B. F. Porshnev and Dr. A. A. Shmakov] with the illuminating title of "Hunting Instructor of the Ministry of Hunting of Dagestan A.S.S.R." This is a man both of parts and of profound precision. I herewith paraphrase his account with due regard to that precision but with considerable compression.

It appears that in late July 1957, this gentleman with three associates was conducting an official investigation of a territory called the Gagan Sanctuary. On August 5 his companions returned to their headquarters as their work was finished, and Leontiev decided to make a few days' tour on his own. He was then at the head of the Jurmut River and spent two days there checking on some glaciers; he then trekked up a tributary stream. He notes that he came across leopard tracks on a patch of snow. After a rest overnight he continued onward and came across a set of quite different tracks on another patch of snow. He says that "you had the impression that this animal was walking on his toes—never getting very heavy on his heels . . . you could see that his big toe was unusually developed, but was it a toe or a claw? These footprints were deformed somewhat because of the snow being slightly in a melted condition."

The next night he camped under an overhanging rock but when preparing for sleep, "All of a sudden there came a strange cry. It stopped as suddenly as it started," he writes. "Then after a pause it repeated again; this time somewhere to the side of the original one. Then it was quiet. The cry was not repeated again. The cry was very loud. It wasn't like the yell of an animal—not any wild mammal or bird known to me could make such a sound, and yet it couldn't be a human being either. [And he is a professional wildlife conservator.] From where I was sitting to the origin of the cry was approximately 100 meters [110 yards], and at the time the cry was repeated, 200 meters. I just say approximately." The following day appears to have been a miserable one so that he decided to camp before dark at the head of the stream in a very dark gap. He ran out of matches and all the wood was wet but he just managed to keep the fire going long enough to brew tea; then, he chanced to look up at a neighboring snowfield to the south. Something moving thereon caught his eye and of this he wrote: "This creature was going across, ascending slightly the upper part, and away from me. At the moment I saw him he was approximately 50 to 60 meters away from me. It was sufficient to have only one glance of him to know that this was a *Kaptar*."

Leontiev goes on to state that it exactly resembled the descriptions he had obtained from all the locals adding, "He was walking on his feet, not touching the ground with his hands. His shoulders were unusually wide. His body was covered with long dark hair. He was about 2.2 meters [about 7 feet] tall." Realizing that this was a chance for the procurement of the most priceless scientific information but also realizing that he could neither catch nor, if he did, overcome the creature, Leontiev took careful aim and fired a shot at its feet. However, by this time the *Kaptar* was at extreme range for his rifle and he does not seem to have hit it for it turned to him and then with incredible speed waltzed about and ran up the slope with tremendous speed, cutting through the snowfield, reaching high rocks beyond and disappearing. Leontiev tried to follow but it was hopeless so he measured and sketched the footprints before it got dark. The next morning he re-examined these, made more sketches, and then spent the day searching around for the creature. Being out of food he had to leave the next day.

Altogether he estimates that he had the *Kaptar* in view for 5 to 7 minutes and pursued him for 9. He saw his back, left side and cheek; when he fired he had just a second's sight of the face for it was late evening, beginning to snow, and he could not see much detail. He then makes some most interesting remarks, to wit: "He was not too tall [7 foot would seem enormous to me, *Author*]; his shoulders were unusually wide; his arms were long— longer than a man's but shorter than a monkey's. His feet were *slightly bent* and very heavy [italics mine], and the whole body was covered with a dark gray fur. The length of the hair on the body was shorter than the hair or fur of a bear. He had especially long hair on his head. I had the impression that the hairs on the head were darker than on the body. I couldn't see anything of a tail. I couldn't see any ears. The head was massive, and when he turned to me, I saw for one second his face. It was somewhat like an elongated animal face, the general outline of the nose, lips, and forehead, or the chin or the eyes I couldn't see. I had the impression that his face, like his body was covered with hair. His back was slightly bent; he was stoop-shouldered. His general appearance was human-like. If you want to compare the *Kaptar* with some living creature the best comparison would be to think of him as a tall, massively built, wide-shouldered man, with a heavy growth on his face and the rest of his body."

Leontiev measured and sketched the *Kaptar's* footprints when only a few minutes old. Of them he says: "This footprint had a very strange formation. The whole print was about 25 centimeters [about 9 inches] long.[4] The general impression was of the toes pushed deeply into the snow. Also around the toes you could see some rough formation.

---

[4] There would seem to be something wrong here. A 9-inch foot for a 7-ft. giant seems most improbable (*Author*).

The explanation is, of course, that he was walking with bent knees and like 'clawing' into the snow. The [outer] four toes did not come very close to each other, as in humans, but they were slightly spread out—about ½ of a centimeter to 1 centimeter. The width of the big toe was 3½ centimeters; in length, 9 centimeters. The length of the other toes about 5 centimeters. You had the impression that on all the toes there were very hard scar tissue formations—that the toes were widely separated and in between there was scar tissue formation. The entire print narrowed down toward the heel, and there were two parallel deep ridges like wrinkles. You had the impression that it was not the whole step, and only the toes. This was not too unusual because when I looked at my own footprints I noticed that I put a little harder on the toes than on a heel and actually, that's the way the *Kaptar* would walk. The large toe was very far apart from the rest and it was very long. It seems when you look this over and study the print, the entire heel of the foot is covered with a thick growth of a tough hide interspersed with all kinds of little growths and heavy wrinkles. There were no claws at all. This footprint has no resemblance to the footprints of any of the animals that I know. It doesn't look like a footprint of a bear, and, of course, is entirely different from a footprint of a human heel.

"The cry of the *Kaptar* is very strange and you cannot compare it with anything else. It consists of several repeating high-and-low pitched sounds, that remind you of the sound of a gigantic chord. There is certainly a kind of metallic quality about them. In the cry you can hear some plaintive note too. I, personally, did not experience any fear hearing this cry, but to me they seem to express the loneliness of a lost creature. I could not hear any coherent sounds, or perhaps I couldn't quite catch the fine shadings of the sound, just the way a human being pronounces them. The name *cry,* or terminology *cry* actually does not describe the sound that the *Kaptar* issues. This cry is peculiar, and so much of its own, that there would be many different ways of describing it and no particular way to give it *real* definition. At any rate, not any of the mammals or birds that I know have a cry similar to the *Kaptar*."

This is by no means the only close encounter with a *Kaptar* in modern times. First there are literally dozens of reports from locals including whole village populations who reported them about at various times, and sometimes for months and at low levels. Then also, one appears to have been captured in 1941 and physically examined by a lieutenant-colonel of the Medical Service of the Soviet Army, by the name of V. S. Karapetyan. I give this report verbatim as supplied to me, already translated, by the courtesy of the Russian Information Service. It goes as follows:

"From October to December of 1941 our infantry battalion was stationed some thirty kilometers from the town of Buinaksk [in the Dagestan A.S.S.R.]. One day the representatives of the local authorities asked me to examine a man caught in the surrounding mountains and brought to the district center. My medical advice was needed to establish whether or not this curious creature was a disguised spy.

"I entered a shed with two members of the local authorities. When I asked why I had to examine the man in a cold shed and not in a warm room, I was told that the prisoner could not be kept in a warm room. He had sweated in the house so profusely that they had had to keep him in the shed.

"I can still see the creature as it stood before me, a male, naked and bare-footed. And it was doubtlessly a man, because its entire shape was human. The chest, back, and shoulders, however, were covered with shaggy hair of a dark brown colour [it is noteworthy that all the local inhabitants had black hair]. This fur of his was much like that of a bear, and 2 to 3 centimeters long. The fur was thinner and softer below the chest. His wrists were crude and sparsely covered with hair. The palms of his hands and soles of his feet were free of hair. But the hair on his head reached to his shoulders partly covering his forehead. The hair on his head, moreover, felt very rough to the hand. He had no beard or moustache, though his face was completely covered with a light growth of hair. The hair around his mouth was also short and sparse.

"The man stood absolutely straight with his arms hanging, and his height was above the average—about 180 cm. He stood before me like a giant, his mighty chest thrust forward. His fingers were thick, strong, and exceptionally large. On the whole, he was considerably bigger than any of the local inhabitants.

"His eyes told me nothing. They were dull and empty —the eyes of an animal. And he seemed to me like an animal and nothing more.

"As I learned, he had accepted no food or drink since he

was caught. He had asked for nothing and said nothing. When kept in a warm room he sweated profusely. While I was there, some water and then some food [bread] was brought up to his mouth; and someone offered him a hand, but there was no reaction. I gave the verbal conclusion that this was no disguised person, but a wild man of some kind. Then I returned to my unit and never heard of him again."

On the little map of Asia in a box at the left-hand upper corner of Map XV, you will see a small vermiform tongue of shading sticking out of the left-hand lower corner of the contained rectangle. This represents the extension of the Hindu-Kush Range, via the Ala-Dagh and the Elburz in Iran, to the Armenian highlands and the Caucasus in the west. This is the farthest west for ABSMs in the Old World unless some really very startling though admittedly vague reports that have just reached me from Sweden should have substance. The Scandinavian countries are hotbeds of myth, legend, and folklore regarding ABSM-like creatures of long ago but these new statements sound suspiciously like our own Northwestern ones. I must admit that this has quite unnerved me and I am not prepared to say any more until I have at least made an attempt to investigate. We may therefore turn east again and will follow that little wormlike strip back to the Roof of the World. Along the way, we pass through the Elburz Ranges.

These are quite surprising for their wildness and the existence therein of such obvious things as Tigers only a day's drive from Teheran. But then, I suppose it is really no more odd than Jaguars wandering about almost within sight of Los Angeles. Nonetheless, there is plenty of space here for lots of big as yet uncaught things and, by jingo, we get an alleged ABSM. This came to me from the indefatigable Bernard Heuvelmans, in the form of a plea for help since we are a sort of private "Bureau of Missing Persons" for the natural sciences, among other things. It transpired that a gentleman in New Jersey had written Bernard and stated: "When I was in the Army [in World War II], one man in my company was an engineer who had worked for an oil company in Persia. He and I talked together for hours and hours, as men do in the army, and I never detected him in a single lie, or what I thought was a lie, or even suspected that he exaggerated anything, but for one curious thing.

"He said that when he was working in Persia, some

Persians brought around a 'gorilla' they had killed in the mountains. I was amazed that he should say such a thing. I assured him that there were no gorillas in Persia, or anywhere else outside of Africa. He said that it was as big as one, and surely looked like one. He saw it, and that was enough. I said that there were no anthropoid apes in Asia closer to Persia than the Malay Peninsula [sic]. He was indignant. Was I telling him that he didn't see it? Of course, he thought also that there were no gorillas outside of Africa—until he saw this one. He was a bit short-tempered about it, so I dropped the subject."

[I have not yet traced the gentleman concerned but his name is Daniel Dotson; his home state is Utah but he was in Washington, D.C. when he joined the Army. If anybody knows him, for the love of mike, please write me; and if you know where he is, don't wait on ceremony but extend to him my invitation to dinner forthwith. He can name the time and place.] [5]

[5] For later information see forthcoming sequel.

The borders of the U.S.S.R., Iran, Iraq, and Turkey, and the Caucasus. Dagestan is one of the Union of Socialist Soviet Republics.

This is the only specifically Iranian (Persian) report that I have but there are others from the Iranian-Turkmen S.S.R. border, and more from the Iranian-Afghanistani border. The geography of this and the adjacent area, which I call that of the Pamirs generally, and to which we will now proceed, is so complicated both physically and politically that I have to resort to the accompanying little maps. Most of the material that immediately follows comes from Russian sources and I am simply following their breakdown of this into regions of their designation.[6] These have political or rather ethnic tabs on them such as Kirghiz, Uzbek, Tadzhik, Kazakh, or simply "Chinese" assigned to them. This is really most muddling for the boundaries of these groups are utterly bewildering and interlocking as the map shows, while all these peoples

[6]These sources are first and foremost four Booklets issued by the Special Commission set up to study the Snowman Problem by the Academy of Sciences of the U.S.S.R., under the Direction of Prof. B. F. Porshnev and Dr. A. A. Shmakov. Bks. 1 and 2 were published in 1958; Nos. 3 and 4 in 1959 in Moscow. Secondly there are a number of articles kindly sent to me by Prof. Porshnev and a voluminous report made available by the Russian News Services.

The borders of the U.S.S.R., China, Pakistan, and Afghanistan. About these borders is the Pamir Range. B.A.A. is the Badakshan Autonomous Area.

have been surging about for centuries, elbowing each other, and dozens more peoples, in and out of valleys and off plateaus, gradually getting themselves worked into a sort of political pudding. Also lots of them are still nomadic, while families and sometimes whole villages just up and move somewhere else. Then the tab "Chinese" in this case means simply that the place is on the Chinese side of the border, here principally Sinkiang, but also a whole host of other border provinces, autonomies, and such. Finally, a considerable percentage of the place names cited are not on any map; not even the most excellent, modern, Russian maps. This area must therefore be understood to encompass not only the Pamirs themselves, but the adjacent mountainous portions of Afghanistan, the Uzbek, Tadzhik, Kirghiz, and Kazakh S.S.R.'s and the Badakshan Autonomous Area [to be called simply the A.A.] unless otherwise stated. This of course runs off into the Karakorams to the east and the Ala-Tagh and Tien-Shan to the north. Most of the information from these regions was unearthed by the 1958 Expedition of the Russian Academy of Sciences to investigate the "Snowman" problem there.

In one of the Russian booklets cited, a map was included showing the distribution of myth, legend, and folklore about ABSMs in Eurasia; the areas from which reports of sightings, encounters, and tracks have been recorded within this century; and a dark globular blob covering this general Pamirs region. The legend states that this blob or blot was considered by the Soviet scientists to be the last remaining stronghold and the only remaining breeding ground of the Asiatic ABSMs. This is a very curious notion and not strictly in accord with either the published opinions of Prof. Porshnev himself [due to a certain very pertinent, and in my opinion, correct observation that he makes in one of his articles] nor with those of the Mongolian and Chinese scientists. In fact, I am of the mind that it was an idea imposed on the Commission by a sort of backhanded tradition stemming from the days before ABSMs were taken seriously even in Russia. Once again it was probably due to the old "*snow*man" bit; the everlasting reiteration that the creature or creatures *lived* in the perpetual upland snowfields, the obvious corollary to which was the biggest and most perpetual snowfields were the most logical places to look for them.

Professor Porshnev however states in what I can only describe as a stirring article in a magazine entitled *The*

Contemporary East: "The expression Snowman is not supposed to mean a creature living among perpetual snow (or exclusively in the snow.) Similar expressions are used in connection with some animals, like the Snow Leopard. It means only that this specimen (species) belongs to the fauna of the high mountain ranges. He appears on the snowfields or glaciers only while migrating. He lives, however, and finds his food *below* the snowline, among the rocks and alpine meadows, sometimes even in the subalpine zone, in the forests, as well as among the rocky sands of the desert and in reedy thickets. The alpine zone [i.e. Upper Montane coniferous forest] is known for its rich and lush vegetation and the variety of its animal life." Professor Porshnev is so exactly right.

Neither the Pamirs themselves nor the area generally are wholly snow-clad; as a matter of fact the whole is a vast hodge-podge of deep valleys, gorges, canyons, and intermediate ridges, and all the former are heavily forested up to considerable heights being at a rather low latitude. This may be called a wilderness area but it is not, strange as it may seem, anything so much like one as our own Northwest. There have always been people there, or barging through it, since most ancient times and today there are meteorological stations dotted all about it, while the extensive international boundaries that meander through it are not exactly left to the imagination or desires of the locals. Both the Russians and the Chinese have conducted rather thorough explorations into the area, while the Afghans live there, as do most of the Tadzhiks and Kirghiz, and quite a lot of other people.

Practically everybody who does live, or even camps there, is of a single mind about the existence among them, and all over the lot, of ABSMs. This is another case such as that of the Himalayas, the Great Gutter, and the southern Tibet Rim, where the cases reported are just too numerous to detail as well as too consistent to be worth recording specifically. Such a procedure would be quite silly: rather like recording sightings of Mountain Lions from our Southwest. The bloody things are everywhere and seem always to have been; nobody locally paid much more attention to them than they did to other large wild fauna until outsiders started asking about them. Then they mostly clammed up; for two very different reasons, however.

First, the ancient animism mentioned above, is here even more deeply ingrained, but more shallowly covered by modern faiths such as Buddhism, and Islam than it is in the Caucasus, so that ABSMs being only just not men are regarded as ideal recipients for departed souls and should not be molested. This leads to taking special pains to steer foreigners away from them, while not mentioning their real names but referring to them vaguely, in generic terms. Secondly, to put the matter frankly, boiled ABSMs produced the most extremely potent and magical medicines for which really vast sums, in bar gold, were once paid in Russia, China, and especially in India. These medicines were known to the most ancient Chinese, to the Mongolians, the Tibetans, and to all Mongolic peoples all the way to Turkey. In the Pamirs area, the boiling, preparation, export, and marketing of these ABSM extracts (*moomuyam*) [called *mumer by* some] was carried on principally by Gypsies—referred to as the Luli or Asiatic Gypsies—who wandered all over the lot but mostly in directions exactly contrary to the normal annual migrations of the nomads for very obvious trade purposes. These Gypsies held a very peculiar and unique position in this part of the world. They were regarded as having sort of direct lines of communication both with God and the Devil, [and the whole pantheons of other entities to boot] and so to be both able and sanctioned to tamper with most venerated things. Actually, like their Western congeners, they were consummate poachers, and since they could not be prevented from hunting anything, however sacred, and did not seem to suffer any dire consequences from doing so, they were assumed to have some special immunity or divine dispensation. At the same time, the whole concept of "Extract of ABSM" was probably a hang-over from most ancient ritual cannibalism, whereby token consumption of special parts of a powerful quarry or enemy [or even fellow citizen] was believed to transfer to you some of his powers. I witnessed just this process in the Cameroons, West Africa, when an enormous male Gorilla was killed. The local Juju-chap begged bits of certain glands—and he knew his anatomy as well as any college demonstrator—and other parts of the body, made a brew out of these, and passed it around to all the hunters who took a token sip and smeared some on their gun barrels.

These two factors—the deep-seated reverence for ABSMs by the locals on the one hand, and their value as "medicine" on the other—have proved to be most potent ones in keeping information about the creatures from all outsiders. Personally, I suspect that there is something of the first attitude current among both the Northern and Southern Amerinds. This whole attitude in both its aspects comes to light in another way. This is the careful preservation of the heads and hands of ABSMs—and other Primates, as well, it may be noted. The head, dried whole, has special significance, not for ingestion, like the extract, but as an object with its own medicinal qualities, and like any other sacred reliquary is kept hidden. This custom is pre-Buddhist but has been incorporated into Lamaist practice. The hands have another significance. They are kept as mere talismans, not having any deep religious significance, but rather because the hands of Primates (and men) have always seemed a marvel to Mongolian peoples, being literally the key to the success of both. There are mummified or desiccated hands kept in monasteries and by private individuals of communities all over Eastern Eurasia, from the Great Barrier, east. A few in Nepal have been shown to foreigners; others have been shown to Mongolian and Chinese scientists; and there are a few reports of them recorded in the Russian publications.

This is not the only aspect of ABSMery that presents a completely different face once we pass east, up and on to the great highlands of the Middle Mongoloid peoples. Here is the true heartland, not only of the greater part of modern humanity, but of culture also, for learning was apparently thriving there when even the Greeks were yet occupied in little else but bashing the Minoans' and each others' heads in, while we in the far west were running about clothed in blue paint and chipping flints. The ancient repositories of knowledge and of documents lie sprawled up the great "basin" that forms the center of these eastern uplands, between the Great Barrier on the west, the southern Rim of Tibet on the south, and the escarpment on the east that fronts onto the lowlands of Manchuria and China proper. Around the periphery, along the Himalayas, through the Pamirs, and northeast up the Great Barrier to the region of Lake Baikal, there is only a second-hand knowledge of this ancient erudition or of its records of such matters as ABSMs; this knowledge moreover is often vague and distorted. The peoples of the western Pamirs were mountaineers, hunters, shepherds, and agricultural peasants; those of the Barrier itself mostly nomadic herders, who moved back and forth along the steppes that fringe the Barrier to the west and north, and stretch west to the Caspian. They were not literate and they did not support centuries-old libraries in monasteries, as did the inner Mongols. The Chinese on the other side of the uplands were settled agriculturists and at an early date took to city dwelling and the formation of city-states. They too developed an advanced "learning" but, despite the fact that "China" has for centuries nominally spread west to the Pamirs and to the inside of the Great Barrier, it absorbed more culture from those inner regions than it exported to them, while China proper was itself constantly overrun by Mongols coming notably down from the north through Manchuria.

When we get onto the great plateau, or rather into its great basin we will meet for the first time straight talk about ABSMs, rather than rumors, hearsay, and the somewhat dumfounded disbelief that we have encountered everywhere else, even among the most erudite. Educated Mongolians, using that term in its widest and proper sense to include all the peoples from the Siberia border to Nepal, and from Sinkiang to the Chinese escarpment, have a wealth of historical record about ABSMs, and are brought up to the notion that they still exist, *in several distinct forms,* all over their country, in isolated pockets, and all around its periphery in an almost unbroken line. Modern scientists of the Mongolian Peoples' Republic are fully aware of this and are beginning to restudy, reappraise, and make known to the world this store of knowledge, but they have as yet only just scratched the surface. The matter of ABSMs is really a rather abstruse item in their fund of knowledge. Mongolians are very practical people and although they have for millennia delved into every aspect of life, ethnology per se was one of the last of their interests. Wildlife was important, and medicine very much so, and it is in these literatures that amazing facts about ABSMs are found, as we shall see in the next chapter.

14. The Eastern Horizon

CURRENT CONDITIONS ON THE GREAT MONGOLIAN UPLANDS

Russian scientists appear to have been just as stunned as those of the West about a decade ago when they were confronted with the new turn in ABSMal events that took place after the Shipton foot-tracks uproar. Further, despite the fact that their jurisdiction has for a long time marched with the Great Barrier, and the expansion of their country was in the past centuries eastward, just as ours was westward, while their interests in inner Mongolia were multifarious, they don't seem to have known much more about this huge, truly mysterious subcontinent in upland eastern Eurasia than any other outsiders did. While the Westerners, led by the British, had been nibbling away at its southern border via India, and the Americans had shown some interest via China, neither had really even penetrated the great triangle. Some travelers, considered rather intrepid, had crossed it and a few naturalists had accomplished bizarre tasks like unearthing nests of fossil dinosaur eggs therein, but the accumulated *lack* of knowledge about it mounted steadily. This is not to say that Europeans had not been traveling through it since very early times, for some became immortalized for their accomplishments like Marco Polo and the great Russian explorer Prjewalski in the last century. There were also lesser known but equally intrepid explorers, such as one Johann Schiltberger of Bavaria in the years 1396 to 1427. In modern times there have been men of exceptional perspicacity such as J. Nicholas Roerich and the Englishman Peter Fleming. The list is of course almost endless, and in all this Russians have played a most prominent part. Yet, despite the fact that a very high percentage of these travelers throughout the ages seem to have mentioned

ABSMs, and not just casually, the concept of the continued existence over enormous areas of some of our primitive ancestors, of sub-men, and possibly even of sub-hominids simply did not penetrate the collective mind of Russian scholarship any more than it did that of Westerners. The Russian expedition to the Pamirs went out every bit as unprepared as the Western expeditions to the Himalayas, with all the same preconceived notions and misconceptions, and it came back just as mystified and empty-handed.

However, the Russians had in the meantime made special investigations in the Caucasus, and they had sent another party to the northern face of the Everest Block —which ended in a sad disaster—and they had offered their Chinese and Mongolian colleagues co-operation in investigating the whole matter. This intelligent approach was prompted in part by the growing tumult in the popular press and in scientific circles in the West about the "Abominable Snowman," and in part by certain historic discoveries of what may be called a purely bureaucratic nature by Prof. Porshnev. These prove to be a sad commentary on just about everything, but somehow make one feel a little better about some things. They demonstrate that we are not the only dumb clucks, or the only ones to let our scientific hierarchy obliterate any signs of novel thinking or unexpected discovery. I would like to tell this story in full not only for the sake of humanity but because its various facets point up just about everything that has been wrong with the study of ABSMery during the past century. Space does not permit and all I can give is the bare bones.

There lives in Moscow today a scientist by the name of V. A. Khakhlov who in 1913 submitted a full and detailed report on the east Asiatic ABSMs to the Russian Imperial Academy of Sciences. This priceless material was shelved, he was denied funds to continue his field investigations, and he was frankly told to shut up. Professor Porshnev happened to stumble on these reports in 1959 and sought out Dr. Khakhlov. He writes of his first interview: "Here he sits in front of me, this white-haired man, an emeritus scholar, a Professor of comparative animal anatomy, a scientist who made valuable contributions in the field of zoology. He talks about the discoveries he was about to make while he was a young man; his talk is enthusiastic and bitter at the same time. He is bitter not only at the general attitude taken by the pre-revolutionary Academy of Sciences, but at the action of his former advisory professor, P. P. Suschkin. In 1928, Suschkin came out with a startling, at the time, hypothesis; namely, that the region where the change from a monkey (sic) to a man took place was on the high plateaus of Asia . . . but not one word about the extensive contributions made by him [Khakhlov] or about his reports of the existence of 'Wild Men' in Central Asia." Need I say more?

Nor was Khakhlov the only enlightened scholar and enthusiastic field worker who was rapped over the knuckles and threatened with limbo at that time for the same reason. There was a young man named B. B. Baraidin who in 1905–07 specialized in Eastern folklore. He was given a commission to travel through Mongolia to Tibet on assignment from the Russian Geographical Society of [then] St. Petersburg. While doing so he encountered an ABSM at close range, while in company with many others in a caravan, and a young monk pursued the creature, which the locals called an *Almas*. Baraidin made a full report on this, but his boss, one S. F. Oldenburg, head of the geographical society and Secretary of the Academy of Sciences, ordered him to delete all mention of the matter from his report, stating that "no one will ever believe that, and it may prove embarrassing." At least, they were direct about it in Imperial Russia!

Young Baraidin had been befriended by a Mongolian scholar named Z. G. Jamtzarano, and when he told him of the incident, the latter was inspired to devote much time to pursuing ABSMs. This he did with the help of two assistants named A. D. Simukov and a Dr. Rinchen. The latter is now a Professor at the University at Ulan Bator, Mongolian D.R., still most actively engaged in pursuing the matter, and has given a great deal of information to the Russian Special Commission. It was these "discoveries" in the attics of Russian science that did more than all the firsthand reports of tracks and encounters along the entire length of the Great Barrier to aid Prof. Porshnev in mounting a proper investigation of ABSMery in Russian territory. Yet there remained a great skepticism, right up till the time of departure of the expeditions and investigators. In the previous year (1957) one A. J. Pronin, a hydrographer from Leningrad University, had made the world press with a story that he had observed an ABSM twice, for a brief time but at some distance on the Fedchenko Glacier in the Pamirs. This had at first been proclaimed by, but then just as violently decried in the Russian press, to such an extent that the inevitable debunking

—which as usual amounted to nothing more than some "expert" saying that he did not believe him—was seized on by everybody as final and absolute proof that all ABSMs have never been anything but myths. I am sincerely sorry for Mr. Pronin, but I must say that this also makes me feel a little better: for it is manifest that our press also is not the only muddleheaded group or the only one that jumps to grovel in abject compliance with the least pontification on the part of an "expert." Reviewing press reports on the 1958 expedition to the Pamirs, I find an almost similar story—first considerable enthusiasm and even pride in this open-minded and truly scientific endeavor, then a sad retrogression to the age-old bolt-hole . . . "Sorry to have to do this, dear Readers, but I'm afraid we have finally to bury the poor Snowman. He turns out to be just a myth after all. We hate to see a good myth die; we need them in this day and age, but . . . etc., etc, etc." I have a whole file on these periodical requiems on ABSMs, the latest, as of writing, a highly facetious lead editorial in the *Christian Science Monitor* anent Hillary's scalps. They make amusing reading but are a sad commentary on intelligence in whatever part of the world.

Nonetheless, although this expedition to the Pamirs did not bring back a pickled ABSM, it did bring to light a wealth of most fascinating reports. Not a few of these were from resident Russians. One of the most notable only came to light later in a communication to Prof. Porshnev, who remarks of it in one of his articles: "Not only the 'authority of official science' acts as a hindrance to obtaining more information about the 'snow men.' There are other obstacles as well, which incidentally still remain: lack of co-ordination in gathering data is the most important [or most detrimental of all]. Investigators working in different regions are not aware that similar data is being collected in another area and, lacking this most basic tool of science—comparison—they are unable to accomplish anything. As an example we can cite a recent communication from a geologist by the name of B. M. Zdorick. He writes that much to his regret while he was in the Pamirs in 1926–38 he had no information about the Himalayan ABSMs [called *yeti*], and just could not understand all the stories he was told about furry men, *or even what he had seen himself* (italics mine, *Author*)."

"In 1934 Zdorick accompanied by his guide was making his way through a narrow path among a growth of wild oats on a little alpine plateau at about 8000 feet altitude between the Darwaz Ridge and the eastern reaches of the Peter the First Range. Unexpectedly the path leveled off and one could see how the grass was trampled on, the ground giving evidence that someone was digging around. There were splotches of blood on the path and remains of a gopher's skin. Just a little way from Zdorick and his guide, on a mound of freshly upturned earth, was a creature, asleep on his belly, fully stretched out. He was about a meter and a half in length (approximately 4 feet 10 inches). The head and the forward limbs could not be seen because they were hidden by a growth of wild oats. The legs, however, could be seen. They had black naked soles, and were too long and graceful to have belonged to a bear; his back was also too flat to be a bear's. The whole body of this animal was covered with fur, more like the fur of a yak, than the rich fur of a bear. The color of the fur was a grayish-brown, somewhat more prominent brown than a bear's. One could see the sides of the creature moving rhythmically in his sleep. The fear that took possession of the guide transmitted itself to Zdorick and they both turned around and ran for their life, scrambling and falling in the tall, wild grass.

"On the following day Zdorick learned from the local residents, who were much alarmed by the news, that he came across a sleeping 'dev.' The local residents used another word in naming the creature, and Zdorick had the impression that they were using the word 'dev' just for him, so that he could understand better. The local residents ventured the information that in valleys of Talbar and Saffedar there were a few families of these 'devs' —men, women and children. They were considered like beasts, and no supernatural power was ascribed to them. They cause no harm to the people, or their stock, but meeting them is considered a bad omen.

"The geologist was very much surprised to hear that the 'dev' was listed as an animal, and not a supernatural creature. He was told that the 'dev' looked like a short stocky man, walking on two hind legs, and that his head and body were covered with short grayish fur. In the Sanglakh region the 'dev' is seen very rarely, but they do roam about, either singly, or in pairs—male and female. No one had seen any young ones, but last summer they caught a grown one at the flour mill, where he evidently was eating either flour, or grain. This was at the eastern foothills of Sanglakh, only a few kilometers from Tutkaul. The captive was chained for about two months by the mill and was fed raw meat and flour pancakes. After that he broke his chain and escaped. They also pointed out a man who had a large scar on his head from a wound supposedly inflicted by the 'dev.' "

The list of encounters with, let alone mere sightings of ABSMs throughout the Pamirs region generally (as defined above) are literally endless. The same can be said of the other major areas of the Mongolian upland triangle. These areas are as follows: first the super-upland plateau of Tibet with its three principal super mountain ranges, in the south the Rim with the Karakoram, in the middle the Kunluns that turn south to the head of Indo-China, and along the north the Altyn Tagh, that leads into the Nan Shans and on to the Tsin-Lings of China. Second, north of the Pamirs lie the Alai-Tagh, and from them stretch the Tien Shans to form the northern boundary of the Tarim Basin of Sinkiang. Next, north of these come the Grand Altai, forming the southern border of Mongolia proper. North of these are the Tannu-Ola and the mighty Khangai between Mongolia and Tannu Tuva. Still north again come the Sayan complexes and the Baikals, lying along the shore of the great lake of the same name. Then, in the Gobi Desert lie the Yablonovoi Mountains. Finally there are the Khingans running north to south between the Gobi and the eastern lowlands of Manchuria. There is some suspicion that ABSMery may have to be extended still farther north through the Stanovois, to the Dzhugdzhurs and Gidan Mountains which border the Sea of Okhotsk. There is also a most important triangle sandwiched in between the Nan Shans, the eastern end of the Tibet Rim and the upper end of the Indo-Chinese Peninsula, that has no collective name, but is filled with immense north to south ranges. This lies in Sikang, now incorporated into the Chinese Province of Szechwan. [All these sub-areas or natural provinces will be found on Map XV with the exception of the penultimate group which are in far eastern Siberia, and from which we have no definite ABSMery.] I cannot stress too forcibly the sheer volume of such reports and of those of foot-tracks, droppings, and other corollary evidence that have been found year after year all over all of these subareas within the great upland Mongolian Triangle. The full record of those that have been published—some 200, that have been properly investigated and assessed scientifically by competent specialists—will form the subject of another book.[1] For now, I shall have to confine myself to a few samples and some further explanatory remarks about the country, vegetation, and general background against which they were recorded.

First, in the general Pamirs region, the Russian expedition brought to light half a dozen most recent and categoric reports. One was supplied by a man, described as a "quite well-to-do," resident in Chesh Teb, who did a lot of hunting for pleasure. In 1939, in the spring, about 4 o'clock in the afternoon, while he was walking around he saw some man who actually jumped on him. "They started wrestling. This was a *Gul-Biavan*. The hunter was very strong and tall and heavy and once he was able to lasso a bear. Now, this hunter wrestled with *Gul-Biavan*. The *Gul-Biavan* was covered with short, soft wool and the man could not get hold of anything. On the face of this man there was also short wool and there was a terrible odor coming from him. Finally, the hunter was able to throw the *Gul-Biavan* to the ground, but at the same time he lost consciousness himself. The villagers came upon the man and brought him home. When he came to, it was late in the evening and he told how he met the *Gul-Biavan*, and the villagers told him that he was lying on the ground, and the ground around him bore evidence of this wrestling match."

In the same area intelligent local people made many sworn statements such as "A man in Roharv was traveling with two others through the Pass of Karategin and Vahio, when they saw a naked man covered with short black hair, who was slightly taller than an average ordinary man, and which had *a very strong smell*" [italics mine]. As elsewhere all over the world, this matter of a strong stink, attached to ABSMs keeps cropping up throughout the east Eurasian cases. Then, there was the hunter, Andam Kerimov, from a place called Uskrog between Roharv and Bodaudi, who called the creature he encountered a *Voita* (just another local name for an ABSM). It was not much bigger than a man, was covered with hair but not much on its chest. It had a bare face, and ears sticking out, the nose was wide, and "over the nose and on the ears he did not have much hair." Rather pleasantly the report states that "At the time Andam met the *Voita* he was leading a goat but gave way to him—the *Voita*." A group of hunters named Alaer, Altibai, Matai, Beksagir, and

Tastambek who were with the reporter and his father, one Abdurahmanov Abdulhamid, when encamped for the night, heard "something treading lightly on the grass" and running out apparently with a light saw what they called a *Gul-Biavan* about 6 feet 6 inches tall covered with hair. "It had a powerful and unpleasant smell." That was in 1951.

Some of the most interesting information collected on east Eurasian ABSMs comes from Khakhlov's original inquiries at the beginning of this century, mentioned above. Khakhlov obtained most of this through that group of the Kazakh nation which had moved northeast and settled along the edge of the Great Barrier, north of Kirghiz territory and north of Lake Balkhash, in the area lying between the Abakan Mountains and Tannu Tuva. These people were actually foreigners to and were not acquainted with the uplands beyond the Barrier but they penetrated into it via certain lowland basins having entrances pointing to the west. The most notable of these is called Dzungaria which is an immense lowland pocket, into which the western steppes [i.e. prairies, to us] penetrate via two great valleys separated by the Tarbagatai Mountains. Patient inquiry by Khakhlov elucidated the fact that reports gathered by the Kazakhs from a wide area seemed all to come from Dzungaria. Khakhlov makes a point of noting that these reports came from herders, hunters, and those engaged in other pursuits strictly in that order numerically. His first most astonishing discovery, which has recently been much confirmed, was that the ABSMs from that region had "been seen, captured, left footprints in sand, had an odor, resisted capture and yelled, and lived in captivity for a while."

"One witness, a Kazakh, stated that he was in the mountains of Iran-Kabirg and once, together with local herders, was taking care of a herd of horses at night. Toward dawn they saw some man prowling around and suspecting a thief, they jumped in the saddle taking along long poles with nooses which are used to catch horses, 'arkans' [lassos]. Because the 'man' was running awkwardly and not too fast, they succeeded in capturing him. While he was being captured, the 'man' was yelling, or rather screeching 'like a hare.' Looking the captured creature over, the herder explained to the visitor that this is a 'Wild Creature' not doing any harm to any one, and that he should be released.

"The 'wild man' was a male, below average height,

covered with hair 'like a young camel.' He had long arms, far below his knees, stooped, with shoulders hunched forward; his chest was flat and narrow; the forehead sloping over the eyes with prominently arched brows. Lower jaw was massive without any chin; nose was small with large nostrils. The ears were large without any lobes, pointed back [like fox's]. On the back of his neck was a rise [like a hound's]. The skin on the forehead, elbows and knees hard and tough. When he was captured he was standing with his legs spread, slightly bent in the knees; when he was running he was spreading his feet wide apart awkwardly swinging his arms. The instep of the 'wild man' resembled a human, but at least twice the size with widely separated fingers [toes]; the large toe being shorter than that of humans, and widely separated from the others. The arm with long fingers was like a human arm, and yet different.

"When the 'wild man' at the insistence of the herders was allowed to go free, both Kazakhs followed him and discovered the place into which he had vanished: an indentation under a hanging rock strewn with high grass. The local residents offered additional information about these creatures: that they lived in pairs, seldom seen by people, and not at all dangerous to humans.

"A second witness found by Khakhlov stated that for several months he observed a 'wild man' in the region of the River Manass, or Dam. This creature of female sex was for some time chained to a small mill but was also allowed to go free. The general description was the same as of the male: hairy cover of the skin, stooped, narrow chest, shoulders were inclined forward, long arms; bent knees, flat insteps, spread out toes resembling a paw, the contact with the ground flat without the instep. The head is described in the same fashion—absence of a chin and a rise in the back.

"This creature seldom issued any sounds and usually was quiet and silent. Only when approached she bared her teeth and screeched. It [sic] had a peculiar way of lying down, or sleeping—like a camel, by squatting on the ground on its knees and elbows, resting the forehead on the ground, and resting the wrists on the back of the head [see sketch]. This position accounts for the unusually hard skin of the elbows and knees—like camel's soles. When offered food, the female ate only raw meat, some vegetables and grain. She did not touch cooked meat, or grain, although later she was getting used to bread. Some-

(Top) Hypothetical skull of the Ksy-Giik type of Abominable Snowman as reconstructed by Russian scientists.

(Center) A drawing made by Prof. Khaklov of the Almas type of Abominable Snowman sleeping, from native descriptions.

(Bottom, left) An ancient mask from the great Mongolian plateau. (Bottom, right) Reconstruction of head and face of the creature on the mask, drawn by Russian scientists.

times she would catch and eat some insects. She would drink in animal fashion, by lapping water, or sometimes she would dip her arm in water and lick the water. When she was allowed to go free, she ran awkwardly swinging her long arms, to the nearby reeds where she disappeared."

Khakhlov notes that "This creature [2] has nothing in common with the *Jez-Termak* ('Copper-Nails'), or with the *Almas*." This is a most startling statement but one of the utmost significance, and also one that has been totally overlooked. We find on analyzing the reports from the general Pamirs area that, despite variations in coat color, all ABSMs there appear to be of one type. This is about man-size, and in many respects very manlike with, as is frequently mentioned, something like a primitive language or at least a vocal communication system more elaborate than anything known among animals. Its footprints, while having a very widely separated and extra-large big toe, are said to be human in form. This type—which incidentally seems to be the same as the Caucasian *Kaptar* —is most commonly called by one of the names in the *Guli-avan* group [due, of course, to the regionality of the languages in the area] and extends north into and along the Tien Shans, and east into the Kunluns and the Karakorams. Moreover, I do not know of any remarks to the effect that there are more than one kind of ABSM throughout these three regions. The larger and more bestial *Meh-Teh* type with *two* semi-opposed toes begins only east of the Karakorams along the Southern Tibetan Rim and, possibly, in the Himalayas; though—and this is exceedingly strange—I cannot actually find a single report of this type from any part of that range.

It would seem that Khakhlov's creatures from around Dzungaria are also of the *Guli-avan* type and that they extend north to the Grand Altai and beyond to the Sayans. The descriptions of those from the Nan Shans [which is to say the *northern* rim of the Tibetan superuplands] seem also to be similar. This creature, which gives every indication of being a Neanderthaler-type of sub-man, and whose footprints *exactly* match those of a Neanderthaler discovered in a cave in Italy,[3] would seem

[2] Known locally by the names grouped around the stems *Ksy* and *Giik.* The latter means "wild" as in *At-Giik,* Wild Horse.

[3] In the spring of 1948 the official caretakers of a cave known as "The Witch's Cave" near Toirano in Italy [all caves in Italy are government controlled] obtained permission to blast through what proved to be 11 feet of flowstone forming a blockage to

to be a mountain dwelling form: in fact, they *are* montane forms, for not one single report of them from down on either the lowlands or even on the Mongolian Plateau itself has ever been recorded.

From the latter, which is to say Mongolia proper [with the Khangai Mountains that arise in its center] and the vast Gobi Desert, together with the Ala Shan, the Ordos, Turfan, and even possibly the lowlands of Dzungaria and the Tarim, we get reports only of the little *Almas*. These are much smaller and apparently even more human, and seem always to have been regarded simply as extremely primitive humans; hairy and without speech understandable to us, but having more or less all the human qualities such as suckling human infants and even, it has been alleged, "trading" with normal humans, in that they would leave skins at appointed places, and take away certain simple basic articles left there by the nomadic tribesmen in return. There is even a report of a scholar in a Mongolian monastery who was a half-breed *Almas*. This report comes from Prof. Rinchen, mentioned previously, and reads: "There was a lama in the Lamin-gegen monastery who was famous for his scholarship, and known under the name of—"a son of an *Almasska*." The father of this lama supposedly was captured by *Almas* and begot a boy with an *Almas* woman. Both father and son eventually managed to escape by joining a passing caravan. The boy was allowed to become a pupil in a monastery and achieved scholarly fame." The same informant, one Gendul from Khuremal of the Bainkhongor District, recently told [Dr. Rinchen] that in 1937 he saw in a monastery, Barun-Khure, an entire skin [or hide] of an *Almas* which was fastened to the ceiling of the temple. This skin was taken off by a cut along the back so that it remained practically intact and one could see that it had human-like

---

one of the cave's passages, in the off-tourist season. They had seen bats flying in and out of a small hole leading into this and had rightly assumed that unexplored areas lay beyond. On breaking through, extensive passages with clean, smooth, wet, clay floors were found. On these there were enormous numbers of foot-tracks of large cave bears, of modern-appearing man, and of what are obvious Neanderthalers, together with many artifacts and even evidence of some kind of game played by throwing clay balls at a circle on the wall. The cave seems to have been finally abandoned and sealed by the flowstone curtain about 50,000 years ago. An outline tracing of one of the Neanderthaler footprints found therein is reproduced, App. A.

legs and arms. The face was framed by long hair hanging from the head. The entire skin was covered with cabalistic signs and painted by the lamas. This *Almas* was supposedly killed in Gobi and brought as a gift to the monastery by a famous hunter, Mangal Durekchi."

Although I am getting somewhat ahead of my story, I would like to point out that the idea of a half-breed Neanderthaler becoming a great scholar is not to be scoffed at. Those submen had relatively large brains, while there is really no evidence that a large brain is necessary for a large intellect. One should take to heart the couplet that states:

> "Little brain, little wit.
> Big brain, not a bit"

and note that Anatole France's gray-matter capacity was only 1100 cubic centimeters while that of a proto-Neanderthaler so lowly as Rhodesian man was 1280!

Professor Rinchen, already mentioned, reports that a man by the name of Anukh, traveling in the South Gobi in 1934 with a companion "noticed in thick growth of saksaul grass a strange, two-legged creature that started running away from them. '*Dzagitmegen*'! [saksaul grandmother] decided both, and, making lassos out of rawhide, they started in pursuit of the creature. The fast Gobi camels had no difficulty in overtaking the creature whose body was covered with short wool. At the sight of people twirling the lassos, the creature issued such a piercing cry that the frightened camels would not budge any further and the creature was able to escape behind a rocky furrow."

Then, again, there is the story of "a caravan on the way to Kuku-khoto in Inner Mongolia. The caravan was traveling from the region of Uliasutan in Eastern Mongolia and approaching the southern borders of Khalkhi when it was decided to stop for rest near a place thickly grown with saksaul grass. When they were ready to start again the man who was sent to get together the camels could not be found anywhere. An old experienced guide told the men that in this location may be some '*Dzagin Almas*,' and advised that more than one man should go searching. After a while the three men who were sent out to search came to a cave and saw on the ground in front of it signs of struggle between two people—one having shoes, the other barefoot. The frightened men did not attempt to enter the cave and, recovering the camels, returned with their observations to the caravan, insisting that all should go to the help of their companion. The old guide again cautioned them against such an act. He stated that the *Almas* never kills people but, having captured one, will hole up for a while and will not come out of the cave. He suggested that they should wait till they came by on their way back and then attempt to free their comrade.

"And so on their way back they came to the same spot and, arming themselves with a gun, they decided to hide near the cave and wait till the *Almas* came out. They waited a whole day, and then toward sunset out of the cave emerged a two-legged creature covered with hair all over. A shot sounded and the creature fell dead. Reloading the gun, the men ran into the cave looking for their lost companion. They found him, but he seemed wild and listless. He never told anyone what occurred in the cave, he avoided talking to people, and in two months time he died."

Reverting to the creatures called *Jez-Termak* [4] which is alleged to mean *Copper-Nails* [meaning, of course, "fingernails"] we should note that this name is applied to a larger, grosser, and more bestial type of ABSM than the Dzungarian *Ksy-Giik*, and is alleged to be found on the super-uplands of Tibet. It is said to be clothed in rather long, shaggy, very dark gray to black hair, and to have fingernails of copper. The implication in the folklore on this type and in all undocumented stories about it asserts that their nails are actually made of copper. This idea is illogical and as near impossible as anything could be but there could be a very simple and logical explanation for it. It is that the fingernails of some primates and notably adult gorillas are quite often bright copper-colored and even look burnished. The explanation seems to be that they are stained—as the material of which all nails and claws are made, known as keratin, so readily is—by the juices of certain fruits, barks, or berries on which they feed. I have collected monkeys of more than one species in Africa that displayed remarkable variations from the described coat-color and pattern by reason of bright red areas in the inguinal region; sometimes on the lower face, and even on the chest and inner arms. After preparing skins, it is a custom to wash them in warm soap and

[4] This term actually means "The Mountain one that scrambles using its hands."

water before drying them for museum preservation. On doing this to these monkey pelts we were amazed to find that all this bright copper color washed out and left the fur pure white or yellow. Experiment elicited the fact that the ingestion of certain fruits, selected for us by local people, although looking green and otherwise quite innocent, produced this vivid red stain on the pelt of caged monkeys within a matter of days by dribbling from the mouth or anus; and, when said fruits were eliminated from their diets, the color persisted for weeks. Their fingernails also remained bright copper-colored until they grew out from the bottom up.

While everybody has for centuries been alluding to Tibet as the real center of ABSMery, there turns out to be surprisingly little of a concrete nature from that vast land. This may appear astonishing but should not be regarded as indicating that there are no ABSMs there. Quite the contrary, it appears to be the true "heartland" of the whole matter but, as I have been at pains to try and explain above, there is a deep-seated, proto-religious prejudice against speaking of the matter to foreigners while, at the same time, the number of foreigners to visit Tibet throughout the ages has really been extraordinarily small. However, almost all of those who have visited the country and written about their travels have mentioned ABSMs.

The American William W. Rockhill wrote in 1891 of hearing many stories from Tibetans in Pekin, China, and elsewhere of the "Hairy Mountain People" of their country but he discounted these reports as being merely cases of mistaken identity; namely, of bears. However, he goes on to say: "One evening, a Mongol told me of a journey he had once made to the lakes in the company of a Chinese trader who wished to buy rhubarb from the Tibetans, who annually visit their shores [i.e. the lakes of central Tibet]. They had seen innumerable herds of yaks, wild asses, antelopes, and *Gérésun Bamburshé*. This expression means literally "wild men"; and the speaker insisted that such they were; covered with long hair, standing erect, and making tracks like men's; but they could not speak."

W. M. McGovern in his book *To Lhasa in Disguise* (1924) says: "In nearly all parts of Tibet one finds the tradition of the existence of a primitive race of men, former inhabitants of the land who have been driven out of the plains by the Tibetans and who now dwell only in the passes and in inaccessible mountain crags. My own servant referred to them as snow men. They are said to be great hairy creatures, huge in size, and possessed of incredible physical strength. Although having a certain low cunning, they are deficient in intelligence, and it is the intellectual superiority of the Tibetans that has enabled them to oust the primitive snow men from the plains. It has been permitted to no white man to meet these snow men." He adds at another point that "Rockhill, who came across this tradition in the extreme eastern part of Tibet [i.e. the land of the *Dzu-Teh*] suggests in his *Land of the Lamas* that the wild men may be nothing other than bears! For other parts of Tibet this explanation could scarcely be valid, since in many parts of Tibet, as, for example, in Kampa Dzong, Pari, and the surrounding districts, bears are unknown."

This is a rather significant statement in view of the constant insistence that all kinds of bears [though all varieties of the Eurasian Brown Bear] are found all over Tibet. Actually, it does not matter a "tuppenny-damn" whether they are so found or not, because the Tibetans know their local animals and their distribution much better than any outsiders do, have completely different names for bears and ABSMs with qualifying terms for the various kinds of each—none of which for one kind of creature could in any way be confused with those for the other—and would never for one moment confuse one with the other. Further, Rockhill himself states in another passage that "Lieutenant Lu Ming-Yang, when speaking of wild tribes to the north of the Horba country, assured me that men in a state of primitive savagery were to be found in Tibet. Some few years ago [that was before 1890, *Author*] there was a forest fire on the flank of Mount Ka-Lo, east of Kanze, and the flames drove a number of wild men out of the woods. These were seen by him; they were very hairy; their language was incomprehensible to Tibetans; and they wore most primitive garments made of skins."

This is a pretty startling statement, for Rockhill was a rather nasty kind of skeptic, given to debunking anything possible and imbued not only with the then current pomposity of all Western travelers, but with an almost modern craze for mediocrity and the disposal of all things that did not fit the accepted pattern. Having disposed of ABSMs proper as "bears standing on their hind legs" he then fell with a wallop into a report on primitive "humans," *with hairy bodies,* in a place where they "ought not to have been" [at least by Victorian estimation], and all on the say-so of a Chinese lieutenant. It is a strange commentary on the closed mind of even a famous traveler and at the same time an eye opener on our subject, for we must not forget that there is still ample room for whole hosts of mere "primitives" let alone ABSMs all over this vast Triangle. Further, we must not forget those forlorn people; still, at least until recently, maintaining a Bear-cult, called the "Hairy Ainu" of the Japanese island of Hokkaido. They seem to have been Caucasoids of an extremely early vintage and they certainly were hairy [and in some cases still are, despite their persecution!]. Hairy chaps, wearing skins, running out of burning Tibetan forests do not quite coincide with then [1890] or even current anthropological beliefs but this is no reason to gainsay their previous or continued existence. Apparently Tibetans took, and still take, all this quite complacently.

Just to make matters worse, this same Rockhill must add still another brief passage that states "Legends concerning wild men in Central Asia were current in the Middle Ages. King Haithon of Armenia, in the narrative of his journey to the courts of the Batu and Mangu Khans, in 1254–55 A.D., speaks of naked wild men inhabiting the desert southeast of the present Urumchi." Almost everybody who has traveled in Tibet both before and since the date of these statements have reported the same thing and some have said they have met the creatures. But, I stress again, these are all foreigners, since the Tibetans themselves just won't talk about the business. One story that has always fascinated me is that of a Kirghiz named Saikbaia Karalaein who told the Russian investigating commission about a Chinese family who had started wandering during the war and finally settled in Tibet. It appears that one of their women disappeared and they thought her to be dead. However, "a year later she came back, and told them the story that she was taken, while gathering wood, by what she called a *Kish-Kiik,* or wild man. He was comparatively little different from an [ordinary] man but was covered with hair and could not speak. She also said that she was expecting a child by him. Hearing that, her husband killed her; and he was taken by the police. The woman also told where the wild man's den was. They went up there and actually saw wild men and women all covered with hair."

On several occasions Tibetans of higher education have said (see Chapter 12) or have been reported to have stated that they know of three distinct types of ABSMs in or around the periphery of their super-upland plateau, while, in addition, they speak of two "animals" with man-like or super-anthropoid characteristics. These latter they identify as, first a giant monkey and, secondly, the *Meh-Teh*. Of the other three "Man-Creatures" they are quite cognizant, affirming that they are first, the little dwarf *Teh-lma* of the lower valleys; second, the man-sized hairy one [i.e. the *Kaptar, Guli-avan,* or *Ksy-Giik* type]; and, third, something quite else. This is the mighty *Dzu-Teh* type known to the Chinese as the *Gin-Sung;* a real giant, shaggy-coated, and able to stay for long periods in the ruggedest country; dangerous, a stock raider, but possessed of an almost exactly human-type foot. This, they and everybody else agree is not found along either the Himalayas or the Southern Tibetan Rim, nor even in the Nan Shans, but is confined to the unnamed triangle between these, upper Indo-China, and the Chinese escarpment. This same type seems to prevail also in the Tapa Shan, the Tsin-Lings, the ranges between Shensi and the Gobi, and again north along the mighty Khingans that separate the Gobi from Manchuria, and on into the little Khingans that lie athwart the northern edge of that province. Also, as I said before there are indications that this type of ABSM may exist still farther north in the Stanovois, Dzhugdzhurs, Gidans, and even in the Anadyrs. This is of the utmost significance since it is only a skip from there to Alaska, while this *Dzu-Teh* type ABSM seems to conform very closely, if not be identical with, our *Sasquatch*es and *Oh-Mahs.*

Here indeed is a strange situation to contemplate. We start out with a suggestion that there *might* possibly be some one kind of as yet uncaught and undescribed animal, probably an anthropoid [or a race of runaway human delinquents] in the Himalayas which somehow got colorfully called "Abominable Snowmen" and we end up with a whole galaxy of unknowns, spread over five continents, and concentrated in eastern, upland Eurasia, where, by the word of those people who know most about the subject locally, speak the local languages, and have devoted the most time to the matter, there appear to be no less than five very distinct types, each with its own characteristics and habitat; namely, (1) the Mountain Neanderthalers of the West, (2) the little *Almas;* also Neanderthalers, or mere primitives, of the hot deserts, (3) the bestial *Meh-Teh* of the Tibetan upper plateau, (4) the giant *Dzu-Teh* (*Gigantopithecus?*), *Tok,* or *Sasquatch*-type and (5) the tiny tropical, forest-dwelling *Teh-lma* of the southern valleys. This may sound fabulous but, the deeper you delve into the reports and the background, the more obvious and logical this becomes.

The distinctive nature of each of the five is perfectly in accord with the varying nature of other groups of mammals. Take for instance the wild sheep of this area. There are distinctive species and/or races in each of the great mountain blocks, while other hoofed animals replace these on the lowlands or comparative lowlands; one set on the *hot* deserts, another on the upland *cold* deserts. Then also, the actual geographical distribution is also perfectly consistent, in that one kind inhabits the far west (the Caucasus) and the western fringe of the plateau; another the comparative lowlands of the middle; a third the eastern mountainous edge; still another the Tibetan Plateau and its superimposed mountain ranges; and the last only the warmer valleys of the extreme southern periphery of the area. These divisions, furthermore, coincide with the distribution of both vegetation and vegetational types of growth. For instance, the arrangement of the latter going north from the Pamirs to the Sayans up the Great Barrier parallels (but is different botanically from) that going up the eastern escarpment from Indo-China to the Stanovois in Siberia. The whole picture, in fact, despite its enormous complexity [and our gross over-all lack of knowledge of the area] is perfectly logical and consistent with all natural facts and factors.

To reiterate—and I cannot help doing this and for some very real reasons—we should wipe away our sense of helplessness and hopelessness on taking our first look at Map XV, and just remember that this tremendous mishmash may be quite simply divided into five parts: the Great Barrier on the west; the central desert basins; the Great Barrier and escarpment on the east fronting Manchuria and China; the Tibetan super-uplands and their mountains; and, last, the fringe area of the Himalayas. This is eastern Eurasia in, as it were, a nutshell. The only things left over are the two enormous masses of uplands and mountains in Siberia, west and east of the Lena River respectively. These, however, do not at the moment concern us.

And so we find ourselves ending our world tour in an area that is only one stage removed from where we started. The animal life and much of the vegetation of far eastern Siberia is identical to that of our extreme northwest. What is more, as you go south from the Bering

Strait on either side—down through Siberia on the Asian side, or through Alaska to the Yukon, and British Columbia on the American, you pass through the same succession of vegetational belts and mountainous zones at each latitude. Many large animals, like the Brown or Dish-faced Bears and the large Red Deer or American Elk, have crossed from one to the other in comparatively recent times. The Amerinds seem to have done the same too; and the Arctic or Eskimo-type Mongoloids even later [unless they were on both sides all the time]. As I asked at the outset, what was there to prevent the Neo-Giants from doing so also, at some time? They are, of all the ABSMs, apparently the most rugged, surpassing in this respect the Neanderthaler *Kaptar-Guli-* (or *Gulb*) *-avans,* the desert-dwelling *Almas,* and the little warm-forest *Teh-lmas.* That the *Meh-Tehs* did not do likewise seems to me fairly reasonable for it would appear that they are more apes than men and, like all of that ilk, are neither catholic in their tastes nor so readily adaptable as are the Hominids. Like the Gorillas in Africa and the Orangs in Indonesia they got into a special environmental niche and have remained stuck therein.

Appendix A

THE IMPORTANCE OF FEET

The study of footprints and foot-tracks—the difference between which was discussed earlier in this book—form the subject of a very precise science called *Ichnology*. This discipline is employed in quite a number of fields, notably in police work and in palaeontology. The identification of the tracks of living animals in snow and mud has, of course also been an art in hunting since time immemorial, and it is of great interest to the field naturalist. Its more psychological aspects were also discussed when we first introduced the matter of ABSM tracks. We should now consider the details of this discipline.

Tracks [the word I shall use from now on, unless dealing specifically with a single print] are caused by gravity. The first requirement is that the object on top that presses down be composed of a denser material than that upon which it is pressed, but this does not mean that tracks will invariably result. Thus, a body made of steel if rolled across a sheet of lead need not leave tracks. There appears here another factor—that of weight—which results in the beginning of the erection of a complicated formula. Above a certain weight the upper body will leave tracks, but the point at which it starts to do so is also dependent upon the compressibility of the under body, or surface. Then again, tracks can be either pressed or punched into a substance: in other words energy, in addition to mere gravity, may be exerted. In this case the point at which an impression begins varies according to quite a number of factors which fortunately need not concern us since they lie in realms of engineering that do not apply to purely biological matters. Nevertheless, one must bear in mind that there is a considerable difference in appearance between a print made

327

by pressing and one made by punching an object downward into a surface. The former will be found to be surrounded by little cracks all running inward to the "gutter" of the print, while the latter will be surrounded by a sort of levee or ridge.

One of the easiest ways to spot an artificially made print is to find such an *impact ridge* around a print where there is no cause for it under the natural conditions pertaining on the terrain. By this is meant, where the creature [and this does not apply to machines] had no cause to *jump*. Jumping results in the application of "weight" to the normal gravity and so is equivalent to "punching." Thus a creature running, rather than walking, will leave differently formed individual prints, and when going downhill, they will be quite other than when it is going uphill. Already the matter becomes, as you may readily agree, complicated. But there are several further complexities.

Perhaps the most notable is the area of the object which makes any print and, in the case of animals, the number of such objects [i.e. hands, feet, tail, or other appendages) employed in so walking, running, hopping, jumping, or otherwise progressing. The other most important factor is naturally the nature of the material or surface into which the tracks are impressed. This is itself an enormously complicated subject.

Tracks may be left in gravels or sands, all of which are of course much denser than any animal foot that passes over them. This is due to their particulation or "looseness." They are dry, and such substances range widely in consistency from what are called screes, of sometimes enormous boulders piled against the sides of mountains, to dry plaster of Paris. Much finer substances have now been artificially developed but in Nature we need not concern ourselves with anything much finer than what we call a fine dried silt, which is a little coarser than dry plaster.

There are two other types of solids in which imprints may be left. These are, first, materials, such as lead, that are themselves malleable or what is commonly called "soft" and, secondly "solutions" in the widest sense of that word. This means, popularly speaking, *wet*. We need not overly concern ourselves with the first since such substances may be regarded as nonexistent in Nature—that is to say in the nonhuman world. The second is of course the most important type of material in which the tracks of animals appear —and this goes for snow, which in many respects holds an intermediate position, since, dependent upon temperature, it may be either a particulated material, or a mere wet mixture. Prints can thus be left in three kinds of substances —(1) dry, as sands, (2) wet, as in muds, or (3) snow, which has to be separately classified.

There are those, such as the technologists of police laboratories and road-construction engineers, who know so much about the factors just named and the results of making impressions in various substances that it would really startle you. On another hand, certain palaeontologists have made profound studies of this subject, and most notably in connection with the interpretation of fossil footprints of early amphibians, reptiles, mammals, and birds. The findings of all three groups of specialists of course coincide for, as I say, Ichnology is a very precise science. However, most unfortunately, totally insufficient application has been made of their findings in ABSMery. Also, there has been an extraordinary lack of appreciation of the basic theorem of Ichnology which is, simply stated, that a print can be left only by an object that exactly "mirrors" it—a term that should be self-explanatory. This brings us to the questions arising from the conformation of vertebrate animals' feet.

For some reason—and there may well be *no* real reason —it just so happens that the first creatures with backbones to crawl out of water on to land dispensed with all but five of the rays (digits) on the four appendages they retained. This gave all of us land vertebrates a basic pentadactyl pattern—i.e. four "legs" each with five "fingers" or toes. True, there are some animals like whales that have somehow again reduplicated the number of phalanges in their digital extremities. This is, actually, one of the most extraordinary things in zoology as it flies in the face of one of the basic precepts of genetics; namely, that a characteristic once lost cannot be resuscitated from the same source. [The additional phalanges of the Cetaceans are phylogenetically developed by reduplication.] This basic five-fingered and five-toed pattern speaks much for the unitary origin of all land vertebrates—the amphibians, reptiles, birds, and mammals.

Many forms of all these major groups have at one time or another lost one or more phalanges on various digits, whole digits, or even whole limbs. The snakes, for instance, have lost everything. The results may be the most readily seen in the [mirrored] prints left by the hands and feet of the various types; and from such prints a great deal about their makers may, by inference from known types, be reconstructed. This brings us to the classification of feet and specifically of mammalian extremities. Happily we do not have to go into this vast question and may concentrate upon those of the Primates—i.e. the *Order* to which we belong, together with the apes, monkeys, lemuroids, and a few more abstruse types like the Feathertails.

The Primate foot [as opposed to their hands, which we may also from now on ignore] is pentadactyl—i.e. five-toed—but is otherwise of a variety of forms. These forms may be classified in various ways but two sets of factors are of particular interest to us. The first is whether they are what is called wholly *plantigrade* or not; the second, whether the big, great, or first toe is opposed to or lies alongside and points in the same direction as [and/or is bound to] the other toes. A plantigrade foot means that its owner stands and walks with the whole under surface, from the tips of its toes to its heel—which is to say the last bone of the ankle—on the ground. Some Primates, such as the tiny Tarsiers, do not do this, the ankle bones being greatly elongated. Men (Hominids), Apes (Pongids), and most Monkeys (Semioids) are plantigrade. Further, none of these three groups of higher Primates have long enough nails to produce clawlike excrescences which touch the ground and leave noticeable marks though those of some Cynocephaloids (i.e. Baboons and Macaques) may do so when they are running or galloping. There are few —if any, as a matter of fact—other mammals that do *not* leave claw marks. Then again, claws and nails although having a similar origin anatomically, are not identical structures: but this also need not, fortunately, concern us further.

In dealing with Primate footprints we are therefore primarily concerned with the nature and position of the big or great toe. The only one that does not have an opposed big toe is the Hominid group. Nonetheless, this digit in Hominids also varies considerably in the degree to which it is set off from the other four toes. From both the prints found in the cave at Toirano in Italy and from the skeleton of a whole foot found in the Crimea, we now know that the big toe of the Neanderthalers was rather widely separated. There are people living today who have feet not unlike those of Neanderthalers—notably certain Amerinds from the extreme southern end of South America (see a photograph in an article by Dr. Carleton S. Coon, in *Natural History,* January, 1961) and some Australoids. However, there is no indication, even among those which we know, of any evidence whatsoever of a truly "opposed" big toe, among any Hominid.

One known fact about abnormalities among human feet is nonetheless of some significance to our story. This is that shown in the two photographs of a strange type in which the second toe is longer than the first, sometimes more massive, and also widely separated from the remaining three toes. This is the more odd in that the second and third toes of normal Modern Man are partially webbed. If a foot, normal or abnormal, of this nature developed [or even merely occurred] one would have supposed that the second and third toes [together] would have become widely separated from, on the one hand the big toe, and on the other, the remaining two. When this abnormality occurs, both the big and the second toes tend to curl downward and inward not unlike those of the *Meh-Teh.* But they are still not opposed.

Let us now analyze or try to analyze the prints left by the four types of ABSMs. These, we will arrange in the following order: (1) the Proto-Pigmies, (2) the *Almas,* (3) the Neo-Giants, and (4) the very different *Meh-Teh* type. It will be seen from the sketches of the outstanding types of known human feet [accompanying this Appendix] that those of the living pigmy human types such as the Negrillos and Negritos show a distinct tendency toward a very short broad foot with rather large [in proportion] and widely splayed toes *and a very constricted* or narrow heel. It is hardly even a "step" from them to the *Sedapas, Teh-lmas,* and other alleged pigmy ABSMs. Such a tiny, human-type, plantigrade, flat foot does not however begin to approach the form of the various bears, and not even the Malayan Sun Bear (*Helarctos*).

Coming to the prints allegedly left by what I have called the *Alma* type, one finds that they are hardly in any respect different from those of the Neanderthalers left in the cave in Italy. This, in turn, perfectly accords with the now expressed belief of the Russian scientists that the former are but living representatives of the latter. Despite their relatively low plantar index [i.e. the number of times their width goes into their length] they are hardly at all non-human: in fact, they can be matched by the prints left by not a few Modern Men living today and most notably by persons who have never worn shoes or other footgear. We hardly have to discuss these tracks any further, except to mention that such have been rumored from many places other than eastern Eurasia—such as, I may say, northwest North America, South America, and Africa. But how are we to tell whether such prints—if they ever really existed—were left by some wild thing or by local men, walking without footgear and happening to have Neanderthaloid-type feet?

Our real problems begin with the Neo-Giants. Here, I want first to try and wipe away a lot of dross. It has been said, and repeatedly, that such tracks and prints have been found all over northern Indo-China, and on northward through the arc formed by the uplands and mountains of Szechwan via the Tsin Lings to Manchuria. The same— up to 20-inch-long humanoid-type prints—are also said to have been found in the Matto Grosso and in Patagonia in South America. This may be so but after, lo, these many years, I have been completely unable to obtain any photograph or even sketch of one that is stated to have been made on the spot. I have several "sketches" made by members of expeditions to these places but sketches made in retrospect after questioning and mostly in my apartment in New York, but nothing "original." The only areas from which I have been able to obtain such first-hand photos or sketches, *and* plaster casts has been from British Columbia and northern California.

These prints at first look wholly human and, I may say, a bit ridiculous. However, on further analysis they display other qualities. As may be seen from the accompanying sketch, they show one or two extremely old characteristics that are definitely not typically human. As photographs of whole tracks of these monsters have shown, they walk with their feet pointing straight forward: not pigeon-toed, like bears, or in any may out-turned like most men. Thus, they must flex about [or across] a line that forms an arc at right angles to that line of travel behind the toes. Then this means that, although the whole foot is enormous and at first looks very long, it is really a very *short* and broad one [with an index of only 1.61].

A friend of mine, Mr. Fred Laue, long in the shoe business, has worked out the trade equivalents of these proportions. Working from one of our plaster casts with an over-all length of 15¾" and a width of 7", a No. 21 shoe would be needed but no less than 13 sizes in width greater than

(1) HUMAN adult (West Caucasoid). Imprint in clay mold.
(2) HUMAN Adolescent, 14½ years (West Caucasoid). Wet imprint of left foot on hard surface. (3) HUMAN CHILD, 10½ years (West Caucasoid). Wet imprint of left foot on hard surface. (4) HUMAN Infant, 2½ years (West Caucasoid). Wet imprint of left foot on hard surface.

(5) HUMAN Adult (Cromagnon Man). From clay floor of cave in France. (6) HUMAN Adult (Southern Amerind). From mud of river bank Chishue, Patagonia. (7) SUBHUMAN (Neanderthaler). From moist clay floor of cave, Toirano, Italy. (8) ABSM (Guli-yavan type). From a sketch of track in mud, Kirghiz S.S.R.

(9) ABSM (Meh-Teh). From photo of cast made from photo of print in snow, by Eric Shipton. (10) APE (unknown form). Sketch made by Charles Cordier in the Congo (over-all, 30 centimeters). (11) APE (Lowland Gorilla). From photo of cast of foot. (12) APE (Chimpanzee). Outline of extended foot from plaster cast.

(13) HUMAN Adult (Bushman). From a sketch made from a cast. (14) ABSM (Sasquatch). From tracing of deep print in firm wet clay. (15) ABSM (Dzu-Teh). Drawn by author under supervision of Gerald Russell. (16) ABSM (?) (Kakundakari). Sketch made by Charles Cordier in the Congo. (Over-all, 10 centimeters)

(17) HUMAN (Malayan Negrito). From photo of cast. (18) ABSM (Sedapa). Traced from print found in Danau Bento Swamp, Sumatra, by Dr. Jacobson. (19) ABSM (Teh-Ima). From sketch made by the author, under supervision of Gerald Russell. (20) ABSM (Apamandi). Sketch made by Charles Cordier in the Congo. (Over-all, 20 centimeters)

(21) APE (Orang-utan). Outline of extended foot from plaster cast. (22) APE (Orang-utan). Imprints of knuckles and foot, ex Huevelmans. (23) APE (Silvery Gibbon). Outline of extended foot from plaster cast. (24) MONKEY (Old Male Rhesus). Drawn from live specimen, ex Osman Hill.

(**Top row, left**) ASIATIC BROWN BEAR (**Ursus arctos**). Left hind and right fore foot imprints. (**Top row, right**) NORTH AMERICAN BLACK BEAR (**Euarctos americanus**). Left hind and right fore foot imprints.

(**Center row, left**) PUMA (mountain lion) (**Profelis concolor**). Right hind foot. (Fore and hind prints of the large cats are very similar; so also are all prints of the Great Cats.) (**Center row, right**) NORTH AMERICAN PORCUPINE (**Erethizon dorsatum**). Left hind and right fore foot imprints.

(**Bottom row, left**) THE FAMOUS FOOTPRINTS OF CARSON CITY JAIL. The outlined portion was "restored" by Dr. Harkness. This was a left foot print in sandstone. The tracks were not found in the jail yard but some miles distant. (**Bottom row, right**) EXTINCT GROUND SLOTH (**Mylodon**). Skeleton of a left foot from the side.

the widest shoe made—i.e., a EEE. Second, it means that the curious double inner pad under the ball of the foot has something to do with the basal joint of the big toe and not with the end or outer end of the first metacarpal. If this is so, and the foot bends or flexes along the arc that runs between the two pads all the other toes are not just extraordinarily but so exceptionally long that they cannot be of the typically human form. But, if they are that long, why don't they splay or, alternatively, why does not the mud in which the tracks were left well or squeeze up between them as it does with even a normal human foot?

In all the tens of thousands of prints that have now been found and examined of these creatures this has never been observed to have occurred. The only thing that I know of that could prevent this—and at the same time produce such a sharp left-to-right ridge under the flexure of the toes—is an almost complete *web between all of them*. Thus, although the Neo-Giant prints at first look almost completely human they are not. They have a double first subdigital pad; they are extremely short and broad for their size; and, the second to fifth toes seem to be conjoined. The significance of these points should by now be appreciated.

This leaves us with the most abominable problem of all —the *Meh-Teh*-type prints—and abominable this is, indeed. These simply do not fit into any pattern. They are definitely not Pongid in that the big toe though enormous is not truly opposed. Similarly, they are no more Hominid in that said big toe *is* "set off." However the second toe looks for all the world like a semi-opposed digit. Such a condition is not known in any mammal. As we already pointed out, the development of such a condition is somewhat more likely to be able to be undertaken by a Pongid [with an already offset and opposed big toe] than by a Hominid without one. These prints are *not* those of a string of foxes all jumping into the same hole in the snow as we by now know all too well; also, and this has perhaps not yet been sufficiently stressed, the prints show very clear indication of a rather complex musculature which, although so far unknown in any other animal, accords perfectly with what would be expected if one developed such a foot and was bipedal.

Most but by no means all of the *Meh-Teh* tracks have been found in snow. The others have been in mud and sometimes first in one and then in the other in a continuous line. This absolutely and positively disposes of another proposition that has constantly been put forward; namely, that the prints were made by a comparatively small creature and were then subsequently enlarged by melting of the snow with or without regelation. Considerable work has now been done on this phenomenon and it is true that small prints may become large ones in this way, and it is an extraordinary fact that the tracks *seem* or appear in some uncanny way to grow to fit them. By this I mean that, optical illusion or whatever, the stride seems to grow. This of course is physically impossible whereas exactly the reverse should occur because, as the prints get bigger and bigger, their peripheries must get closer together. I observed this most closely at my farm by excluding all from going near a set of tracks made by my small wife wearing close-fitting boots in fresh firm snow from the house to the trash-disposal affair beyond our lawn. In a few days her prints had grown to enormous proportions and looked incredibly sinister and as seen from an upper floor window appearing for all the world like those of a positive giant—and with a giant stride. Actual measurement however showed that the stride had of course remained as originally laid down. Nevertheless, none of these things, actual or illusory can occur in *mud*.

The *Meh-Teh* tracks and prints are, in fact, by far the most puzzling of all, and especially since such persons as Shipton, Bordet, and others obtained clear photographs of them taken from directly above. Here is obviously a bipedal creature of considerable size and weight that inhabits the Himalayas and the ranges north of the Tibetan Plateau. It was the original "Abominable Snowman" and it comes out as the last "abominable enigma."

Appendix B

*The Known Mammalian
Fauna of the Himalayan Area*

The known mammalian fauna of the Tibetan Plateau, the Pamirs, and the Himalayan ranges is very extensive. In the last area we find a combination of typical Eurasian and Oriental forms, together with several unique types not found elsewhere. We are concerned, in our discussion, only with mammals, in that other animals do not have hair; and it has been hair above all else [other than footprints and tracks] that has been brought forward in exposition of ABSMs; and especially in these areas. Moreover, for some reason—but one which does not seem quite logical to me—it has been the larger mammals that have been suggested as the possible origins of these hairs which have been said to be of *yetis*.

This actually need not be final for there are many medium-sized and small mammals the hairs of which are just as long, and sometimes almost as sturdy as those alleged to be from ABSMs. Some alleged ABSM remains have been proved to have been made from the goatlike animal called the Serow; while some of the Californian hairs have been identified, on the one hand as those of a Moose [not found in the area, incidentally], and on the other as "those of a large cat" [i.e. the belly-hairs from a Puma, *Profelis concolor*]. Therefore it is of first importance to list those larger mammals known from the Tibetan and Himalayan areas that might be used to make "yeti artifacts." The most outstanding of these are:

Primates
 Hoolock Gibbon (*Hylobates hooloch*)
 Langurs (*Semnopithecus schistaceus, entellus*, etc.)
 Snub-nosed Monkey (*Rhinopithecus roxellanae*)

Carnivora

Snow-Leopard (*Panthera uncia*)
Giant Panda (*Ailuropoda melanoleucus*)
Lesser Panda (*Ailurus fulgens*)
Wolf (*Canis lupus, subsp.*)—Eurasian form (*not* the Wolf *Canis pallipes*)
Red Bear (*Ursus arctos, subsp.*)
Blue Bear (*Ursus arctos pruinosus*)
Snow Bear (*Ursus arctos isabellinus*)
Himalayan Black Bear (*Selenarctos thibetanus*)
Sloth-Bear (*Melursus ursinus*)

Artiodactyla

(1) Camelines (*Camelidae*)
   Bactrian Camel (*Camelus bactrianus*)
(2) Cervines (*Cervidae*)
   Red Deer—Hangul (*Cervus kashmirianus*)
   Red Deer—Shou (*Cervus wallichi affinis*)
   Thorold's Deer (*Cervus albirostris*)
(3) Bovines (*Bovinae*)
   Yak (*Bos grunniens*)
   Mithan (*Bos frontalis*)
(4) Antelopines (*Gazellinae*)
   Zeren (*Procapra gutterosa*)
   Goa (*Procapra picticaudata*)
(5) Goat-Antelopes (*Saiginae*)
   Saiga (*Saiga tatarica*)
   Chiru (*Panthalops hodgsoni*)
(6) Rock-Goats (*Rubicaprinae*)
   Goral (*Naemorhedus cinereus*)
   Serow (*Capricornis sumatrensis thar*)
(7) Sheep-Oxen (*Ovibovinae*)
   Takin (*Budorcas taxicolor, B. tibetanus,* and *B. bedfordi*)
(8) Goats (*Caprinae*)
   Ibex (*Capra ibex, subsp.*)
(9) Sheep (*Ovinae*)
   Bharal (*Pseudovis nahura*)
   Argali (*Ovis ammon*)

Bibliography

Aelianus, C. [Ill Century] (1832). *Aeliani de natura animalium libri XVII*. Verba ad fidem librorum manuscriptorum constituit (et annotationibus illustravit F. Jacobs. Intextae sunt curae secundae postumae J. G. Schneideri Saxonis). Adjecti sunt indices, rerum et interpretatio Latina Gesneri a Gronovio emendata. (Cum addendis et conjecturis ineditis J. J. Reiskii.) Jenae: imprensis Friderici Frommanni, 2V.

Agassiz-Harrison The Advance Newspaper (1960). "Sasquatch Watches Berry Picker Near Nelson," Oct. 20, B.C., Canada.

Ali, S., & Santapau, H. (1954). "The Abominable Snowman." *J. Bombay nat. Hist. Soc.* Bombay, 52, 594–8.

Almazov, A. (1957). "Does the snow man exist?" *Evening Moscow*, Apr. 24, p. 3.

American Karakoram Expedition, 1st, 1938 (1939). *Five Miles High.* New York (Dodd, Mead & Co.).

American Naturalist (1882). "The Recent Discoveries of Fossil Footprints in Carson, Nevada." v. 16, pp. 921–23. Phila.

Barnier, H. (1958). "Sur les traces de l'homme des neiges." *L'humanité Dimanche*, Feb. 9.

Bartels, M. (1881). "Über Menschenschwanze." *Arch. Anthrop.* vol. 13, pp. 1–41. Braunschweig.

Bartels, M. (1884). "Die Geschwanzten Menschen." *Arch. Anthrop.* vol. 15, pp. 45–132. Braunschweig.

Ibn Batuta (1829). *The Travels of Ibn Batuta.* Translated by Rev. Samuel Lee. pp. 187–8. London.

Beauman, E. B. (1937). Letter to the Editor: "The Abominable Snowman." *The Times*, July 17. London.

Bolinder, G. (1959). *We Dared the Andes.* London. (Abelard-Schuman).

Bolm, D. (1957). *Das Schnitthaarbuck.* Müchen. (Mayer Verlag).

Bontius, J. (1658). *Historiae Naturalis et Medicae Indiae Orientalis.* Amsterdam.

Bordet, P. (1955). "Traces de yeti dans l'Himalaya." *Bulletin Museum nat. histoire natur.* vol. 27, no. 6, pp. 433–439. Paris.

Bordet, P. (1956). "Traces de yeti dans l'Himalaya." *Montagne et alpinisme*, no. 7, pp. 206–209.

Boule et Vallois (1952). *Les Hommes Fossiles*. 4th ed. Paris. (Masson).

Bourdillon, J. (1956). *Visit to the Sherpas*. London.

Bowler, L. P. (1911). *Gold Coast Palaver*. London.

Brandt, K., & Eisenhardt, H. (1939). *Fahrtenund Spurenkunde*. 6th ed. Berlin. (P. Parey)

Brasser, J. C. (1938). *Mes Chasses dans la Jungle de Sumatra*. Paris.

Britton, S. W. (1955). "Man Walks Upright Because of Snow." *Science News Letter*, Apr. 23, Washington.

Broom, R. (1950). *Finding the Missing Link*. London.

Broom, R., & Robinson, J. T. (1950a). "Man Contemporaneous with the Swartkrans Ape-Man." *Amer. J. phys. Anthrop.* vol. 8, pp. 151–5, Philadelphia.

Broom, R., & Robinson, J. T. (1950b). "Ape or Man?" *Nature*, vol. 166, pp. 843–4. London.

Broom, R. (1952). "Swartkrans Ape-man Paranthropus crassidens." *Transv. Mus.*, Mem. No. 6.

Bruce, Gen. C. G. (1924). *L'Assant du Mont Everest, 1922*. Macon. (Protat Freres).

Bruller, J. (1953). *You Shall Know Them*. Translation of Les Animaux Denatures. Boston. (Little, Brown). (Pseud. "Vercors").

Bucks, I. (1959). Letter to the Editor: "The Snowman." *Man*, 337. London.

Buddhacarita (1934). (Pali Theological Treatise, a well-known Buddhist Text. Available in English translation by Rhys David.) Benares.

Burns, J. W. (1929). "Introducing B.C.'s Hairy Giants" *Maclean's Magazine*, Apr. 1, Toronto, Ontario, Canada.

Burns, J. W., & Tench, C. V. (1940). "The Hairy Giants of British Columbia." *Wide World Mag.* Jan., pp. 296–307, London.

Burton, M. (1956). "The Snowman." *The Illustrated London News*, Nov. 3. London.

Busson, B., & Leroy, G. (1955). *Les derniers secrets de la terre*. Paris.

Byrne, P. (1958a). "Frogs Lure Abominable Snowman." *New York Journal-American*, June 5.

Byrne, P. (1958b). "Searching for the Abominable Snowman." *New York Journal-American*, June 15.

Cepilli, T. (1954). "Does the man of the snows exist?" *In Defense of the World*, no. 4, pp. 92–94.

Chaigneau, A. (1954). *Empreintes et voies des animaux gibier et des Musibles*. Paris.

Chard, J. R. S. (1936). *British Animal Tracks*. London. (C. A. Pearson).

Chenu, J. C. (1850–8). *Encyclopedie d'Histoire Naturelle*. Paris.

Chevalley, G. (1953). *Avant-premières à l'Everest*. Paris.

Clark, L. (1953). *The Marching Wind.* London. (Hutchinson)

Clifford, Sir H. (1897). *In Court and Kampong.* London.

Cobb, E. H. (1952). "The Abominable Snowman." *Country Life,* III, 163. London.

Combe, G. A. (1926). *A Tibetan on Tibet.* London. (T. Fisher Unwin Ltd.).

Coon, C. S. (1954). *The Story of Man.* New York. (Alfred A. Knopf).

Cope, E. D. (1883a). "The Nevada Biped Tracks." *American Naturalist,* v. 17, pp. 69–71. Philadelphia.

Cope, E. D. (1883b). "The Carson Footprints." *American Naturalist,* v. 17, p. 1153. Philadelphia.

Ctesias (1612). *"Indica Opera"* in Photius: Myriobiblon. Geneva.

Dammerman, K. W. (1924). "De Orang Pandak van Sumatra." *Trop. Natuur,* 13, 12, 177–82. Weltevreden.

Dammerman, K. W. (1930). "The Orang Pendek or Ape Man of Sumatra." *Proc. 4th Pacific Sci. Congr.* vol. III, Biological Papers, Batavia-Bantoeng.

Dammerman, K. W. (1932). "De Nieuw-ontdekte Orang Pendek." *Trop. Natuur,* 21, 8, 123–31. Weltevreden.

Davis, H. (1940). *Land of the Eye.* New York. (Henry Holt & Co.)

Delaquys, G. (1952). *L'homme de neiges.* Paris.

Delavaille, J. H. (1862). "Les Hommes a queue." *Hist. nat.* 1st series, p. 243. Paris.

Denman, E. (1954). *Alone to Everest.* New York.

Diringer, D., D. Litt. (Univ. of Florence). *The Alphabet, A Key to the History of Mankind* with a Foreword by Sir Ellis Minns, Emeritus Professor of Archaeology, Cambridge, Second Edition, Revised. New York (Philosophical Library, n.d.)

Dollman, G. (1937). Letter to the Editor: "The Abominable Snowman." *The Times,* July 19. London.

Downing, G. R. (1954). "The Snowman: The Strangest Story Yet." *Daily Mail,* Jan. 7. London.

Drennan, Prof. M. R. (1953). "A new race of prehistoric men: The Salhanha skull, found with stone and bone tools, and the fossil remains of extinct South African animals." *The Illustrated London News,* Sept. 26. London.

Dubois, E. (1894). Pithecanthropus erectus: eine menschenahnliche Ubergangsform aus Java. Batavia.

Dutt, N., M.A., B.L., Ph.D., D.Litt. (1934). *The Pancavimsatisahasrika Prajnaparamita.* No. 28 in the Calcutta Oriental Series; Accepted as thesis (pt. ii) for the Degree of Doctor of Literature in the University of London. London. (Luzac).

Dyhrenfurth, G. O. (1952). *Zum dritten Pol.* Müchen (Nymphenburger Verlagshandlung).

Dyhrenfurth, Prof. G. O. (1955). *To the third Pole.* London. (W. Laurie)

Eickstedt, E. Freiherr von (1942). *Rassenkunde und Rassen-*

geschichte der Menschheit. Stuttgart. (Ferdinand Enke Verlag)

Elwes, H. J. (1915). "On the Possible Existence of a Large Ape, Unknown to Science, in Sikkim." *Proc. zool. Soc. Lond.* p. 294, London.

Enjoy, P. D. (1896). "L'Appendice Caudal dans les Tribus Moi." *Anthropologie,* 7, 531–5. Paris.

Estoppey, G. L. (1959). "Qui est l'abominable homme des neiges?" *Les Alpes,* 35, Lausanne.

Evans, C. (1956). *Kangchenjunga.* London. (Hodder & Stoughton)

Finot, L. (1928). "A propos des Moi a queue." *Bull. Amis Vieux Hue,* no. 4, pp. 217–21, Hanoi, Haiphong.

Fitter, R. (1960). "Mask provides new clue to the Snowman." *The Observer,* Oct. 23, London.

Frank, L. (1802). *Memoire sur le Commerce des Negres.* Paris.

Franklin, S. (1959). "The Sasquatch." *Weekend Magazine,* Apr. 4, v. 9. no. 14. Canada.

Frechkop, S. (1937). "Le Pied de l'Homme." *Mem. Mus. Hist. nat. Belg.* 13, 19, Brussels.

Frechkop, S. (1938). *Exploration du Parc National Albert, Mission G. F. de Witte (1933–35).* Brussels. (Institut des Parcs Nationaux du Congo Belge)

Friedenthal, H. (1911). *Tierhaaratlas.* Jena. (Fischer)

Fürer-Haimendorff, G. (1954). "Scalp of an Abominable Snowman?" *The Illustrated London News,* vol. 224, no. 5997, p. 477, London.

Gant, D. (1956). *Ascent to Everest.* Translated from English. Moscow.

Gatti, A. (1936). *Great Mother Forest.* London. (Hodder & Stoughton Ltd.)

Gemelli-Careri, G. F. (1745). *A Voyage Round the World* in J. Churchill: A Collection of Voyages and Travels. vol 4, p. 410. London.

Gromier, E. (1948). *La Vie des Animaux sauvages de l'Afrique.* Paris. (Payot)

Gupta, M. (1958). "The Snowman: Does he exist?" *The Illustrated Weekly of India,* vol. 79, Feb. 2, pp. 10–11.

Haeckel, E. (1865). *Generalle Morphologie der Organismen.* Berlin.

Hagen, V. W. von (1940). *Jungle in the Clouds.* New York. (Duell, Sloan and Pearce)

Hardie, N. (1957). *In highest Nepal,* our life among the Sherpas. London. (G. Allen & Unwin)

Hardy, M. E. (1920). *The Geography of Plants.* Oxford. (The Clarendon Press)

Herwaarden, V. (1924). "Een Ontmoeting met een Aapmensch." *Trop. Natuur,* 13, 103–6, Weltevreden.

Heuvelmans, B. (1952a). "L'Homme des Cavernes a-t-il connu des Géants measurant 2 a 4 Métres?" *Science et Avenir,* no. 61, Mai, Paris.

Heuvelmans, B. (1952b). "L'Homme des Cavernes a-t-il connu des Géants measurant 3 a 4 Métres?" *Science et Avenir*, no. 63, Mai, p. 207, Paris.

Heuvelmans, B. (1955). Sur la piste des bêtes ignorées. t. 1, ch. 6, Paris.

Heuvelmans, B. (1958). "Oui, l'homme-des-neiges existe." *Science et Avenir*, no. 134, Avril, p. 174, Paris.

Heuvelmans, B. (1958). *On the Track of Unknown Animals*. London. (Rupert Hart-Davis)

Hill, W. C. Osman (1945). "Nittaewo, an Unsolved Problem of Ceylon." *Loris*, 4, 251–62, Colombo.

Hillaby, I. (1957). "The Kwangsi Jaw." *Amer. J. phys. Anthrop*. 15, 281–5, Philadelphia.

Hillary, E. (1955). *High Adventure*. London. (Hodder & Stoughton)

Hillary, Sir. E. (1960). "Abominable—and Improbable?" *New York Times Magazine*.

Hooijer, D. A. (1949). "Some Notes on the Gigantopithecus question." *Amer. J. phys. Anthrop*. 7, 513–18, Philadelphia.

Hooijer, D. A. (1951). "The Geological Age of Pithecanthropus, Meganthropus and Gigantopithecus." *Amer. J. phys. Anthrop*. 9, 265–2.

Hooker, J. D. (1854). *Himalayan Journals*. v. II, pp. 14–15, London. 2V. (J. Murray)

Hoosier Folklore (1946). "Strange Beast Stories." v. 5, p. 19, March. Indianapolis. (Published for the Hoosier Folklore Society by the Indiana Historical Bureau.)

Hooton, E. A. (1937). *Apes, Men, and Morons*. New York. (G. P. Putnam's Sons)

Howard-Bury, Col. C. K. (1922). *Mount Everest, the Reconnaissance*. London.

Hunt, A. (1957). "The West Coast's Abominable Treemen." *The Globe Magazine*, July 6. (Toronto Globe and Mail)

Hunt, J. (1954). "Siege and assault." *The National Geographical Magazine*, v. 106, no. 1, pp. 1–44.

Illustrated Times (1956). "Travelling Snowman; Abominable Snowman tracks." Jan. 23, London.

Izzard, R. (1954). *The Innocent on Everest*. Mount Everest expedition, 1953. New York. (E. P. Dutton & Co. Inc.)

Izzard, R. (1955). *The Abominable Snowman Adventure*. Account of the Daily Mail Himalayan expedition, 1954. London.

Jackson, J. A. (1955). *More Than Mountains*. London. (George G. Harrap & Co. Ltd.)

Jacobson, E. (1917). "Rimboeleven in Sumatra." *Trop. Natuur*, 6, 69. Weltevreden.

Jacobson, E. (1918). "Nog eens de Orang pandak." *Trop. Natuur*, 7, 173. Weltevreden.

Jaschke, H. A. (1889). *Tibetan-English Dictionary*. London.

Jaschke, H. A. (1954). *Tibeton Grammar*. New York. (Frederick Ungar)

Jeimin Jibao (1959). "The mystery of the snow man will be uncovered." An interview by the correspondent of the newspaper Jeimin Jibao with Prof. B. Porshnev (in Chinese). Apr. 18.

Kalmpffert, W. (1956). "Abominable Snowman is a bear?" *Science Digest,* no. 4.

Kaulback, R. (1937a). "20 Months in Tibet." *The Times,* July 12, London.

Kaulback, R. (1937b). "The Mountain Men." *The Times,* July 13, London.

Keane, A. H. (1920). *Man Past and Present.* Cambridge. (The University Press)

Keel, J. A. (1958). *Jadoo.* London. (W. H. Allen)

Keith, Sir A. (1929). *The Antiquity of Man.* vols. I & II. London. (Williams and Norgate, Ltd.)

Kisliakow, N. (1959). "Snow man? No, a legend!" *Literature and Life,* Aug. 23.

Kleinenberg, E., & Porshnev, B. (1959). "Studies in the Soviet Union in connection with the snow man. *Huanmin Jibao,*" Feb. 11 (in Chinese).

Koenigswald, G. H. R. von (1935). "Eine fossile Saugetierfauna mit Simia aus Sudchina." *Proc. Acad. Sci. Amst.* 38, (8), pp. 872–9. Amsterdam.

Koenigswald, G. H. R. von (1947). "Search for Early Man." *Nat. Hist. N.Y.* 56, I. New York.

Koenigswald, G. H. R. von (1956). *Meeting Prehistoric Man.* New York. (Harper & Brothers)

Komsomol Truth (1959). "Facts and assumptions." An interview with A. Pronin and D. Evgeniev. Jan. 19.

Korolev, A. (1957). *Beyond the Border of Asia.* pp. 70–71. Moscow.

Korovnikov, V. (1959). "The Mystery Snow Man." *Soviet Russia,* Feb. 25.

Lal, R. N. (1947). *The Student's Practical Dictionary.* Containing Hindustani Words with English Meanings in Persian Character. Eleventh Edition, Revised. Allahabad, India.

Lambert, R. S. *Exploring the Supernatural:* The Weird in Canadian Folklore. Ch. 10, pp. 167–180. London. (Arthur Barker, Ltd., n.d.)

Lane, F. W. (1955). *Nature Parade.* 4th ed. revised. London.

Le Bret (1885). "Notice sur l'Existence d'une Race d'Hommes a Queue." *Arch. gen. Med.* February, Paris.

Le Conte, J. (1883). "Carson Footprints." *Nature,* vol. 28, London.

Le Double, A. F., & Houssay, F. (1912). *Les Velus.* Paris.

Le Gros Clark, W. E., F.R.S. (1950). *History of The Primates.* London. (British Museum [Natural History])

Leroi-Gourhan, Prof. A. (1952). "Among the ten most ancient human remains yet discovered: early Mousterian jawbones found at Arcy-sur-Cure on a unique site continuously oc-

cupied for 140,000 years." *The Illustrated London News,*
Nov. 29. London.

Letavet, A. (1958). "Was it a Snowman?" *Moscow News,* Jan.
22.

Lewis, F. (1919). "Notes on Animal and Plant Life in the
Vedda Country." *Spolia zeylan.* 10, 119–65, Colombo.

Ley, W. (1955). *Salamanders and Other Wonders.* Ch. 4: The
Abominable Snowmen. New York.

Lochte, T. (1938). *Atlas der menschlichen und tierischen Haare.*
Göttingen, Leipzig. (Schoeps)

Lonnberg, E. (1932). "Ett avalojat swindelforsok meddenfelan
de lanken." *Fauna och Flora,* 249–54, Uppsala.

Lyell, D. D. (1929). *The Hunting and Spoor of Central African
Game.* London. (Seeley, Service & Co.)

McGovern, W. M. (1924). *To Lhasa in Disguise.* London.
(Thornton Butterworth)

McGovern, W. M. (1924). *To Lhasa in Disguise.* New York.
(The Century Co.)

MacIntyre, Maj.-Gen. D. (1889). *Hindu-Koh.* Edinburgh. (W.
Blackwood & Sons)

MacIntyre, N. (1936). *Attack on Everest.* London. (Methuen &
Co.)

Maier, R. (1923). "De Orang pandak of Orang pendek." *Trop.
Natuur,* 12, 154. Weltevreden.

Maitre, H. (1912). *Les Jungles Moi, Exploration et Histoire des
Hinterlands Moi du Cambodge, de la Cochin-chine, de
l'Annam et du Bas-Laos.* Paris.

Mariagin, G. (1958a). "Almas—the snow man?" An interview
with Prof. Rinchen. *Literature and Life,* Nov. 12.

Mariagin, G. (1958b). "Almas—the snow man?" Reply from B.
Porshnev. *Literature and Life,* Nov. 16.

Marques-Riviere, J. (1937). *L'Inde Secrete et sa Magie.* Paris.

Marsh, O. C. (1883). "On the supposed human foot-prints recently found in Nevada." *American Journal of Science,*
Ser. 3, vol. 26, New Haven, Connecticut.

Mason, G. F. (1943). *Animal Tracks.* New York. (William
Morrow & Co.)

Master, J. (1959). "The Abominable Snowman." Harper's Magazine, January.

Mayet, Dr. B. (1942). *Recherche de l'espece animale par
l'examen des poils des fourrures.* Lyon. (Bosc Freres, M.
et L. Riou)

Megasthenes (1846). *Indica, fragmenta* in E. A. Schwanbeck:
Megasthenis Indica. Greek text. Bonn.

Mendis, W. (1945). "Where the Pygmies of Ceylon Lived."
Loris, December, p. 262, Colombo.

Merejinsky, U. (1959). "From the ancient manuscripts." *Evening Kiev,* Oct. 23 (in Ukrainian).

Merrick, H. (1954). "Abominable Snowman." *New Statesman
and Nation,* v. 27, no. 6, p. 152. London.

Moore, G., M.D. (1957). "I Met the Abominable Snowman." *Sports Afield,* May, New York.

Morin, M. (1953). *Everest du premier assaut à la victoire.* Grenoble.

Morland-Hughes, W. R. J. (1947). *Grammar of the Nepali Languages in the Roman and Nagri Scripts.* London. (Luzac)

Moscow Komsomolets (1958). "Snow man—Who is he?" An interview with the science editor Prof. of Anthropology, A. Shmakov. Jan. 26.

Murie, O. J. (1954). *A Field Guide to Animal Tracks.* Boston. (Houghton Mifflin)

Murray, W. (1953). *The Story of Everest.* New York.

Murray, W. (1953). "Is there an Abominable Snowman?" *Scots Magazine,* May, pp. 91–97.

Mus. J. Phila. (1915). "Guatemala Myths." vol. 6, no. 3, pp. 103–115.

Nebesky-Wojkowitz, R. von (1956). *Where the Gods Are Mountains.* London. (Weidenfield & Nicolson)

Neff, E. D. (1948). "Nature's Model-T Man." *Nature,* December. London.

Nevada, a guide to the Silver State (1940). Writers program. American guide series. p. 16.

Nevill, H. (1886). "The Nittaewo of Ceylon." *Taprobanian,* February, pp. 66–8, Bombay.

Newman, H. (1937). *Indian Peepshow.* London. (G. Bell & Sons)

Noel, Capt. J. (1927). *The Story of Everest.* Boston. (Little, Brown & Co.)

Northern Neighbors (1959). "Abominable Snowman again." November, Ontario, Canada.

Noyce, W. (1954). "The Ascent of Everest." *Asian Rev.,* April, p. 128, London.

Oakley, Dr. K. P., & Hoskins, Dr. C. R. (1950). "New Evidence on the Antiquity of Piltdown Man." *Nature,* Mar. 11, pp. 379–382. London.

Obruchev, S. (1957). "The footprints of the snow man in the Himalayas." *News of the Geographical Society,* v. 87, edition 1, pp. 71–73.

Obruchev, S. (1957b). "New materials about the snow man yeti." *News of the Geographical Society,* v. 89, edition 4, pp. 339–342.

Obruchev, S. (1959). "Present day evaluation of the snow man." *Nature,* no. 10, London.

Ostman, A. (1957). "I Was Kidnapped by a Sasquatch." *Agassiz-Harrison The Advance,* Aug. 22, British Columbia, Canada.

Pai-HSin (1958). "Information of a Chinese moving picture director Pai-HSin, how he had seen the snow man." *Beiden Jibao,* Jan. 29 (in Chinese)

Palladius, Bishop (1665). *Palladii de Gentibus Indiae et Bragmanibus.* Latin & Greek texts. London.

Parker, W. (1960). "Europe: How Far?" *The Geographical Journal*, vol. cxxvi, part 3, London.

Passarelle, C. (1958). "Alerte au yeti (vers la certitude)." *Science et vie*, April, no. 487, pp. 86–92.

Peissel, M. (1960). "The Abominable Snow Job." *Argosy Magazine*, December.

Pei Ven-Jun, U Ju-Kand, Gow Min-Gen (1958). "The riddle of the snow man." *Huanmin Jibao*, Feb. 27 (in Chinese).

Pei, Wen-Chung (1956). "New Material on Man's Origins." *China Reconstructs*, August, Peking.

Pei, Wen-Chung (1957). "Find Man-Like Ape." *Science News Letter*, Oct. 5, Washington.

Petzsch, H. (1958a). "Der Schneemensch ist Kein Hirngespinst." Liberal Demokratische Zeitung, Jan. 23.

Petzsch, H. (1958b). "Nochmals der der problematische Schneemensch." *Liberal Demokratische Zeitung*, Feb. 15.

Pianikov, P. (1959). "It is not a legend." *Komsomol Truth*, Feb. 1.

Pijl, L. van der (1938). "De Orang Pendek als Sneeuwman." *Tropische Nat.* 27, 53, Weltevreden.

Pliny the Elder (1601). *The Historie of the World*. Translated by Philemon Holland. vol. I, p. 157, London.

Poliakov, A. (1957). "Only footprints and legends." *Physical Culture and Sport*, no. 4, pp. 20–22.

Polo, M. (1818). *The Travels of Marco Polo, a Venetian, in the Thirteenth Century, being a Description by that Early Traveller of Remarkable Places and Things in the Eastern Parts of the World*. Translated with notes by William Marsden. London.

Poppe, N. (1954). *Grammar of Written Mongolian*. Studies on Asia, Far Eastern and Russian Institute. University of Washington at Seattle/Porta Linguarum Orientalium Wiesbaden (Otto Harrasowitz [WGB GmbH])

Pora, E. (1959). "Poate exista yéti—omul zapexilor?" *Natura*, v. 2, no. 2.

Porshnev, B. (1958a). "Does the snow man exist?" *Evening Moscow*, Nov. 13.

Porshnev, B. (1958b). "Does the snow man exist?" *Evening Moscow*, Nov. 29.

Porshnev, B. (1958c). "Legends? But they may be the real thing." *Komsomol Truth*, June 11.

Porshnev, B. (1959a). "Search for a snow man." *Komsomol Truth*, Feb. 15.

Porshnev, B. (1959b). "From the pages of ancient manuscripts." *Komsomol Truth*, June 7.

Porshnev, B. (1959c). "The riddle of the snow man." *Contemporary East*, no. 8, pp. 56–57.

Porshnev, B. (1959d). "The riddle of the snow man." *Contemporary East*, no. 9, pp. 52–55.

Pranavananda, S. (1950). *Exploration in Tibet*. Calcutta.

Pranavananda, S. (1955). "Abominable Snowman." *The Indian Geographical Journal*, 30, 3, 99–104.

Pranavananda, S. (1955a). "The Abominable Snowman." *J. Bombay nat. Hist. Soc.* 54, 358–64, Bombay.

Pranavananda, S. (1955b). "Footprints of Snowman." *J. Bombay nat. Hist. Soc.* pp. 448–50, Bombay.

Prjevalsky, N. (1876). *Mongolia, the Tangut country, and the solitudes of Northern Tibet*. London. (S. Loro)

Pronin, A. (1958). "An encounter with a snow man." *Komsomol Truth*, Jan. 15.

Publications (4 booklets) (1958–9). The Special Commission formed to study the problem of the Snowman by the U.S.S.R. Academy of Sciences. Compiled under the supervision of Prof. B. F. Porshnev and Dr. A. A. Shmakov. Moscow (in Russian).

Quatrefages de Breau, A. de (1887). *Les Pygmees*. Paris.

Rahul, R. (1960). "Stories Increased Search for Yeti." *The Christian Science Monitor*, Dec. 17.

Ramstedt, G. J. (1902). *Bergtscheremissische Sprachstudien*. Helsinki. (Societe Finno-Ougrienne)

Ratsek, V. (1959). "According to me . . . no more of him." *Physical Culture and Sport*, no. 4, pp. 20–23.

Rendall, E. B. (circa 1957). *Healing Waters*.

Reuben, D. E. (1955). "The Abominable Snowman." *J. Bombay nat. Hist. Soc.* 54, 3, Bombay.

Rinchen, Prof. (1958). "Almas—Mongolian relative of the snow man." *Contemporary Mongolia*, no. 5, pp. 34–38.

Rockhill, W. W. (1891). *The Land of the Lamas*. London. (Longmans, Green Co.)

Roerich, N. *Altai Himalaya*, a travel diary. London. (Jarrolds, n.d.)

Roosevelt, T. (1893). *The Wilderness Hunter*. New York. (G. P. Putnam's Son)

Rosenfeld, A. (1959). "About some dated (out dated) ancient beliefs of the people of Pamir, in connection with the legend of the snow man." *Soviet Ethnography*, no. 4. ....

Rosenfeld, M. (1931). *Across Mongolia in an automobile*. Moscow.

Russel, Dr. S. (1946). *Mountain Prospect*. London. (Chotto & Windus)

Ruttledge, H. (1934). *Everest 1933*. London. (Hodder & Stoughton)

Ruttledge, H. (1937). *Everest: The Unfinished Adventure*. London. (Hodder & Stoughton Ltd.)

Sanderson, I. T. (1950). "The Abominable Snowman." *True Magazine*, May, New York.

Sanderson, I. T. (1955). *How to Know the American Mammals*. New York. (Hanover House)

Sanderson, I. T. (1957). *The Monkey Kingdom*. New York. (Hanover House)

Sanderson, I. T. (1959). "The Strange Story of America's Abominable Snowman." *True Magazine,* December, New York.

Sanderson, I. T. (1960). "A New Look at America's Mystery Giant." *True Magazine,* March, New York.

Science (1956). "Abominable Snowman." 123, 1024.

Science (1956). "Again the Abominable Snowman." 126, 3210, 22, July 6, Washington.

Science News Letter (1956). "Abominable Snowman." 69, 26, 405, June 30, Toronto.

Schaefer, E. (1951). *Grandes Chasses sur le Toit du Monde.* Paris.

Schiltberger, J. (1879). *The Bondage and Travels of J. S. in Europe, Asia, Africa, 1396–1427.* London. (Hakluyt Society Works, v. 58)

Schlegel, H., & Muller, S. (1839–44). Bijdragen tot de Natuurlijke Historie van den Orang-oetan (Simia satyrus) *in* Verhandelingen over de Natuurlijke Geschiedenis der Nederlandsche Oederzeesche Bezittingen, door de Leden der Natuurkundige Commissie in Indie en Andere Schrijvers). p. 12, Leiden.

Seton, E. T. (1958). *Animal Tracks and Hunter Signs.* New York. (Doubleday)

Shalimov, A. (1957). "The snow man in Pamir?" *Around the World,* no. 7, pp. 29–32.

Shipton, E. (1938). *Blank on the map.* pp. 202–3, (Ch. by H. V. Tilman) London. (Hodder & Stoughton)

Shipton, E. (1951). "A Mystery of Everest: Footprints of the Abominable Snowman." *The Times,* Dec. 6, London.

Shipton, E. (1952). *The Mount Everest Reconnaissance Expedition, 1951.* London. (Hodder & Stoughton)

Shipton, E. (1952). "Everest: 1951 Reconnaissance of the Southern Route." *The Geographical Journal,* June, London.

Shipton, E. (1953). "The expedition to Cho Oyn." *The Geographical Journal,* 119, 2, 126–133, London.

Shipton, E. (1955–56). *Men against Everest.* Englewood Cliffs, N.J. (Prentice Hall)

Shipton, E. (1956). "Fact or fantasy." *The Geographical Journal,* 122, 3, 370–72, London.

Simonov, E. (1957). "Snow man—myth or reality?" Literaturnaya Gazeta (Literary Newspaper). Notes by S. Obruchev, A. Alexandrov, A. Litovet and N. Sirotkin.

Simonov, E. K. (1959). "To the highest elevation on the globe." *Geography in the school,* no. 1, pp. 29–38.

Simonov, J. (1959). "Po stopach sněžnéo muže." *Veda a technicka mladeze,* no. 10, v. 2, pp. 12–15.

Simpkins, F. J. (1952). "Himalayan footprints." *The Field,* July 12, London.

Skeat, W. W., & Blagden, C. D. (1906). *Pagan Races of the Malay Peninsula,* vol. II, pp. 281–3, London.

Smythe, F. S. (1930). *The Kangchenjunga Adventure.* London.

Smythe, F. S. (1937). "Abominable Snowman." *The Illustrated London News*, Nov. 13, p. 848, London.

Smythe, F. S. (1938). *The Valley of Flowers*. London.

Snaith, S. (1937). *At Grips with Everest*. London. (The Percy Press)

Solecki, Prof. R. S. (1960). "Neanderthal Men in the Heart-Land of Human Evolution: Discoveries at Shanidar Cave, in Northern Iraq." *The Illustrated London News*, May 7, p. 772, London.

Soule, G. (1952). "The World's Most Mysterious Footprints." *Popular Science*, December, p. 133.

Speakman, F. J. (1954). *Tracks, trails and signs*. London.

Spittel, R. L. (1933). *Far-off Things*. pp. 61–74, Colombo.

Spittel, R. L. (1936). "Leanama, Land of the Nittaewo." *Loris*, 1, 37–46, Colombo.

Stansfeld, Lt.-Col. H. S. (1952). "Himalayan footprints." *The Field*, Aug. 2, p. 194, London.

Stanukowitch, K. (1957). "Golub-Jawan." *News of the Geographical Society*, v. 89, pp. 343–345, edition 4.

Staudinger, P. (1932). Einige Angaben über den Orang Pendek oder Orang Letjo. S. B. Ges. naturf. Fr. Berlin.

Stonor, C. (1955). *The Sherpa and the Snowman*. London. (Hollis & Carter)

Stonor, C. (1958). *Sherpas and the Snow Man*. Moscow.

Straus, W. (1956). "Abominable Snowman." *Science*, 123, 3206, 1024–1025, June 8, Washington.

Struys, J. (1791). *Voyage en Tartarie, Perse, Inde*. vol. 1, pp. 88, 100, Rouen.

Stuart, J. (1959). "Canada's Abominable Snowman." *Argosy Magazine*, December.

Technika for Youth (1959a). "Who is he?" no. 4, pp. 31–34.

Technika for Youth (1959b). "Who is he?" no. 5, pp. 37–39.

Teilhard de Chardin, P. (1947). "Sur une Manibule de Meganthropus." *C. R. Soc. geol. Fr.* 15, 309–10, Paris.

Tenzing, N. (with Ullman, J. R.) (1955). *Tiger of the Snows*. New York. (G. P. Putnam)

Teuwsen, E. (1936). *Fährten und Spuren*. Neudamm. (J. Neumann)

Tilman, H. W. (1937). *Snow on the Equator*. London. (G. Bell & Sons Ltd.)

Tilman, H. W. (1938). "The Mount Everest Expedition of 1938." *The Geographical Journal*, v. 92, pp. 481–498, London.

Tilman, H. W. (1946). *When Men and Mountains Meet*. London.

Tilman, H. W. (1948). *Mount Everest, 1938*. Cambridge. (University Press)

Tilman, H. W. (1949). *Two Mountains and A River*. Cambridge. (University Press)

Tilman, H. (1952). *Nepal Himalaya*. Cambridge. (Univ. Press)

Tombazi, A. (1925). *Account of a photographic expedition to* the southern glaciers of Kangchenjunga in the Sikkim Himalaya. Bombay.

Topley, Mrs. M. (1960). Letter, *Man*, 60, no. 33, February, London.

Tschernezky, W. (1954). "Nature of the Abominable Snowman." *Manchester Guardian*, Feb. 20.

Tschernezky, W. (1958). "On the nature of the Snow Man." Added to the book of R. Izzard, *Following the Footprints of the Snow Man*. Moscow.

Tschernezky, W. (1960). "A reconstruction of the foot of the Abominable Snowman." *Nature*, 186, 4723, 496–7, May 7, London.

Tulpius, N. (1641). *Observationum Medicarum, Libri Tres*. Amsterdam.

Turner, S. (1800). *An Account of an Embassy to the Court of the Teshoo Lama, in Tibet*. London.

Tyson, E. (1699). *Orang-utang, sive Homo Sylvestris, or the Anatomy of a Pygmie Compared with that of a Monkey, an Ape, and a Man*. London.

Udin, T. (1959). "Five expeditions to the Himalayas." *Evening Moscow*, Feb. 7.

Ullman, J. R. (1947). *Kingdom of Adventure: Everest*. New York. (W. Sloane Assoc., Inc.)

Urbain, A., & Dekeyser, P. L. (1953). "Le Gorille." *Naturalia*, no. 3, December, Paris.

Urysson, M. (1958). *Das Geheimnis des Yeti. Freie Welt*, Heft 17, Apr. 24, s. 14–17.

Usinger, A. (1954). *Fahrten, Spuren und Gelaufe*. München.

Vandivert, W. & R. (1957). *Common Wild Animals and their Young*. New York. (Dell)

Vercors (see Bruller, J.)

Verma, B. K. (1959). "Man's Nearest Living Cousin: The Yeti." *The Illustrated Weekly of India*, Sept. 27.

Virchow, R. (1885a). "De la Queue chez l'Homme." *Zbl. Chir.* p. 539, Leipzig.

Virchow, R. (1885b). "L'Appendice Caudal chez l'Homme." *Gaz. hebd. Med. Chir.* p. 29, Paris.

Vlcek, E., M.D. (1958). "Co vime o sněžnem muži?" Ziva Roenik VI (XLIV), Brezen, no. 2.

Vlcek, E., M.D. (1959). "Old literary evidence for the existence of the 'snow man' in Tibet and Mongolia." *Man*, v. 50, August, London.

Waddell, Maj. L. A. (1899). *Among the Himalayas*. London. (Archibald Constable)

Waddell, Maj. L. A. (1905). *Lhasa and Its Mysteries*. p. 482, New York.

Wals, H. (1938). *La Chasse a Java*, Paris.

Weidenreich, F. (1945). "Giant Early Man from Java and South China." vol. 40, part 1, New York. (Anthropological papers of the American Museum of Natural History)

Weidenreich, F. (1946). *Apes, Giants and Man*. Chicago.

Weiner, Dr. J. S. (1955). *The Piltdown Forgery*. Oxford. (The University Press)

Weinert, H. (1946). "Über die Neuen Vorund Fruhmenschenfunde aus Afrika, Java, China und Frankreich." *Z. Morph. Anthr.* Stuttgart, xlii.

Weinert, H. (1949). "Menschenaffen oder Affenmenschen, das Unlosbare Problem der Neuen Africa-Funde." *Orion*, 4, pp. 169–74, Munich.

Weinert, H. (1951). "Zur Frage des Gigantenproblems der Summoprimaten." *Anat. Anz.*, 98, pp. 279–87, Leipzig.

Weinman, A. (1945). "Nittaewo." *Loris*, 4, no. 2, pp. 337, Colombo.

Wendt, H. (1960). *Out of Noah's Ark*. Boston. (Houghton Mifflin)

Westenek, L. C. (1918). "Orang Pandak (Boschmenschen) of Soematra." *Trop. Natuur.*, 7, p. 108, Weltevreden.

Wood, W. W. (1948). "Snowman or Monkey." *Country Life*, 103, p. 1234, London.

Wormington, H. M. (1957). *Ancient Man in North America*. Denver, Colo. (The Denver Museum of Natural History)

Wynter-Blyth, M. A. (1952). "A Naturalist in the Northwest Himalaya." *J. Bombay nat. Hist. Soc.*, 50, pp. 559–72, Bombay.

Wyss-Dunant, E. (1953). "The first Swiss expedition to Mount Everest." *The Geographical Journal*, September, London.

Zaborowski, S. (1897). "Les Hommes a Queue." *Bull. Soc. Anthrop.* series 4, 8, pp. 28–32, Paris.

Zerchaninov, U. (1959). "Following the footprints of Kaptar." *Komsomol Youth*, Aug. 29.

Zorza, V. (1960). "Farewell, Soviet Snowman." *Manchester Guardian Weekly*, Feb. 11.

BOOKS BY IVAN T. SANDERSON

Travel

ANIMAL TREASURE	1937	Viking (& Pyramid)
CARIBBEAN TREASURE	1939	Viking (& Pyramid)
LIVING TREASURE	1941	Viking (& Pyramid)

Juveniles

MYSTERY SCHOONER (P-N)	1941	Viking
ANIMALS NOBODY KNOWS	1944	Viking
THE SILVER MINK	1952	Little, Brown
JOHN & JUAN IN THE JUNGLE	1953	Dodd, Mead
THE STATUS QUO (P-N)	1956	Merlin Press

Collected Works

ANIMAL TALES	1946	Knopf
"THINGS"	1967	Pyramid

Reference

HOW TO KNOW THE NORTH AMERICAN MAMMALS	1951	Little, Brown (& NAL)
LIVING MAMMALS OF THE WORLD	1955	Hanover House
FOLLOW THE WHALE	1956	Little, Brown
THE MONKEY KINGDOM	1957	Hanover House & Chilton
ABOMINABLE SNOWMEN	1961	Chilton
THE CONTINENT WE LIVE ON	1961	Random House
THE DYNASTY OF ABU	1962	Knopf
THE BOOK OF GREAT JUNGLES	1965	Messner
THIS TREASURE LAND	1966	Putnam
UNINVITED VISITORS	1967	Cowles

In preparation

OUR ANIMAL ALLIES	Prentice-Hall
INTERMINABLE WOOODSMEN	Pyramid
MORE "THINGS"	Pyramid
RAIES—THE CARIB	Pyramid

INDEX

Abakan Mts. 313
Abidjan (Guinea), 204, 207
Acheulian Man, 119
Achin (Sumatra), 229-230
Adiopodoumé, Inst. of Ed.
  (Guinea), 204
ADVANCE, THE (Agassiz, B.C.),
  85, 106, 111
Afghanistan, 301-302
Afghans, The, 302,
Africa, 115, 201, 204, 226-227, 251,
  263, 278, 300, 320, 332
Africans, 69, 106, 115
Afropavo, 201
Agassiz, B.C., 77, 99, 104, 107
Agogwe, 208, 212
Aharon, Yonah N. ibn, 290
Akalché, 174
Akunakunas, The, 211
Alabama, 122, 127
Ala-Dagh Mts., 289, 299
Alai-Tagh Mts., 302, 312
Ala-Shan Desert, 63, 324
Alaska, 63, 68, 77-78, 80, 129, 321,
  323, 326
Ala-Tau Mts., 63
Albany (Ore.), 164
Albasty, 293
Algeria, 215
Allen, Mrs. Elizabeth (Betty), 133,
  157, 159-161
Alligator Lake (B.C.), 77
Alligators, 77
Almas, 107, 294, 309, 317-320, 324,
  326
Almasty, 107, 294
Alouatta, 181
Altai (The Grand) Mts., 63, 312
Alto Planos (of the Andes), 188
Altyn Tagh Mts., 289, 312
Amazon Basin, 177-178, 188, 201
Ameghino, Prof. Florentino, 193
Ameranthropoides loysi, 190
American Geographical Society,
  173
Americans, The, 307
Amerinds, 68, 70, 72-75, 79, 81, 83,
  98, 102, 106-107, 111, 114-115,
  119, 128, 132, 141, 143-144, 146,

Amerinds—Continued
  151, 153, 161-162, 167, 175, 185,
  192-193, 196-198, 246, 253, 262,
  305, 325, 326
Anadyr Mts., 324
Andaman Islands, 37
Anderson, Alexander C., 68
Andes, The, 29, 176, 178, 201
Angola, 201, 219
Annam Mts., 249
Anteater, Giant, 142
Anthropoids, 166, 223, 267, 289, 300
Anthropoidea, 127
Aötes, 181
Apamandi, 224
Apes, 59, 66, 84, 88, 95-96, 106, 118,
  122, 127, 191, 202-204, 207, 219,
  223-226, 230, 233, 235, 250-251,
  255, 260-261, 274, 279, 299, 326
Arabia, 226-227
Arakan (Burma), 249, 265
Arawaks, The, 197
Arctic, 19, 64, 79
Arctictis, 253
Argentina, 192
Argentine Himalayan Expd., 270
ARGOSY MAGAZINE, 284
Arkansas, 122
Armenia, 289, 292, 299
Arun Valley (Nepal), 270
Asia, 226, 230, 248, 300, 309, 322,
  323
Assam, 63, 270
Ateles, 189-190
Atrato River (Colombia), 178
Atu, 231
August, Adeline, 107
Aurochs (*Bos primigenius*), 250
Australopithecines, 94-95, 203, 212,
  225, 227
Avars, The, 292, 294
Avarskoy Koysu River (U.S.S.R.),
  290, 291
Azerbaijan, 289, 291

Baboons, 208-209, 215, 217, 219,
  261, 278-279
Badakshan A, A., 301-302
Baikal, Lake, 305

355

Canada, 48, 63, 71, 82-83, 120, 128, 140, 148, 246
Canadians, The, 77-78, 291
Capilano, The *S.S.*, 73
Capricornis, 285
Caribbean, The, 27, 176
Caribs, The Amerind, 197
Caribs, The Black, 185-186
Carnivorous ABSMs, 183, 191, 242, 253
Carson City (Nev.), 141-142
Carvings (of ABSMs)—*see Depictions*
Cary, Oliver, 213
Caspian Sea, 288, 290, 304
Cascades, The, 21, 25, 129, 144
Cassowaries, 226
Casuarius, 226
Caucasoid Race, The, 211, 288, 294, 323
Caucasus, 59, 63, 289-290, 293-294, 300, 308, 325
Cavally River (Guinea), 207
Cax Vinic, 179
Cebidae, 190
Ceboid Monkeys, 37, 230, 278
Central America, 27, 119, 176, 178-179, 263
Ceratotherium cottoni, 212
Cercocebus, 260
Cervus albirostris, 279
Ceylon, 33, 226-227
Chaldeans, The, 282
Chapman, Mr. and Mrs. George, 98, 100-101
Chechen (U.S.S.R.), 291
Cheetah, 247
Chehalis, The, 83
Chellean Man, 96, 119
Chesh Teb (Pamirs), 302, 310, 313
Chetco River (Cal.), 143
Chetri, Bombahadur, 46-47
Chiapas (Mex.), 27, 174-175, 179
Chilliwack (B.C.), 75-76, 85, 105
Chimpanzees, 94, 148, 164, 188, 190, 203, 214-215, 217, 219, 276
China, 37, 48, 59, 78, 96, 249-252, 254, 263, 301, 304-306, 312, 325
Chinese, The, 251, 302-303, 306, 308
Chinese Escarpment, 324
Chinyanjas, The, 218
Choyang Valley (Nepal), 270, 276-277
CHRISTIAN SCIENCE MONITOR, THE, 309
Christie, Robert, 86
Chumbithang, 46
Chu River, 268
Clanton (Ala.), 127
Clear Lake (Cal.), 25, 129
Coastal Ranges (U.S.A.), 21
Coban (Guat.), 184
Coelacanth Fishes, 59
Coloboid Monkeys, 226, 240, 278, 281

Colombian Massif, 178, 188
Congo Basin, 31, 63, 155, 201-202, 210-211, 219, 334
Conser, Lake (Ore.), 164
CONTEMPORARY EAST, THE, 303
Cook, S. V., 209
Cope, Prof. E. D., 142
Copper-nails, 317, 320
Cordier, Charles, 220, 224, 333-334
Cotton's Ceratothere, 212
Cougar Lake (B.C.), 77
Courtenay, Roger, 210
Courteville, Roger, 191
Crew, James, 151
Crew, Jerald, 150-151, 153-154
Crocodilians, 78
Cromagnon Man, 118
Crossley-Batt, Jill, 282
Cross River (Nigeria), 211
Crystal Mts., 201
Cubulco (Guat.), 180-181
Cynopithecidae, 278
Cynopithecoid Monkeys, 278, 280
Cynopithecus, 230

Dagestan A. S. S. R., 291, 300
Dahinden, René, 86
DAILY BRITISH COLONIST, THE, 63, 67
Daily Mail Expd., 270
DAILY MAIL, THE (of London), 55, 57
Dammerman, Dr. K. W., 231, 238-239
Dan, Frank, 102-103
Darjeeling, 46, 49, 268
Dart, Dr. Raymond, 96
Darwaz Ridge (Pamirs), 311
Darwinism, 202
Da Tempa, 276
David, The Abbé Pierre, 280
Davis, Hassoldt, 253-254
Dawson, Charles, 202
Deedees (Didis), 197
Deer, 279, 292, 326, 339
Del Norte County (Cal.), 150
Demerara River (B.G.), 200
Denis-Roosevelt Asiatic Expd., 253
DE TROPISCHE NATUUR, 232, 234
Dev, 311
Devil Sakai, 227, 241
DISCOVERY (a pub.), 208
Djakarta (Java), 230
Dog-faced Monkeys, 278
Dogs, 56, 101, 105, 157, 183, 186, 247
DOUBT (a periodical), 79
Douc Monkeys, 240, 250
Dravidians, The, 84
Drawings (of ABSMs)—*see Depictions*

Drill, 278
Dromicetus, 226
Droppings (of ABSMs)—*see Excrement*
Dubois, Dr. Eugène, 96
Dunckel (hunter), 207
Dung (of ABSMs)—*see Excrement*
Durango (Mex.), 175
Dwa Ngombe Hills (Uganda), 209
Dwendis (Duendes), 186-187
Dyrenfurth, Dr. N. G., 270
Dzagin Almas, 317
Dzugdzhur Mts., 312, 324
Dzungaria, 314, 317-318
Dzu-Teh, 254, 260, 263, 274-275, 278, 281, 284, 322, 324

Earthworms, Giant, 188
East Africa, 63, 96, 119-120, 203, 226-227
East Indies, 57
Edwards, Ernest A., 74
Eel River (Cal.), 169
Elburz Mts., 289, 292, 299
Elephants, 228
El-Juf Basin, 31
Ellengassen, 192
El Quiché (Guat.), 181
Elwes, Henry J., 49-50, 267
Emberre Plains (Uganda), 209
Embu (Uganda), 209
Emus, 226
Eng-gano Island, 229
Eskimos, The, 326
Essequibo River (B.G.), 199
Eurasia, 31, 40-41, 48, 50, 202, 249, 263, 265-266, 281, 287-290, 302, 305, 307, 324-325
Eureka (Cal.), 132, 154, 158, 169
EUREKA DAILY LEADER, THE, 138
Europe, 248, 250, 289
Europeans, 287
EVENING STANDARD, THE (Salisbury, S. Rhodesia), 219
Everest, Mount, 40, 51, 53-54, 59, 85, 249, 264-265, 268, 278, 308
Excrement, 266-267, 270, 274, 312

Faeces (of ABSMs)—*see Excrement*
Fantasma humano, 179
FATE MAGAZINE, 64
Feathertails, 228
Fedchenko Glacier, 310
Fernando Po, 31
Fireti (Ufiti), 212, 218
Fleming, Peter, 307
Flood (B.C.), 111
Flood, Charles, 77
Florida, 78, 123, 282
Footprints, 101, 107, 112-113, 127-128, 135-138, 140-144, 147, 152, 162, 217, 219-220, 224, 233-235,

Footprints—Continued
263-264, 267-271, 274-278, 284-285, 295, 297, 307, 312, 314, 317, 321
Formosa (Taiwan), 37
Fort, Charles, 60, 79
Fort Langley (B.C.), 85
France, Anatole, 319
Franklin, Stephen, 67
Fraser River, 23, 63, 66, 71, 75, 80, 98-99, 112, 293
French, The, 57
Frogs, 277
Frostis, Jan, 269
Fukien (China), 34-35
Fukuoka Daigaku Expd., 271
Fürer-Haimendorf, Prof. C. von, 55, 271

Gabun, 201-203
Gagan Sanctuary (U.S.S.R.), 294
Galago, 226
Ganges River, 268
Garwhal (India), 268
Gatti, Mrs. Attilio, 223
Gelada Baboon, 278
Gent, J. R. O., 49, 267
Genzoli, Andrew, 154-155
GEOGRAPHICAL JOURNAL, THE, 289
Geophagy, 182, 273
Georgia (U.S.S.R.), 291-292, 294
Gérésun Bamburshé, 321
Ghurkhas, The, 46, 265
Giants, 75, 94, 103, 107, 112, 133, 140-143, 148, 157, 162, 221, 224, 260, 263, 266, 274, 297, 324, 326
Gibbons, 84, 203, 229, 233, 250
Gidan Mts., 312, 324
Gigantopithecus, 60, 254, 274, 324
Gilgit, 288
Gilmore, Harry, 234
Gini, Prof. Corrado, 231
Gin-Sung, 254, 263, 274, 281, 324
Goa (Portuguese India), 32
Goats, 272
Gobi Desert, 312, 318-319, 324
Gold Coast (Ghana), 221
Golden Monkey, 251
Gondwanaland, 226
Gorillas, 83-84, 94, 191, 203-204, 217-219, 221, 225, 276, 300, 304, 320, 326
Gosainkund Pass (Nepal), 256
Grand Altai Mts., 317
Grant's Pass, 150
Great Barrier (Eurasia), 41-42, 305, 307, 309, 314, 325
Great Barrier (N. Am.), 19, 21, 79
Great Basin, The, 21, 140
Great Central Lake (Vancouver Is.), 73
Green, John W., 85, 111
Ground-Sloths, 29, 142, 191